ANALYSIS OF LINEAR TIME-INVARIANT SYSTEMS

McGRAW-HILL ELECTRICAL AND ELECTRONIC ENGINEERING SERIES

Frederick Emmons Terman, *Consulting Editor*

W. W. Harman and J. G. Truxal, *Associate Consulting Editors*

ANALYSIS OF LINEAR TIME-INVARIANT SYSTEMS

WILLIAM M. BROWN

Associate Professor of Electrical Engineering & Research Engineer
of the Institute of Science and Technology, University of Michigan

McGRAW-HILL BOOK COMPANY, INC.

New York   San Francisco   Toronto   London

ANALYSIS OF LINEAR TIME-INVARIANT SYSTEMS

TO CHERYL AND MARK

PREFACE

The object of this book is to develop in considerable depth operational analysis and its applications to the study of linear time-invariant systems. Now that undergraduates are usually trained to some degree in the use of one-sided Laplace transforms, there is a need for a text suitable for the second exposure to such material. The early work is generally directed at quickly displaying the role of operational calculus in solving differential equations, and a study in depth with two-sided transforms and advanced applications is a natural follow-up of such a first exposure. The book is self-contained and hence prior study of operational analysis is not required; however, in the absence of such background it seems helpful to demonstrate the use of Laplace transforms in some simple problems dealing with electrical transients (without attention to mathematical details) before proceeding with the careful treatment given in Chapter 2.

The theory of two-sided Laplace transforms is given in detail in Chapter 2; of course Fourier transforms and ordinary Laplace transforms are discussed as important special cases. Also, elementary and intermediate applications are included with the development of the theory.

In Chapter 3 the important conceptual aspects of the analysis of linear time-invariant systems are brought into sharp focus; among other things, an all-inclusive formulation of operational calculus is developed. Actually Chapter 3 is self-contained (does not logically require results from Chapters 1 and 2). It serves all of the following purposes: (1) it establishes the existence and uniqueness of operational theory for which there is a multiplicative notion of transfer function; (2) it provides a review (and extension) of Chapters 1 and 2; and (3) it provides a basis for the use of Part II of the book without further reference to material in Part I. The author uses the material in Part II as a one-semester introductory graduate course in the analysis of linear time-invariant systems.† Part I is used as a course in operational analysis for seniors and first-year graduate students.

In Part II there is no attempt to cover all the existing important applications and extensions of the basic theory developed in Part I; however, all the topics covered are important and occasionally exciting. Topics such as the following are covered thoroughly in Part II: complex representation of signals and systems, response time (or resolution), Hilbert transforms, and discrete (or sampled-data) systems and Z transforms. In addition, the role of statistical considerations in system analysis and optimization is introduced in Chapter 8; and then many of the results obtained in Part II are applied, in Chapter 9, to radar and communication systems.

The last chapter is intended mainly as reference material. Based on a small number of assumptions about Lebesgue integration, this chapter gives in detail the mathematics of operational calculus. Actually, Chapter 10 is a small book in itself, suitable as a basis for a serious two-credit course in the mathematics of Fourier transforms.

The book stresses fundamentals, and it is slanted toward system evaluation (and optimization) rather than toward detailed design work. Although the material is fundamental, much of what follows Chapter 2 was not available prior to this book. Some standard topics such as loop and nodal analysis have been omitted in view of their ready availability in almost all other related books. The applications stress simple electronic systems, but many analogies to other types of systems are obvious. Save for Chapter 9, the emphasis is on analysis rather than the study of specific systems. The study in depth of elaborate electronic systems is introduced in Chapter 9. Actually the material in the book, along with the theory of random processes, provides a good basis for detailed study in depth of electronic systems such as radar, sonar, and communications.

The reader is expected to know elementary calculus and the elementary theory of differential equations (solutions by "classical" methods). Some background in electronic circuits is helpful in understanding many of the examples, and prior knowledge of the theory of functions of a complex variable is helpful for the study of Section 2-4. Mathematical maturity is probably a good substitute for specific background training, and it is hoped that in the use of the book some mathematical maturity is gained along with the learning of skills and results. The mathematical style (definitions, lemmas, theorems, etc.), which is rather common now in analytical material intended for engineers and scientists, is valuable in that its use provides a clear picture of the logical development of the theory.

Occasionally concepts are introduced and results are derived at a pace too fast for normal self-teaching. Specifically, the review of functions of a com-

† To a large extent the word system rather than circuit or filter is used to avoid creating a narrow impression about the domain of applicability of the theory.

plex variable in Section 2-4 is concise since many readers will have covered the material in another course, and a few of the advanced topics are treated quickly.   When the book is used with a course the lecturer can easily adjust the pace to fit the background of the students.

I am grateful to many friends and acquaintances for the help and information they offered me.   In particular, my debts to George Comenetz and Carmen Palermo are very great.   Where the material is clear and correct it is a reflection of my exposure to Dr. Comenetz.   I have benefited greatly from a long research collaboration with Dr. Palermo, and in connection with this work he had a strong influence on and contributed many results to Part II of the book.   Finally, support for research related to the book was very helpful.   This was provided mainly by the Electronics Technology Laboratory of the Aeronautical Systems Division of the Air Force.

William M. Brown

CONTENTS

1

OPERATIONAL ANALYSIS

The first three chapters of the book provide a rather detailed development of operational analysis. The mathematical level is higher than that found in most engineering texts; however, an even higher-level treatment is certainly possible. The level used here seems to be well suited to the needs of applied work while at the same time it provides more than a superficial understanding of the material. The remaining chapters cover numerous important applications and theories.

The most important conceptual aspects of operational analysis are covered in Chap. 3, while Chap. 2 covers the down-to-earth useful material. In Chap. 3 exponential functions are shown to provide the basis of the theory. Also, the theory is shown to be unique under the condition that a multiplicative notion of transfer function is desired. Of course, it is important to prove uniqueness, for otherwise it would seem necessary to develop (many) other theories.

1

INTRODUCTION AND OPERATIONAL ANALYSIS FOR EXPONENTIALLY AMPLITUDE-MODULATED SINUSOIDS

Some of the important concepts in operational analysis are introduced in this short chapter and are developed in depth in later chapters. In Sec. 1-2 the theory of *sinusoidal steady state* is given in detailed mathematical terms. The results of Sec. 1-2 are of some interest as part of the theory of operational analysis, and some rather important basic mathematics is included in the development of the theory.

3

1-1 NATURE OF OPERATIONAL ANALYSIS

The systems (also called circuits or "black boxes") considered will normally have an output which is a real- or complex-valued function of the real variable time. The input is also such a function. The role of the system is to transform the input into the output. The generalization to systems in which the input and output consist of many functions of time (vector-valued functions of time) is not given much attention in the book. Some notations to be used during most of the book will be introduced before operational analysis is defined. For the most part, terms being defined will be *italicized*.

Essentially all mathematical topics involve sets and functions. Of course, a *set* is simply a collection of things. Recall the following definition and notation for functions: A *function* with domain D and outer range V is a set of correspondences such that to each element of the set D there corresponds a unique element of the set V. If Φ denotes such a set of correspondences,† we shall write $\Phi: D \to V$, which is read: Φ maps D into V. If q is an element of D, the element of V which corresponds to q is denoted by $\Phi(q)$ and is called the value of Φ at q. We shall sometimes abbreviate *q is an element of the set D* by writing $q \in D$.

As a simple example of a function, sin denotes a function where the domain is normally taken as the set of all real numbers and the range is the interval of real numbers $[-1, 1]$. Of course, any set of real numbers which contains the interval $[-1, 1]$ can be taken as an outer range. As a different kind of example, a specific collection (set) of people with their corresponding ages is a function.

It may be that the elements of the domain or range of a function are themselves functions. Such is the case for a circuit; the domain is the set of possible (or interesting) inputs which are functions of a real variable. The range is the set of outputs which can be produced. The function for a circuit is the set of correspondences between inputs and outputs. Important terms such as set and function have many synonyms. The following terms mean set: class, collection, ensemble, and aggregate. Some of the synonyms of function are mapping, transformation, and operator. It is sometimes useful to reserve some of the terms for special types; e.g., class usually means a set for which the elements are sets. With this

---

† What is called a function here is sometimes called a single-valued function. A very good approach (cf. Ref. 1 in the list of references at the end of the book) is to first define *relation* as a set of ordered pairs. The set of all first elements is the domain of the relation, and the set of all second elements is the range. A relation is a function if for any given first element there is one and only one element of the relation having this first element; i.e., the first element uniquely determines the second. As an example, $\leq$ is a relation but not a function. The relation $\leq$ consists of all ordered pairs of real numbers (x, y) such that $x \leq y$.

agreement on the use of the word class we might refer to a football team as a set and then refer to the class of Big 10 football teams. We shall use the terms *transformation* and *operator* to mean functions for which the domain is a set of functions. Thus, a circuit is viewed mathematically as a transformation. As an example, suppose D is the set of all real-valued functions of time which have a derivative everywhere. Then d/dt can be viewed as a transformation having domain D (an outer range is all real-valued functions of a real variable).

Let $\Phi: D \to V$ denote the transformation performed by a system. Let f denote an arbitrary element of D and let g denote the corresponding element of V; that is, $g = \Phi(f)$. The general situation for operational analysis can be viewed as shown in Figure 1-1. We start with some interesting transformation Φ for which it may not be easy to compute $g = \Phi(f)$, given f. We then define some transformation on f and g, here called the operator L with $F = L(f)$ and $G = L(g)$. Since f and g are related (with the relation

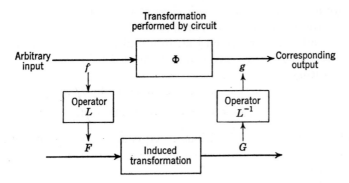

FIGURE 1-1.   A diagram for operational analysis.

denoted by Φ), we expect F and G to be related by what might be called the relation induced by Φ under the operator L. Generally, the operator L is considered useful if the induced relation is simpler than Φ in some sense. For example, Φ may be implicitly defined by differential or integral equations while F and G are related by a simple algebraic equation. In fact, for the Φ's and L's discussed in the book, G will be equal to F times a fixed function called the transfer function. Thus, given the problem to find $\Phi(f)$, we find $F = L(f)$, from which $L(g) = G$ is easily obtained. Finally, given G, we assume that g can be found; i.e., we assume that L has an essentially unique inverse. One reason that operational analysis of a problem is sometimes easier than direct analysis is that for many physical systems the induced explicit relation can easily be obtained, while Φ is available only in an awkward form. As a preliminary to the detailed study of the operational analysis obtained when L is taken as the Laplace transform, a more elementary operational analysis will now be reviewed briefly.

1-2 EXPONENTIALLY AMPLITUDE-MODULATED SINUSOIDS

It does not appear to be possible or entirely desirable† to develop a single operational theory which can handle any input (or output) which might be of interest.   Instead, we restrict our attention to some set of functions for which a useful operator can be defined.   For example, in Chap. 2 we consider a set of functions f, for which

$$\int_{-\infty}^{\infty} e^{-\sigma t}\,|f(t)|\,dt < \infty$$

for some real σ.   Such a function is two-sided Laplace-transformable. Here we consider a small class of functions which are *not* two-sided Laplace-transformable.   In this chapter let p denote an arbitrary fixed complex number ‡ $p = \sigma + j\omega$, where σ and ω are real.   Let D_p be all functions of the form $f(t) = Ae^{\sigma t} \cos(\omega t + \alpha)$ for all real t, where A and α are real numbers. The (complex) frequency of f is p, and f is called a real wave of frequency p. Clearly, we are considering a *small* class of functions; however, this small class is important in applications, and, as shown in Chap. 3, it is tied in with the basis for all operators which lead to a multiplicative notion of transfer function.   Also, the theory given here is needed in that it is not a special case of the theory of Chap. 2.

The operator appropriate for D_p will be denoted by L_0 and is defined thus:

$$L_0(f) \equiv L_0[Ae^{\sigma t} \cos(\omega t + \alpha)] \equiv Ae^{j\alpha}$$

(the symbol $\equiv$ is used in definitions).   Of course, $Ae^{j\alpha}$ denotes a complex number which is called the phasor of f, and it can also be written as $A \cos\alpha + jA \sin\alpha$.

At the risk of being pedantic, we shall recall the following definition: The *complex number system* consists of all ordered pairs of real numbers with the following rules for equality, complex addition $+'$, and complex multiplication $\times'$:

$$(x_1, y_1) = (x_2, y_2) \qquad \text{iff§ } x_1 = x_2 \text{ and } y_1 = y_2$$
$$(x_1, y_1) +' (x_2, y_2) \equiv (x_1 + x_2, y_1 + y_2)$$
$$(x_1, y_1) \times' (x_2, y_2) \equiv (x_1 x_2 - y_1 y_2,\ x_1 x_2 + y_1 x_2)$$

Of course, only real addition and multiplication are involved on the right sides of the definitions.   After making the definitions, we no longer carry the special symbols for complex addition and multiplication.   It is con-

---

† The very general theories are complicated to the point of decreasing their utility.

‡ If $\sigma = 0$, the theory given here is called sinusoidal steady state.

§ iff means if and only if.   Also, the notation (a, b) is used for the ordered pair of numbers a *and then* b as well as for the interval on the real line between a and b.   That is, (a, b) sometimes means all x such that $a < x < b$.   In this context a bracket is sometimes used in place of a parenthesis to close a side of the interval; for example, $(a, b]$ is all x such that $a < x \leq b$.   However, the ordered-pair or interval meaning for (a, b) either will be stated or will be clear from context.

venient to define multiplication of a complex number by a real number: $a(x, y) \equiv (ax, ay)$. Of course, we define $(0, 1) \equiv j$ and use $x + jy$ to denote $(x, y) = (x, 0) + (0, 1)(0, y)$. Given the above definitions, we can prove many theorems. For example, for arbitrary complex numbers z_1, z_2, z_3, $(z_1 z_2)z_3 = z_1(z_2 z_3)$. One simple theorem will be discussed which illustrates a situation of importance that occurs often in mathematics and in particular in operational analysis. Let C_r denote the set of complex numbers having zero imaginary parts, i.e., numbers of the form $(x, 0)$. Let R denote the real numbers. When the number system is "extended" from the reals to the complexes, it is hoped that the new system contains the old as a special case. However, since an element of C_r is an ordered pair $(x, 0)$ we cannot quite say that $(x, 0)$ is the same as x—they are not even the same kind of objects. On the other hand, we could well use C_r in place of R in any situation. The precise relationship can be summarized as follows.

Theorem 1. Let $J: C_r \to R$ thus: $J[(x, 0)] = x$ for any $(x, 0)$ of C_r; then J is a one-to-one† mapping and $J[(x_1, 0) +' (x_2, 0) \times' (x_3, 0)] = x_1 + x_2 \cdot x_3$; that is, $(C_r, +', \times')$ is isomorphic to $(R, +, \cdot)$ under the mapping J. The proof is very simple. The fact that one very seldom makes any distinction between real numbers and complex numbers having zero imaginary parts indicates that isomorphic systems might as well be considered the same. In other words, C_r and R have the same mathematical structure but involve different labels. The formal definition of isomorphic is implied by Theorem 1. Loosely speaking, systems are isomorphic iff there is a one-to-one mapping which is preserved by corresponding operations.

When two mathematical systems seem to be very different at the offset, a theorem depicting the strong tie of an isomorphism may be very illuminating. In what follows it will be seen that D_p and C (the set of real waves of frequency p and the set of all complex numbers) enjoy a grand isomorphism under the mapping L_0—this is hardly obvious at the outset. Here, proofs will be given which preserve the nonobvious impression; however, in Chap. 3 the isomorphism between C and D_p is demonstrated more simply.

Theorem 2. D_p is closed with respect to addition and multiplication by real constants; i.e., if one forms any real linear combination of exponentially amplitude-modulated sinusoids of complex frequency p, that combination can be written as a single function of said type. In mathematical terminology the theorem states that D_p is a linear space‡ over the field of real numbers.

PROOF: Clearly, $(aA)e^{\sigma t} \cos(\omega t + \alpha)$ is of the form of elements of D_p for any real a. It remains to be shown that any sum of the form

$$A e^{\sigma t} \cos(\omega t + \alpha) + B e^{\sigma t} \cos(\omega t + \beta)$$

can be written in the form $C e^{\sigma t} \cos(\omega t + \gamma)$.

† Of course $\Phi: D \to V$ is one-to-one iff for any $g \in V$ there exists one and only one $f \in D$ such that $\Phi(f) = g$.

‡ Let D be a set (the elements of which are sometimes called vectors). Let $+$ denote

One way to see that such is the case is to expand the sum by using trigonometric identities so that it becomes

$$(A \cos \alpha + B \cos \beta)e^{\sigma t} \cos \omega t - (A \sin \alpha + B \sin \beta)e^{\sigma t} \sin \omega t$$

We want to find a C and a γ such that the above equals

$$(C \cos \gamma)e^{\sigma t} \cos \omega t - (C \sin \gamma)e^{\sigma t} \sin \omega t$$

We can take

$$C = [(A \cos \alpha + B \cos \beta)^2 + (A \sin \alpha + B \sin \beta)^2]^{\frac{1}{2}}$$

and γ as the angle shown in Figure 1-2, which completes the proof.

We now continue with most of the important theorems for L_0. These theorems will then be applied to some familiar problems. A transformation

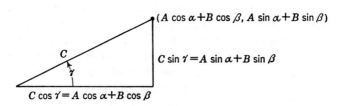

FIGURE 1-2.   Construction for C and γ.

$L: D \to V$ is linear iff (1) D is a linear space; (2) for any f in D and any number a, $L(af) = aL(f)$; and (3) for any f and g in D, $L(f + g) = L(f) + L(g)$.

Theorem 3.   If $L_0: D_p \to C$ is defined as $L_0[Ae^{\sigma t} \cos (\omega t + \alpha)] \equiv Ae^{j\alpha}$, then L_0 is a linear (the scalars are taken as real numbers) one-to-one transformation.

PROOF: It was proved in Theorem 2 that D_p is a linear space. It is clear that for any $f \in D_p$, $L_0(af) = aL_0(f)$; that is,

$$L_0[aAe^{\sigma t} \cos (\omega t + \alpha)] = aAe^{j\alpha} = aL_0[Ae^{\sigma t} \cos (\omega t + \alpha)]$$

---

an operation (called addition) for pairs of vectors of D; and if $x \in D$, let ax denote *multiplication of x by the scalar a* (the scalars are usually taken as real numbers or complex numbers). Then D is a linear space (also called vector space) iff:

1. For any $x \in D$ and $y \in D$, $(x + y) \in D$.
2. For any $x \in D$ and any scalar a, $ax \in D$.
3. The operations of addition and multiplication by scalars are well behaved, specifically,

$$x + y = y + x$$
$$(x + y) + z = x + (y + z)$$
$$\text{If } x + y = x + z \text{ then } y = z$$
$$1x = x$$
$$a(x + y) = ax + ay$$
$$(a + b)x = ax + bx$$
$$a(bx) = (ab)x$$

For D_p, x, y, and z are real-valued functions and hence condition 3 is obviously satisfied.

The only point remaining is to show that, if $f + g = h$, where $f + g = Ae^{\sigma t} \cos (\omega t + \alpha) + Be^{\sigma t} \cos (\omega t + \beta) = Ce^{\sigma t} \cos (\omega t + \gamma) = h$, then $L_0(f + g) = L_0(h) = Ce^{j\gamma} = L_0(f) + L_0(g) = Ae^{j\alpha} + Be^{j\beta}$. If we refer back to the proof of Theorem 2, we see that C and γ were such that

$$Ce^{j\gamma} = (A \cos \alpha + B \cos \beta) + j(A \sin \alpha + B \sin \beta)$$

and this clearly equals

$$Ae^{j\alpha} + Be^{j\beta} = (A \cos \alpha + B \cos \beta) + j(A \sin \alpha + B \sin \beta)$$

Finally, as for the one-to-one property, it is clear that, since p is fixed, given $Ae^{j\alpha} = L_0(f)$, f is unique.

It might be observed that any element of D_p can be written in the form $f(t) = Ae^{\sigma t} \cos \omega t + Be^{\sigma t} \sin \omega t$, in which case $L_0(f) = A - jB$. Also, $L_0[Be^{\sigma t} \sin (\omega t + \beta)] = -jBe^{j\beta}$.

Theorem 4. If $f \in D_p$, then f' is in D_p and $L_0(f') = pL_0(f)$, where $f' \equiv df/dt$.

PROOF: Let $f(t) = Ae^{\sigma t} \cos (\omega t + \alpha)$.   Then

$$f'(t) = \sigma Ae^{\sigma t} \cos (\omega t + \alpha) - \omega Ae^{\sigma t} \sin (\omega t + \alpha)$$
$$f'(t) = \sigma f + \omega Ae^{\sigma t} \cos \left(\omega t + \alpha + \frac{\pi}{2} \right)$$

Thus, by linearity, $L_0(f') = \sigma Ae^{j\alpha} + \omega Ae^{j(\alpha + \pi/2)}$, but since $Ae^{j\alpha} = L_0(f)$, we have

$$L_0(f') = \sigma L_0(f) + \omega e^{j\pi/2}L_0(f)$$
$$L_0(f') = (\sigma + j\omega)L_0(f) = pL_0(f)$$

as was to be shown.

Before going on with additional theorems, we shall discuss a simple example. Suppose a current generator "drives" a parallel RC network thus:

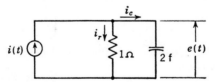

If $i(t) = 5e^t \cos (2t + 1)$, find e;† if the solution is to be unique we must add a restriction such as that $e(t)$ is of the form $Be^t \cos (2t + \beta)$.   Normally we should give the solution by inspection, using familiar impedance concepts; however, this would not display the role of Theorems 3 and 4; therefore, we shall start with the differential equation which relates i and e:

$$i = i_r + i_c \qquad i_r = \frac{e}{R} \qquad q_c = Ce$$

† The letter e is used for both voltage and the base of natural logarithms.

and hence $i_c = Ce'$.   Thus

$$i = \frac{1}{R}e + Ce'$$

We now look for a solution $e(t)$ of the form $Be^t \cos(2t + \beta)$; that is, we look for a solution in D_p.   Throughout the book capital letters will usually be used for the transform of the corresponding lowercase letter.   Thus the L_0 transform of $e(t)$ will be denoted by E; that is, E will denote $L_0(e)$, called the phasor of e for the *operational calculus* now under consideration.

   To start solving the problem we must assume there exists a solution of $i = (1/R)e + Ce'$ in D_p.   Then, taking the L_0 transform of both sides yields

$$L_0(i) = \frac{1}{R}L_0(e) + CL_0(e')$$

by Theorem 3.   Then Theorem 4 gives

$$I = \frac{1}{R}E + pCE$$

Thus,
$$E = \frac{I}{1/R + pC} = Z(p)I$$

For the specific case under consideration,

$$R = 1 \qquad C = 2 \qquad I = 5e^{j1} \qquad p = 1 + j2$$

This gives

$$E = \frac{5e^{j1}}{1 + 2 + j4} = \frac{5e^{j1}}{3 + j4}$$

or
$$E \cong e^{j(1-0.93)} \cong e^{j0.07}$$

So far it has been shown that if there is a solution in D_p, that solution is

$$e(t) = e^t \cos(2t + 0.07)$$

That there is a solution in D_p is established by reading the solution backward.   For said e, we get

$$L_0(i) = \frac{1}{R}L_0(e) + CL_0(e')$$

Now take the inverse transform L_0^{-1}, which is linear and unique; hence, $i = (1/R)e + Ce'$, which establishes $e^t \cos(2t + 0.07)$ as a solution. Under the restriction that the solution was to be in D_p, we actually found that the solution is unique for the specific case treated.   Of course, without any constraints the solution is not unique, for we can always add any homogeneous solution of the differential equation.

   It might be observed that the above method can be used to find a homogeneous solution if we do not fix p. For example, consider

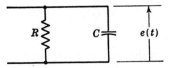

We have $0 = e/R + Ce'$; hence $0 = (1/R)E + CpE$, which is satisfied for nonzero E iff $1/R + Cp = 0$, that is, iff $p = 1/RC$, in which case any E will do.   Thus, if we want a more general solution to

$$5e^t \cos(2t + 1) = e + 2e'$$

we use

$$e(t) = e^t \cos(2t + 0.07) + Ke^{-t/2}$$

where $e^t \cos(2t + 0.07)$ is the particular solution obtained by restricting our attention to D_{1+j2}, and $Ke^{-t/2}$ is an arbitrary homogeneous solution.

Though the above calculation involved only a first-order differential equation, it is clear that the methods can be applied to any linear differential equation with constant coefficients.   For suppose†

$$\sum_{k=0}^{n} a_k f^k(t) = \sum_{i=0}^{m} b_i g^i(t)$$

where, say, f is given in D_p and we wish to find g.   We restrict g to D_p and find the following particular solution where $G = L_0(g)$ and $F = L_0(f)$:

$$G = FH(p)$$

where $H(p)$ is the following rational function of p:

$$\frac{\displaystyle\sum_{k=0}^{n} a_k p^k}{\displaystyle\sum_{i=0}^{m} b_i p^i}$$

Of course, the derivation uses the linearity of L_0 along with the result that

$$L_0(f^k) = L_0\left(\frac{d^k f}{dt^k}\right) = p^k L_0(f)$$

which is obtained‡ by k applications of Theorem 4.   The search for homogeneous solutions involves the equation

$$\sum_{i=0}^{m} b_i p^i G = 0$$

† Superscripts denote differentiation.
‡ Formally we can use mathematical induction.   For if $L_0(f^k) = p^k L_0(f)$, consider $L_0(f^{k+1})$.   We get $L_0(f^{k+1}) = pL_0(f^k)$ from Theorem 4, and then $L_0(f^{k+1}) = pp^k L_0(f) = p^{k+1}L_0(f)$, which establishes the result for all integers k since it is known to hold for $k = 1$.

and it is clear that if $p = \sigma + j\omega$ is a zero of the polynomial

$$\sum_{i=0}^{m} b_i p^i$$

$A e^{\sigma t} \cos (\omega t + \alpha)$ can be added to the particular solution.

Finally, the example now suggests two more problems: (1) If the polynomial

$$Q(p) = \sum_{i=0}^{m} b_i p^i$$

has multiple zeros, how do we find all m linearly independent homogeneous solutions?   (2) In solving for the particular solution, what should be said about the possibility that the particular p under consideration is a zero of $Q(p)$?   For then

$$GQ(p) = \sum_{k=0}^{n} a_k p^k F$$

has no solution if we assume that $F \neq 0$ and

$$\sum_{k=0}^{n} a_k p^k$$

is not zero.   These questions are not very difficult to treat, but they will be left for later.

Two more theorems concerning L_0 will now be given, but the picture will not be complete until Chap. 3 when we return to a careful consideration of the fundamentals.   If f is a function of a real variable, let f_τ denote the function obtained by translating f by an amount τ in time; that is,

$$f_\tau(t) = f(t + \tau) \qquad \text{for all } t$$

Of course, delay lines perform the operation of taking f into f_τ if τ is negative. If we describe Theorem 4 with the remark that p is the transfer function of a differentiator, we should describe Theorem 5 by the remark that $e^{p\tau}$ is the transfer function of a delay line (with the sign convention used, anticipation line would be more appropriate).

Theorem 5.   Let $f \in D_p$ and let $L_0(f) = F$.   Then $f_\tau \in D_p$ and

$$L_0(f_\tau) = e^{p\tau} F$$

PROOF: Let

$$f(t) = A e^{\sigma t} \cos (\omega t + \alpha)$$

where $F \equiv A e^{j\alpha}$.   Then

$$f_\tau(t) = A e^{\sigma(t+\tau)} \cos (\omega t + \omega \tau + \alpha)$$

Thus,

$$L_0(f_\tau) = A e^{\sigma \tau} e^{j(\alpha + \omega \tau)} = A e^{j\alpha} e^{\sigma \tau + j\omega \tau}$$

That is,

$$L_0(f_\tau) = e^{p\tau} F$$

It is common to relate the output of a system to the input implicitly by a differential equation. It is very desirable to have an explicit equation for the output (g) in terms of the input (f). In Chap. 2, we shall show that convolution provides such an explicit formulation. Let h and f be functions of a real variable t. The *convolution* of h and f is a function of t denoted by $h * f$, and its value at t is defined thus:

$$\int_{-\infty}^{\infty} h(t - \tau)f(\tau)\, d\tau \equiv h(t) * f(t)$$

In circuit theory, h is fixed and characterizes the transformation performed by the circuit, f is an arbitrary input, and the output is $g = h * f$. Observe that convolution is commutative:

$$h(t) * f(t) = \int_{-\infty}^{\infty} h(t - \tau)f(\tau)\, d\tau$$

Let $t - \tau = u$. Then

$$h(t) * f(t) = \int_{-\infty}^{\infty} h(u)f(t - u)\, du = f(t) * h(t)$$

As mentioned in Prob. 4, convolution is also associative and distributive with respect to addition; thus convolution has (about) the same algebraic properties as multiplication. Since we have not yet adequately described the role of convolution in the analysis of linear time-invariant systems, Theorem 6 can simply be viewed as an interesting property of L_0.

Theorem 6. Let f be a sinusoid of complex frequency p (that is, f is an element of D_p), let h be real-valued, and define

$$H(p) \equiv \int_{-\infty}^{\infty} e^{-pt}h(t)\, dt$$

which is assumed to exist. Then $g = f * h$ exists and is in D_p, and

$$L_0(g) = H(p)L_0(f)$$

PROOF: Let $f(t) = Ae^{\sigma t} \cos(\omega t + \alpha)$ and consider the following, which we hope exists:

$$g(t) = \int_{-\infty}^{\infty} h(\tau)f(t - \tau)\, d\tau = A \int_{-\infty}^{\infty} h(\tau)e^{\sigma(t-\tau)} \cos(\omega t + \alpha - \omega\tau)\, d\tau$$

or

$$g(t) = Ae^{\sigma t} \cos(\omega t + \alpha) \int_{-\infty}^{\infty} h(\tau)e^{-\sigma\tau} \cos(\omega\tau)\, d\tau$$
$$+ Ae^{\sigma t} \sin(\omega t + \alpha) \int_{-\infty}^{\infty} h(\tau)e^{-\sigma\tau} \sin(\omega\tau)\, d\tau$$

If g exists, it is clearly in D_p, and by the remark after Theorem 3,

$$L_0(g) = Ae^{j\alpha} \int_{-\infty}^{\infty} h(\tau)e^{-\sigma\tau} \cos(\omega\tau)\, d\tau - jAe^{j\alpha} \int_{-\infty}^{\infty} h(\tau)e^{-\sigma\tau} \sin(\omega\tau)\, d\tau$$

That is,

$$L_0(g) = L_0(f) \int_{-\infty}^{\infty} e^{-p\tau} h(\tau) \, d\tau$$

where $p = \sigma + j\omega$.   If

$$\int_{-\infty}^{\infty} e^{-p\tau} h(\tau) \, d\tau$$

exists, it is clear that the derivation can be read backward to establish the existence of $h * f$.

We can summarize Theorems 2 through 6 by the remark that the system† $(D_p$, real linear combinations in D_p, differentiation, and convolution with h) is isomorphic to the system—C, real linear combinations of complex numbers, multiplication by p, and multiplication by

$$H(p) \equiv \int_{-\infty}^{\infty} h(t) e^{-pt} \, dt$$

—under the transformation L_0.   We should not quit with the idea that C and D_p are essentially identical when corresponding operations (for example, d/dt and p) are identified.   The isomorphism does not exist for all

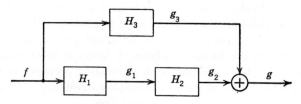

FIGURE 1-3.   Composite system.

interesting operations.   For example, if f and g are elements D_p with transforms F and G, $L_0(fg)$ does not equal FG.   In fact, fg is not even an element of D_p (except in special cases when one factor is zero or $p = 0$); hence $L_0(fg)$ is not even defined.

The transformations induced by L_0 were found to be multiplicative. That is, in Theorems 4 through 6, if f and g denote input and output, respectively, then $L_0(g) = H(p)L_0(f)$, and $H(p)$ is called the transfer function.   Of course, $H(p)$ is p if $g = f'$, $H(p)$ is $e^{p\tau}$ if $g = f_\tau$, and

$$H(p) = \int_{-\infty}^{\infty} e^{-pt} h(t) \, dt$$

if $g = h * f$.   The multiplicative nature of the induced transformation, along with the linearity of L_0, implies that when circuits are cascaded and/or paralleled, the overall transfer function is easily formulated in terms of the individual transfer functions.   The utility of operational analysis rests

† The term system will usually refer to a "black box" of some kind; however, it will sometimes refer to a mathematical system which is a set having certain mathematical operations associated with it.

heavily on this simple observation. Thus the following theorem is as important as it is obvious.

Theorem 7. Multiplying transfer functions corresponds to cascading systems, and adding transfer functions corresponds to paralleling systems. As an example, consider the composite system shown in Figure 1-3. Since

$$L_0(g_1) = H_1L_0(f) \qquad L_0(g_2) = H_2L_0(g_1) \qquad L_0(g_3) = H_3L_0(f)$$

and

$$g = g_3 + g_2$$
$$L_0(g) = (H_1H_2 + H_3)L_0(f)$$

Problems

1. (*a*) If $i = 13e^{2t} \cos(6t + 3)$ for all real t, find i_0 under the assumption that i_0 is an element of D_{2+j6}.

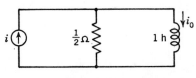

FIGURE P 1

(*b*) Find values of p for which nonzero homogeneous ($i = 0$) solutions exist in D_p.

(*c*) With the i_0 of part a, find $i_0(t)$ under the restriction that i_0 has the value 4 at time $t = 3$, that is, $i_0(3) = 4$.

2. Let a parallel LRC circuit be driven by a current generator $i(t) = Ae^{\sigma t} \cos(\omega t + \alpha)$. Find the voltage across the tank as shown in the sketch. Also, find values of p for which nonzero homogeneous solutions exist.

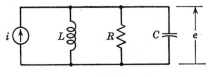

FIGURE P 2

3. Suppose the output of a circuit is implicitly related to the input by the following differential equation where f is the input and g is the output:

$$Tg' + g = f$$

(*a*) Find the transfer function, that is, G/F, where $F = L_0(f)$ and $G = L_0(g)$.

(*b*) If g is related to f explicitly by the following convolution, find the transfer function $H(p)$ as given by Theorem 6.

$$g(t) = \frac{1}{T}\int_0^\infty \exp\frac{-\tau}{T} f(t - \tau)\, d\tau = \frac{1}{T}\int_{-\infty}^t \exp\frac{-(t - \tau)}{T} f(\tau)\, d\tau$$

(*c*) Differentiate the second formulation of (*b*) by using the rule

$$\frac{d}{dt}\int_{-\infty}^t K(t, \tau)\, d\tau = K(t, t) + \int_{-\infty}^t \frac{\partial K(t, \tau)}{\partial t}\, d\tau$$

and show that for any f, $Tg' + g = f$ when g is taken as formulated in (*b*).

4. (a) Show that $(f * g) * h = f * (g * h)$; that is, convolution is associative.

(b) Show that $h * (f + g) = h * f + h * g$ (the proof is trivial); i.e., convolution is distributive with respect to addition. It is a bit more informative to show that $h * (af + bg) = a(h * f) + b(h * g)$ (where a and b are constants), which establishes that convolution is a linear operation.

(c) Show that if $g = h * f$, then $h * f_T = g_T$; that is, translating f by an amount T simply results in translating g by an amount T (trivial). When translating the input simply produces the same translation of the output, a system is called *time-invariant*; thus it is seen that if Φ is a circuit which can be described by convolution, $\Phi(f) = h * f$, then Φ is time-invariant as well as linear.

2

TWO-SIDED LAPLACE
TRANSFORMS WITH
SIMPLE APPLICATIONS

In Chap. 1 an operational theory was developed in nearly complete detail. An analogous theory will be given here, but the class of functions of interest here is not so simple; in turn, the development will be more complicated as far as mathematical details are concerned. It may be that by the end of Chap. 2, we shall find it difficult to see the forest for the trees. However, with the details of the first two chapters serving as background material, the foundations and overall nature of operational analysis are derived deductively in Chap. 3 from basic properties of the systems to be analyzed. Thus, Chap. 3 serves to summarize and determine the final shape of the theory of operational analysis.

Before the definition† of the Laplace transform is given, some notation will be introduced. Let f be a complex-valued (or real-valued) function of a real variable (usually time). The two-sided Laplace transform of f will be denoted by $L(f)$ and by F, if it exists. This transform of f, $L(f)$, will be a complex-valued function of a complex variable; restricting f to be real does not restrict $L(f)$ to be real. Of course, L denotes the transformation and $L(f)$ can be called the value of L at f. Since $L(f) \equiv F$ is itself a function, it has values at complex numbers in its domain of definition. The value of $L(f)$ at the complex number p will be denoted by $L(f)_p$ and by $F(p)$. We are now more or less ready for the definition: p is in the domain of $L(f)$ iff the following exists:

$$\int_{-\infty}^{\infty} e^{-pt} f(t)\, dt$$

And if it does exist, it is the value of $L(f)_p \equiv F(p)$. To make the definition precise, we must specify the type of integral being used; e.g., should we insist on absolute convergence of the integral, should we insist that $f(t)$ be defined for every t, etc. The conventions to be used in most of the book will be given later. The domain of L is all functions f for which $L(f)_p$ exists for at least one complex number p. For the most part we shall not try to deal with the entire domain of L, but rather with various subsets.

One important subset is those functions in the domain which have the value zero for all negative time. The restriction of the two-sided Laplace transform to those f in the domain of L for which $f(t) = 0$ when $t < 0$ will be called‡ the *right-sided Laplace transform of f*. It will be denoted by L_r. Another important special case comes about in quite a different way. We restrict the domain of L to those f such that $L(f)_p$ exists for Re $p = 0$. Then let $p = j\omega$ (with ω real) and consider $L(f)_{j\omega}$ as a function of the real variable ω. This function of a real variable is the *Fourier transform of f*. We shall frequently restrict our attention of the above special cases of the two-sided Laplace transform. A major attraction of the two-sided Laplace transform is that it contains the one-sided (right-sided usually being of interest) Laplace transform and the Fourier transform as important special cases. Another major advantage is that several aspects of the theory can be more easily and completely understood in the setting of L than in the setting of L_r; specifically, inversion by contour integration is clearest when viewed in terms of the two-sided transform. Also, when only the one-sided theory is given, there is seldom any insight for the importance of the point

---

† We should say a *definition* because there are several sets of useful conventions which can be made in the formulation of Laplace transforms; some not covered in this chapter are discussed in Chap. 10.

‡ Laplace transform is usually synonymous with right-sided Laplace transform; however, in this book Laplace transform is synonymous with two-sided Laplace transform.

$t = 0$. However, in the theory for L, an arbitrary (finite) set of values of t can be given this importance in an obvious fashion; not only is this illuminating, but it is also useful in certain problems.

As was already mentioned, we seldom deal with the entire domain of L. One important reason is simply that to obtain needed mathematical results (theorems) various special mathematical restrictions must be placed on the functions to be transformed. Most of the restrictions to be used are familiar ones; however, a few which may not be familiar will now be reviewed before we discuss fundamental theorems for L.

2-1 MATHEMATICAL PRELIMINARIES†

Since $F(p) = L(f)_p$ is defined in terms of an integral, a specific definition of the integral must be selected. The notion of integration usually defined in elementary calculus is called Riemann integration. Some of the first work on Fourier series (which carries over to Fourier transforms and Laplace transforms) was done by Riemann, and this work was based on Riemann integration and was the motivation for the development of a good part of the theory of Riemann integration (2).‡ A respectable inversion theorem can be obtained by using Riemann integration in the definition; by an inversion theorem is meant a prescription which gives f in terms of F— under certain restrictions on f. Specifically, with Riemann integration we can obtain a very satisfactory theory for functions of bounded variation; we shall rely on this theory throughout the book. Hence, some of the properties of functions of bounded variation will be reviewed.

To go much beyond the theory developed for functions of bounded variation, we find that Riemann integration is not an adequately general theory of integration in that there are functions which are not Riemann-integrable which can be generated by Fourier series (as well as L transforms). In turn, the theory of Fourier series, etc., which was developed after Riemann, was based on and was a motivation for Lebesgue integration (3), which can be viewed as simply a generalization of Riemann integration. With Lebesgue integration we can obtain an inversion formula for a more general class of functions than those of bounded variation. This theorem is given in Chap. 10, and it involves *convergence in the mean*, while the inversion theorem of most interest to us involves pointwise convergence. Riemann integration will be adequate for very nearly all the material in the book, and hence it will be used in the definition of L; however, we shall occasionally make use of powerful analytical tools discovered in the development of Lebesgue integration but having application in Riemann integration as well. The use of something other than the best available theory of integration is no more than a minor annoyance in most of our work.

---

† Light coverage of this section is adequate as far as the main objectives of the book are concerned.

‡ Numbers in parentheses are keyed to the references at the end of the book.

FUNCTIONS OF BOUNDED VARIATION

The complex-valued function f of the real variable t is of *bounded variation* on the interval $[a, b]$ iff there exists some real $M > 0$ such that

$$\sum_{i=1}^{n} |f(t_i) - f(t_{i-1})| < M$$

whenever $a = t_0 < t_1 < \cdots < t_n = b$ for arbitrary integer n. The smallest value of M which will serve as an upper bound for

$$\sum_{i=1}^{n} |f(t_i) - f(t_{i-1})|$$

is called the variation of f on $[a, b]$ and will be denoted by $V(a, b)$. When f is real, we can think of $V(a, b)$ as the total "up and down movement" of the graph of f. It is a bit inconvenient to discuss the properties of functions of bounded variation for complex-valued functions; however, the following theorem indicates that there is no loss in generality in discussing only real-valued functions.

Theorem 1. A complex-valued function is of bounded variation iff its real and imaginary parts are of bounded variation.

PROOF: Let $f(t) = x(t) + jy(t)$, where x and y are real. The *only if* follows from the observation that $|x(t_i) - x(t_{i-1})| \leq |f(t_i) - f(t_{i-1})|$ (and the similar equation with y). The *if* part follows from the observation that $|f(t_i) - f(t_{i-1})| \leq |x(t_i) - x(t_{i-1})| + |y(t_i) - y(t_{i-1})|$.

Theorem 2. A real-valued function is of bounded variation on $[a, b]$ iff it can be expressed as the difference of two monotone nondecreasing functions.

PROOF: For the *if* part of the theorem, let f_1 and f_2 be nondecreasing on $[a, b]$. Of course f_1 is nondecreasing on $[a, b]$ iff $f_1(t') \leq f_1(t)$ whenever $t' > t$ and both t' and t are points of the interval $[a, b]$. Suppose $f = f_1 - f_2$. Then it is nearly obvious that f_1 and f_2 are of bounded variation and that the variation of f is no greater than the sum of the variations of f_1 and f_2. The proof in detail follows:

$$\sum_{i=1}^{n} |f(t_i) - f(t_{i-1})| = \sum_{i=1}^{n} |[f_2(t_i) - f_2(t_{i-1})] - [f_1(t_i) - f_1(t_{i-1})]|$$

$$\leq \sum_{i=1}^{n} |f_2(t_i) - f_2(t_{i-1})| + |f_1(t_i) - f_1(t_{i-1})|$$

However, since f_1 and f_2 are nondecreasing, the absolute-value signs are not needed in this last equation, and hence we get *telescoping sums*. To see this, consider the sum involving f_2:

$$f_2(t_1) + f_2(t_2) + \cdots + f_2(t_{n-1}) + f_2(t_n) - f_2(t_0) - f_2(t_1) - f_2(t_2)$$
$$- \cdots - f_2(t_{n-1})$$

which gives the bound

$$f_2(t_n) - f_2(t_0)$$

Finally, since f_1 and f_2 are nondecreasing,

$$\sum_{i=1}^{n} |f(t_i) - f(t_{i-1})| \leq f_2(b) - f_2(a) + f_1(b) - f_1(a)$$

That is, f is of bounded variation.

For the *only if* part, let f be of bounded variation on $[a, b]$. For any t in the interval it is easy to see that f is of bounded variation on $[a, t]$. Let $V(a, t)$ be the variation of f on the subinterval $[a, t]$. Now write f thus:

$$f(t) = V(a, t) - [V(a, t) - f(t)]$$

It is easy to show that this is an expression for f as the difference of nondecreasing functions. Let $t' \geq t$. Then it is (nearly) obvious that

$$V(a, t') = V(a, t) + V(t, t')$$

However, $V(t, t') \geq 0$; therefore,

$$V(a, t') \geq V(a, t)$$

Finally, we wish to show that for $t' > t$,

$$V(a, t') - f(t') \geq V(a, t) - f(t) \qquad \text{or} \qquad V(a, t') - V(a, t) \geq f(t') - f(t)$$

Now the question reduces to

$$V(t', t) \geq f(t') - f(t)$$

This is certainly true if

$$V(t', t) \geq |f(t') - f(t)|$$

This is clearly true since the right side of the inequality is a special case of a sum (a one-term sum with $t_0 = t$, $t_n = t'$, and $n = 1$) of the type for which $V(t', t)$ is an upper bound.

Several interesting results can now be obtained.

Theorem 3.   The set of real functions of bounded variation on $[a, b]$ is a linear space over the field of real scalars.

PROOF: If f is of bounded variation, obviously af is of bounded variation for any a. Also, let f and g be of bounded variation with $f = f_1 - f_2$ and $g = g_1 - g_2$, where the functions with subscripts are nondecreasing. Then $f + g = (f_1 + g_1) - (f_2 + g_2)$, which is clearly the difference of nondecreasing functions, which completes the proof.

Theorem 4.   If f is of bounded variation on $[a, b]$, then

$$\int_a^b f(t) \, dt$$

exists.

PROOF: For the proof we need a definition for the integral. Of course, from now on integral will mean Riemann integral unless otherwise stated. For the proof, upper and lower approximating sums will be formulated for a nondecreasing function thus (let $a = t_0 < t_1 < \cdots < t_n = b$):

$$\bar{S} = \sum_{i=1}^{n} f(t_i)(t_i - t_{i-1}) \qquad \underline{S} = \sum_{i=1}^{n} f(t_{i-1})(t_i - t_{i-1})$$

The integral exists iff $\bar{S} - \underline{S}$ can be made small by taking the largest increment

$$\Delta = \max_i (t_i - t_{i-1})$$

small.   Observe that

$$\bar{S} - \underline{S} = \sum_{i=1}^{n} [f(t_i) - f(t_{i-1})](t_i - t_{i-1}) \qquad \bar{S} - \underline{S} \le \Delta \sum_{i=1}^{n} [f(t_i) - f(t_{i-1})]$$

which again is a telescoping sum; that is,

$$\bar{S} - \underline{S} \le \Delta [f(b) - f(a)]$$

which is small if Δ is small, which establishes the existence of $\int f$ when f is nondecreasing.   Of course, since any function of bounded variation is the difference of nondecreasing functions, it follows from the linearity of integration that any function of bounded variation is integrable.

Theorem 5.   One-sided limits exist for functions of bounded variation, and hence the only discontinuities are jump discontinuities.   Also, there are at most a countable† infinity of points of discontinuity.

PROOF: Again this follows from the corresponding property for nondecreasing functions; i.e., if f is nondecreasing,

$$f(t + 0) = \lim_{\epsilon \to 0} f(t + |\epsilon|) \qquad \text{and} \qquad f(t - 0) = \lim_{\epsilon \to 0} f(t - |\epsilon|)$$

exist since these are limits on monotone bounded functions.   Recall that f is continuous at t iff each of these one-sided limits exists and each is equal to $f(t)$.   A discontinuity at t contributes $|f(t + 0) - f(t)| + |f(t) - f(t - 0)|$ to the variation of f.   If we had a noncountable infinity of jumps on $[a, b]$, then for some positive integer n there would be infinitely many jumps which contribute at least $1/n$ to the variation and hence the variation would not be bounded.   To state this in more detail, let J_n be the set of points that have jumps which contribute more than $1/n$ but not more than $1/(n - 1)$. Each jump point appears in one and only one J_n (we make the convention that J_1 includes all jumps contributing more than one).   If each J_n were finite, we could "count" the jump points.   Thus, if we have a noncountable

† A set is countable iff either it is finite or it can be put into one-to-one correspondence with the positive integers.

infinity of jump points, there are infinitely many points in some J_n. Corresponding to this J_n there is an infinite contribution to the variation, which contradicts the assumption of bounded variation.

Enough formal mathematics for the moment. In elementary calculus continuous functions are emphasized more than functions of bounded variation (because continuity is the proper condition for the fundamental theorem of calculus). However, continuity is neither a necessary nor a sufficient condition for the inversion theorem toward which we are heading. The conditions of continuity and bounded variation are not comparable, because neither implies the other. For example,

$$U(t) = \begin{cases} 0 & \text{for } t < 0 \\ \tfrac{1}{2} & \text{for } t = 0 \\ 1 & \text{for } t > 0 \end{cases}$$

is of bounded variation on any finite interval, but U is not continuous at $t = 0$. On the other hand,

$$f(t) = \begin{cases} t \sin \dfrac{1}{t} & \text{for } t \neq 0 \\ 0 & \text{for } t = 0 \end{cases}$$

is continuous for all t, but it is not of bounded variation on any interval

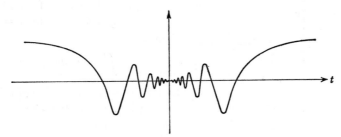

FIGURE 2-1.   Sketch of $t \sin (1/t)$.

having $t = 0$ as an interior point (the proof for a similar function is sketched in Prob. 3).

By the way, the function

$$g(t) = \begin{cases} \sin \dfrac{1}{t} & \text{for } t \neq 0 \\ 0 & \text{for } t = 0 \end{cases}$$

provides an example of a nonjump discontinuity at $t = 0$. Here the discontinuity is due to the fact that the one-sided limits $g(+0)$ and $g(-0)$ do not exist.

As a side remark (of almost no use to us), the following is an equation for variation: If f' is continuous on $[a, b]$, then

$$V(a, b) = \int_a^b |f'| \, dt$$

Thus, continuity of the derivative implies bounded variation. Also, bounded variation and the lack of jumps imply continuity, and in any event bounded variation implies that there are at most a countable infinity of jump discontinuities.

SOME CONVENTIONS AND THEOREMS IN INTEGRATION THEORY

A nearly adequate discussion of integration is given in Chap. 10; only a few points will be made here. In the definition of the (proper) Riemann integral

$$\int_a^b f(t) \, dt$$

$f(t)$ must be defined for all t of the closed interval $[a, b]$. However, it often happens that we integrate functions which are not defined at certain points. For example, if $f(t) = |t|$, we might be interested in

$$\int_{-2}^1 f'(t) \, dt$$

but $f'(t)$ does not exist at $t = 0$. It is easy to see that if we let

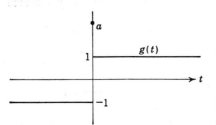

$$g(t) = \begin{cases} f'(t) & \text{for } t \neq 0 \\ a & \text{for } t = 0 \end{cases}$$

then

$$\int_{-2}^1 g(t) \, dt = -1$$

FIGURE 2-2.   Graph of $g(t)$.

no matter what the value of a is. The convention made for the integral of functions not defined at certain points is the following: If arbitrary values are assigned for the points and the function is then properly integrable and if the value of this integral is independent of the assigned values, then (and only then) the original function is considered integrable and of course its integral is taken as the value obtained with any particular assignment of values at the exceptional points.

The function ϕ is called a null function on $[a, b]$ iff ϕ is integrable on $[a, b]$ and

$$\int_a^b |\phi(t)| \, dt = 0$$

Thus a null function is a function which is essentially zero in that it behaves like zero as far as integration is concerned. If f and g differ by at most a null function, we say $f = g$ *almost everywhere* (which means f and g are equal as far as integration properties are concerned; the concept is discussed further in Sec. 10-1).

Theorem 6.   If f and g are functions of bounded variation which are equal at all points where they are both continuous, then f equals g almost everywhere.

PROOF: We wish to prove that

$$\int_a^b |f(t) - g(t)|\, dt = 0$$

and we know that $f(t) = g(t)$ except possibly at jumps in f or g.   Of course, $f - g$ is integrable since f and g are integrable.   Consider the approximating sum

$$\sum_{i=1}^n |f(\xi_i) - g(\xi_i)|(x_i - x_{i-1})$$

where $a = x_0 < x_1 < x_2 < \cdots < x_n = b$; and since $f - g$ is integrable, we can take ξ_i as any point of the interval $[x_{i-1}, x_i]$ with the assurance that in the limit as

$$\max_i (x_i - x_{i-1})$$

goes to zero, the approximating sum will go to the value of the integral. It is now easy to show that we can always make the approximating sum zero and in turn the limit is zero.   For any of the intervals (x_{i-1}, x_i), which are always of nonzero length, there are at most a countable infinity of points where f and g are not equal.   Thus, we merely select any one of the (many) remaining points for ξ_i.   Then $f(\xi_i) = g(\xi_i)$, which makes each term of the approximating sum zero, as was to be shown.

The above theorem will provide us with (a weak form of) the fact that the inverse Laplace transform is unique within a null function.

Prior to the development of Lebesgue integration, the only useful theorem guaranteeing that one could interchange limits and integrals used the hypothesis of uniform convergence.   Though the theorem is sometimes adequate, it is a very weak (nearly trivial) result leaving much to be desired.   We shall use the following less ancient, powerful analytical tool to justify some of our interchanges.

Theorem 7 (*Dominated Convergence Theorem*).   Let $f(t, \theta)$ be integrable as a function of t for each θ in a punctured neighborhood of θ_0 (by punctured is meant that we do not worry about $\theta = \theta_0$), let there exist an integrable function $h(t)$ such that $|f(t, \theta)| < h(t)$ for θ in said neighborhood, let

$$\lim_{\theta \to \theta_0} f(t, \theta) = g(t)$$

and (this last condition is not needed when Lebesgue integration is used) let $g(t)$ be integrable; then

$$\lim_{\theta \to \theta_0} \int f(t, \theta)\, dt = \int g(t)\, dt$$

The theorem holds for an infinite interval of integration as well as for finite intervals. The following theorem is also used occasionally.

Theorem 8 (*Fubini's Theorem*). Consider a function of two variables $f(x, y)$. We shall say f has the property $*$ iff the double integral $\iint f(x, y)\, dx\, dy$ is equal to the iterated integrals $\int [\int f(x, y)\, dx]\, dy$ and $\int [\int f(x, y)\, dy]\, dx$. If $\iint |f(x, y)|\, dx\, dy$ or $\int [\int |f(x, y)|\, dx]\, dy$ exists (Lebesgue case), then f has the property $*$. If, in addition, the double and iterated integrals of property $*$ exist (Riemann sense), then Riemann integration will do. This Riemann version follows from the fact that Riemann integrability implies Lebesgue integrability, and when an integral exists in both senses, the values are equal.

Problems

1. *Prove:* If f and g are of bounded variation, then fg is of bounded variation (it is enough to consider f and g real).

2. Let f be a complex-valued function of t and think of $f(t) = x(t) + jy(t)$ as a parametric equation for a curve in the xy plane. Or (what is the same thing) think of the locus of the values of f as a curve in a complex plane. If f is continuous and of bounded variation, what geometrical quantity corresponds to the variation of f on $[a, b]$?

3. If

$$f(t) = \begin{cases} 0 & \text{for } t = 0 \\ t \exp \dfrac{j}{t} & \text{for } t \neq 0 \end{cases}$$

formulate the variation of f on $(\epsilon, 1)$ as

$$\int_\epsilon^1 |f'|\, dt$$

Show that

$$\lim_{\epsilon \to 0^+} V(\epsilon, 1) = \infty$$

and hence f is continuous on $[0, 1]$ but not of bounded variation on $[0, 1]$.

4. *Prove:* If $a < t < t'$, then $V(a, t') = V(a, t) + V(t, t')$.

2-2 FUNDAMENTAL THEOREMS FOR LAPLACE TRANSFORMS

In this section some insight will be developed as to which functions are transformable, an inversion formula will be derived, and the mathematical nature of functions obtained as the result of taking transforms will be established. The pseudo linearity of L will be considered first.

Theorem 9. If $L(f)_p$ and $L(g)_p$ exist, then for any (complex) numbers a and b, $L(af + bg)_p$ exists and equals $aL(f)_p + bL(g)_p$. This theorem does not imply that L is a linear transformation in that the domain of L is not a linear space. Specifically, $L(f)$ and $L(g)$ may exist only at different points in the complex plane, and in turn $L(f + g)$ would not exist at any points of the complex plane.   For example, suppose

$$f(t) = \begin{cases} 1 & \text{for } t \geq 0 \\ 0 & \text{for } t < 0 \end{cases}$$

Then

$$F(p) = L(f)_p = \int_0^\infty e^{-pt}\, dt = \lim_{A \to \infty} \frac{e^{-pt}}{-p}\bigg]_0^A = \frac{1}{p} - \lim_{A \to \infty} \frac{e^{-pA}}{p}$$

which exists iff Re $p > 0$ and then $F(p) = 1/p$.   Now consider

$$g(t) = \begin{cases} 1 & \text{for } t < 0 \\ 0 & \text{for } t \geq 0 \end{cases}$$

Then

$$G(p) = \int_{-\infty}^0 e^{-pt}\, dt = \lim_{B \to \infty} \frac{e^{-pt}}{-p}\bigg]_{-B}^0 = -\frac{1}{p} + \lim_{B \to \infty} \frac{e^{pB}}{p}$$

which exists iff Re $p < 0$.   Finally, consider $h(t) = f(t) + g(t) = 1$ for all t; then

$$H(p) = \int_{-\infty}^\infty e^{-pt}\, dt$$

which exists for no complex p.   That is, the sum of two-sided transformable functions is not necessarily transformable.

On the other hand, one-sided transforms are linear.   For if $L_r(f)_p$ exists, then $L_r(f)_q$ exists whenever Re $q > $ Re p; that is, for one-sided transforms the convergence is always on a right infinite half plane (or not at all).   In turn, if $L_r(f)$ and $L_r(g)$ each exist at some point, they will simultaneously exist for values of p which have a sufficiently large real part.   The proof of this fact is a bit sticky in the general case (cf. Ref. 4, page 15); however, under various restricting conditions (e.g., see Theorem 10 and Prob. 7) it is quite easy.

Theorem 10 (Sufficient Conditions for Existence of L_r).   Let f be integrable on finite intervals, let $f(t) = 0$ for $t < 0$, and let real numbers c and M exist such that $|f(t)| < Me^{ct}$ for all t; then $L_r(f)_p$ exists for Re $p > c$.

PROOF: Since f was assumed integrable,

$$\int_0^A f(t)e^{-pt}\, dt$$

exists, and we need only show that

$$\lim_{A \to \infty} \int_0^A f(t)e^{-pt}\, dt$$

exists for Re $p = \sigma > c$.   For such p, $|f(t)e^{-pt}| \leq Me^{-(\sigma-c)t}$, from which it is obvious that the indicated limit exists, and in fact we have absolute convergences of $L_r(f)_p$.   The mathematical details of the proof go as follows:

By the Cauchy condition of convergence it is enough to show that

$$\int_{A_1}^{A_2} f(t) e^{-pt}\, dt$$

can be made small for all $A_2 > A_1$ if A_1 is taken sufficiently large.   To see this, observe that

$$\left| \int_{A_1}^{A_2} e^{-\sigma t} e^{-j\omega t} f(t)\, dt \right| \leq \int_{A_1}^{A_2} |e^{-\sigma t} e^{-j\omega t} f(t)|\, dt$$

$$= \int_{A_1}^{A_2} e^{-\sigma t} |f(t)|\, dt \leq M \int_{A_1}^{A_2} e^{-(\sigma-c)}\, dt$$

$$= \frac{M}{\sigma - c} (e^{-A_1(\sigma-c)} - e^{-A_2(\sigma-c)}) \leq \frac{M}{\sigma - c} e^{-A_1(\sigma-c)}$$

which can be made arbitrarily small by taking A_1 large if $\sigma > c$, as was to be shown.

Corollary 1.   If f is integrable on finite intervals and

$$|f(t)| \leq \begin{cases} M e^{c_1 t} & \text{for } t \geq 0 \\ M e^{c_2 t} & \text{for } t < 0 \end{cases}$$

where $c_1 < c_2$, then $L(f)_p$ exists for $c_1 < \operatorname{Re} p < c_2$.   To see this, we consider†

$$L(f)_p = \lim_{B \to \infty} \lim_{A \to \infty} \int_{-B}^{A} e^{-pt} f(t)\, dt$$

$$= \lim_{B \to \infty} \int_{-B}^{0} e^{-pt} f(t)\, dt + \lim_{A \to \infty} \int_{0}^{A} e^{-pt} f(t)\, dt$$

The theorem gives the existence of the second limit for $\operatorname{Re} p > c_1$.   Logic similar to that used in the proof of the theorem gives the existence of the first limit for $\operatorname{Re} p < c_2$.   In turn, both limits exist for $c_1 < \operatorname{Re} p < c_2$. Figure 2-3 summarizes the above results for a specific case:

$$f(t) = \begin{cases} 1 & \text{for } t \geq 0, \text{ which is } \leq 3e^0 \\ 3e^t & \text{for } t < 0, \text{ which is } \leq 3e^t \end{cases}$$

Though Theorem 10 provides only a sufficient test for convergence, the largest interval (c_1, c_2) which can be found often coincides with the entire strip of convergence.

For curiosity's sake we shall now discuss two behaviors of f which illustrate that the exponential bounds of the theorem are not necessary conditions. First, there may be "lots of cancellation of positive and negative humps of $f(t)$."   For example, consider

$$f(t) = \begin{cases} \sin e^t & \text{for } t \geq 0 \\ 0 & \text{for } t < 0 \end{cases}$$

† Except for the inversion formula (Theorem 11), integration over the entire real line will be defined by integrating over a finite interval and then letting the upper and lower limits of integration go to infinity independently.

In the transform p will be taken real, which is all we need to consider in finding the strip of convergence—save possibly for questions at the boundary. The transform is

$$\int_0^\infty (\sin e^t)e^{-\sigma t}\, dt$$

Let $e^t = \theta$. Then we have

$$\int_1^\infty (\sin \theta)e^{-\sigma \ln \theta}\, \frac{d\theta}{\theta}$$

that is,

$$\int_1^\infty \frac{\sin \theta\, d\theta}{\theta^{\sigma+1}}$$

By formulating this as an infinite series, each term of which is obtained by

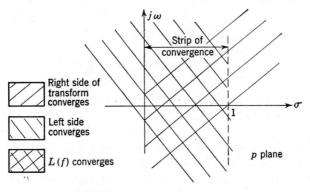

FIGURE 2-3.   Strip of convergence.

integrating over a "hump" of the sine wave, we get an alternating series

$$\sum_{k=0}^\infty (-1)^k a_k$$

If $\sigma + 1 > 0$, then $a_{k+1} < a_k$ and

$$\lim_{k \to \infty} a_k = 0$$

Thus we have convergence for $\sigma > -1$. Also, we get divergence for $\sigma < -1$. The best we could do with Theorem 10 is to observe that

$$|\sin e^t| \le e^{0t} \qquad \text{for } t \ge 0$$

and hence we predict (absolute) convergence for $\sigma > 0$ and miss the strip of conditional convergence $-1 < \operatorname{Re} p < 0$.

Secondly, f may be very spiky; that is, f may not have an exponential bound, yet its large values occur only on very small intervals. For example, let $f(t) = 0$ except when t is in a small interval about the positive integers thus:

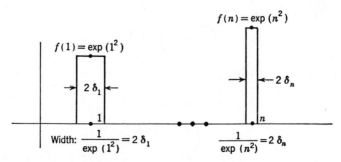

There is no exponential bound for this function; that is, $\exp n^2 > M e^{cn}$ for sufficiently large n. However, $L(f)$ exists for Re $p > 0$. One would guess that $L(f)$ exists for such p by observing that the integral over intervals involving only large n can be approximated thus:

$$\sum_n \int_{n-\delta_n}^{n+\delta_n} (\exp n^2) e^{-pt}\, dt \cong \sum_n e^{-pn}$$

since $e^{-pt} \cong e^{-pn}$ over the very small intervals of integration. This is a convergent series for Re $p > 0$.

To get back to serious matters, an inversion theorem will now be given. Five additional inversion theorems are given in Chap. 10 (see Table I).

Theorem 11 (*Our Most Fundamental Theorem*). Let f be of bounded variation on finite intervals, let there exist a (real) σ such that

$$\int_{-\infty}^{\infty} e^{-\sigma t} |f(t)|\, dt$$

exists (is finite), and let

$$F(p) = \int_{-\infty}^{\infty} e^{-pt} f(t)\, dt$$

Then $\tfrac{1}{2}[f(t+0) + f(t-0)] = \dfrac{1}{2\pi j} \lim_{A \to \infty} \int_{\sigma-jA}^{\sigma+jA} e^{pt} F(p)\, dp$

Of course if f is continuous at t, then the left side of the equation is simply $f(t)$; and if there is a jump discontinuity at t, then the left side is the mean of the values at the ends of the jump. Since $p = \sigma + j\omega$, the right side can also be written thus $(dp = j\, d\omega)$:

$$\frac{1}{2\pi} \lim_{A \to \infty} \int_{-A}^{A} e^{(\sigma+j\omega)t} F(\sigma + j\omega)\, d\omega$$

In applying the theorem we shall usually write

$$f(t) = \frac{1}{2\pi j} \int_{\sigma-j\infty}^{\sigma+j\infty} e^{pt} F(p)\, dp$$

in place of the precise conclusion of the theorem.

PROOF: Consider

$$\frac{1}{2\pi} \int_{-A}^{A} e^{\sigma t} e^{j\omega t} \left[\int_{-\infty}^{\infty} f(u) e^{-\sigma u} e^{-j\omega u} \, du \right] d\omega = \frac{1}{2\pi j} \int_{\sigma-jA}^{\sigma+jA} e^{pt} F(p) \, dp$$

The integrand is absolutely integrable over the indicated infinite strip in the (ω, u) plane; this is a sufficient condition for the interchange of the orders of integration (Fubini's theorem). We then have

$$\frac{e^{\sigma t}}{2\pi} \int_{-\infty}^{\infty} f(u) e^{-\sigma u} \left(\int_{-A}^{A} e^{j\omega(t-u)} \, d\omega \right) du$$

or, for $t \neq u$,

$$e^{\sigma t} \int_{-\infty}^{\infty} e^{-\sigma u} f(u) \frac{\sin A(t-u)}{\pi(t-u)} \, du$$

The integration gives $2A$ at $t = u$; hence $[\sin A(t-u)]/\pi(t-u)$ is replaced with A/π at $t = u$. The proof now consists in showing that when we take the limit as A goes to infinity, the result is

$$\tfrac{1}{2}[f(t+0) + f(t-0)]$$

The function $[\sin A(t-u)]/\pi(t-u)$ is called the Dirichlet kernel, and of course our problem is the classical one of Fourier transforms. To get some insight we first note some properties of the kernel:

1. $\dfrac{\sin A(t-u)}{\pi(t-u)}$ is even about t; that is, $\dfrac{\sin A\theta}{\theta}$ is an even function of θ.

2. $\displaystyle\lim_{u \to t} \frac{\sin A(t-u)}{\pi(t-u)} = \frac{A}{\pi}$, which is the value at $u = t$ by direct evaluation of the integral at $t = u$; that is, the kernel is continuous for all u.

3. Since the kernel equals A/π at $t = u$, the value at $t = u$ goes to ∞ as $A \to \infty$.

4. $\displaystyle\int_{-\infty}^{t} \frac{\sin A(t-u) \, du}{\pi(t-u)}$ exists and is the same for all $A > 0$, and its value is $\frac{1}{2}$. To see this, let $A(t-u) = \theta$ and $-A \, du = d\theta$; then we get

$$\int_{0}^{\infty} \frac{\sin \theta}{\pi\theta} \, d\theta$$

To see that this exists, we simply write it as a sum where each term is the integral over one hump of the sine wave. The series is alternating, and the magnitudes of the terms are monotone decreasing going to zero; hence, the series can be summed (conditionally). We shall show that the value is $\frac{1}{2}$ in an example of integration by residues—the actual value is not very important.

It should now be rather clear that only the values of $f(u)e^{-\sigma u}$ close to t are important as $A \to \infty$ since the value of the kernel at $t = u$ goes to ∞ as $A \to \infty$. The kernel for two values of A is sketched in Figure 2-4.

To complete the proof we could show that

$$\lim_{A \to \infty} \int_{-\infty}^{t-\delta} f(u)e^{-\sigma u} \frac{\sin A(t-u)}{t-u} \, du = 0$$

(Riemann-Lebesgue lemma).   Then the problem is reduced to

$$\lim_{A \to \infty} \int_{t-\delta}^{t} e^{-\sigma u} f(u) \frac{\sin A(t-u)}{t-u} \, du \qquad \lim_{A \to \infty} \int_{t}^{t+\delta} e^{-\sigma u} f(u) \frac{\sin A(t-u)}{t-u} \, du$$

At first glance, we might be tempted to consider continuous f's; however, there exist continuous functions for which the indicated limits do not exist for some values of t (to date it is not known if there exists a continuous f for which the limits do not exist for every t).   On the other hand, if f is of

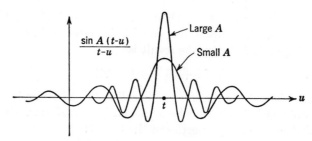

FIGURE 2-4.   Behavior of the Dirichlet kernel.

bounded variation, the limits do exist and are equal to $\frac{1}{2}e^{-\sigma t}f(t-0)$ and $\frac{1}{2}e^{-\sigma t}f(t+0)$.   In turn, the $e^{\sigma t}$ factor outside the integral leaves us with the desired result.   The mathematical details will not be given at this time; however, the inversion formula is established in Chap. 10.   By the way, if f is continuous and the limits do exist, the limit gives $f(t)$ as hoped (see Chap. 10).

The above theorem obviously gives the uniqueness of the inverse of L for functions of bounded variation.   Formally, we have the following corollary.

Corollary 2.   If f and g satisfy the conditions of Theorem 11, they have the same transform F iff f and g differ by at most a null function.   For the *only if* the theorem gives

$$f(t+0) + f(t-0) = g(t+0) + g(t-0)$$

for all t, and of course this means $f(t) = g(t)$ except possibly when f or g has a jump.   But now, by Theorem 6, f and g differ by at most a null function. For the *if* part, we have

$$L(f)_p - L(g)_p = \int_{-\infty}^{\infty} \phi(t)e^{-pt} \, dt$$

where ϕ is a null function.   However, if ϕ is a null function its transform is zero,† and hence $L(f) = L(g)$. The inversion formula will usually be evaluated by using integration by residues, which is covered in Sec. 2-4. However, two sample calculations will be done here; in the first example, both L and L^{-1} will be computed, which will serve as a verification of the theorem.

Example 1.   Suppose we are given $F(p)$ for p purely imaginary.   This is the case when we consider Fourier transforms.   Specifically, let

$$F(j\omega) = \begin{cases} 1 & \text{for } |\omega| \leq W \\ 0 & \text{for } |\omega| > W \end{cases}$$

Observe that the inversion formula has essentially the same mathematical form as the direct transform.   Hence, when it is helpful, we can interchange roles in the theorem and think of F as the function of bounded variation for which

$$\int_{\sigma-j\infty}^{\sigma+j\infty} |F(\sigma + j\omega)|\, dp$$

exists.   When this is done, the direct transform should be evaluated with

$$\lim_{A\to\infty} \int_{-A}^{A} e^{-pt} f(t)\, dt$$

The example now under consideration is a case in point.   With $p = j\omega$ and $dp = j\, d\omega$, we get

$$f(t) = \frac{1}{2\pi} \int_{-W}^{W} e^{j\omega t}\, d\omega = \frac{\sin Wt}{t\pi}$$

Thus the function $(\sin Wt)/t$ can be thought of as a uniform weighting of the frequencies $-W < \omega < W$.   We shall now verify the theorem by computing

$$F(j\omega) = \lim_{A\to\infty} \int_{-A}^{A} e^{-j\omega t} \frac{\sin Wt}{\pi t}\, dt$$
$$= \lim_{A\to\infty} \int_{-A}^{A} \frac{\cos \omega t \sin Wt}{\pi t}\, dt - j \lim_{A\to\infty} \int_{-A}^{A} \frac{\sin \omega t \sin Wt}{\pi t}\, dt$$

The second integrand is an odd function, that is, $g(-t) = -g(t)$; hence, for this term

$$\int_{-A}^{0} = -\int_{0}^{A}$$

† This is obvious; for a proof consider a finite interval of integration for which we have

$$\left| \int_{a}^{b} \phi(t) e^{-pt}\, dt \right| \leq \int_{a}^{b} e^{-\sigma t} |\phi(t)|\, dt$$

This last quantity is bounded between

$$e^{-\sigma b} \int_{a}^{b} |\phi(t)|\, dt \quad \text{and} \quad e^{-\sigma a} \int_{a}^{b} |\phi(t)|\, dt$$

but these are both zero.

and its contribution is zero. For the first term, expand the integrand by using the appropriate trigonometric identity; then

$$F(j\omega) = \lim_{A \to \infty} \frac{1}{2\pi} \int_{-A}^{A} \frac{\sin\left[(W + \omega)t\right]}{t}\, dt + \lim_{A \to \infty} \frac{1}{2\pi} \int_{-A}^{A} \frac{\sin\left[(W - \omega)t\right]}{t}\, dt$$

We are back to the Dirichlet kernel. If $W + \omega$ and $W - \omega$ are greater than zero, we get π for each of the integrals and hence $F(j\omega) = 1$ for $|\omega| < W$. If, say, $W - \omega < 0$ and hence $W + \omega > 0$, then the second term gives

$$-\int_{-A}^{A} \frac{\sin\left[(\omega - W)t\right]}{t}\, dt$$

which gives $-\pi$ when $A \to \infty$ since now $\omega - W > 0$. Of course, the other term is $\frac{1}{2}$ in this case. Thus it is seen that when $|\omega| > W$, one of the terms gives $\frac{1}{2}$ and the other gives $-\frac{1}{2}$. In turn, $F(j\omega) = 0$ for $|\omega| > W$. Finally, suppose $W = \omega$. Then the second term is zero and we have $F(jW) = \frac{1}{2}$.

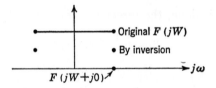

Similarly, $F(-jW) = \frac{1}{2}$. Thus we recovered F at its continuity points, and we got the mean values at the jump discontinuities as expected (actually guaranteed).

Example 2. In this example we would like to establish the following transform pair [let α be real and positive; however, it is only necessary that Re $(1/\alpha^2) > 0$]:

$$L\left(\frac{1}{\sqrt{2\pi}\,\alpha}\, e^{-t^2/2\alpha^2}\right)_p = \exp \tfrac{1}{2}\alpha^2 p^2$$

For this original function, it is seen that any σ will do; that is,

$$\int_{-\infty}^{\infty} e^{-\sigma t}e^{-t^2/2\alpha^2}\, dt < \infty$$

for all real σ since for large t the term involving t^2 "wins." We shall only prove that $e^{\frac{1}{2}\alpha^2 p^2}$ is the transform to the extent that it will serve in the inversion formula to produce the original. Consider

$$\frac{1}{2\pi j} \int_{\sigma-jA}^{\sigma+jA} (\exp \tfrac{1}{2}\alpha^2 p^2)e^{pt}\, dp$$

or, with $p = \sigma + j\omega$, we have

$$\frac{1}{2\pi} e^{\sigma t + \frac{1}{2}\alpha^2\sigma^2} \int_{-A}^{A} e^{-\frac{1}{2}[\alpha^2\omega^2 - j(2\sigma\alpha^2 + 2t)\omega]}\, d\omega$$

Recall that any real σ can be used; therefore, to simplify the problem for specific t, take σ such that $\alpha^2\sigma = -t$. Then only the term $\alpha^2\omega^2$ remains in the exponent of the integrand. Also,

$$\sigma t + \frac{1}{2}\alpha^2\sigma^2 = -\frac{t^2}{\alpha^2} + \frac{t^2}{2\alpha^2} = \frac{-t^2}{2\alpha^2}$$

Thus we get

$$\lim_{A \to \infty} \frac{\exp\left(-t^2/2\alpha^2\right)}{2\pi} \int_{-A}^{A} e^{-\frac{1}{2}\alpha^2\omega^2}\, d\omega$$

which we hope is equal to

$$\frac{1}{\sqrt{2\pi}\,\alpha} e^{-t^2/2\alpha^2}$$

The final problem is to compute

$$I = \int_{-\infty}^{\infty} e^{-\frac{1}{2}\alpha^2\omega^2}\, d\omega$$

Let $\alpha\omega = x$. Then we get

$$I = \frac{1}{\alpha} \int_{-\infty}^{\infty} e^{-x^2/2}\, dx$$

The trick used to evaluate this integral is to compute

$$I^2 = \frac{1}{\alpha^2}\left(\int_{-\infty}^{\infty} e^{-x^2/2}\, dx\right)\left(\int_{-\infty}^{\infty} e^{-y^2/2}\, dy\right) = \frac{1}{\alpha^2}\int_{-\infty}^{\infty}\int_{-\infty}^{\infty} e^{-(x^2+y^2)/2}\, dx\, dy$$

Now go over to polar coordinates to obtain

$$I^2 = \frac{1}{\alpha^2} \int_0^{\infty}\int_0^{2\pi} e^{-\rho^2/2}\rho\, d\theta\, d\rho$$

The θ integration gives 2π, and we have

$$I^2 = \frac{2\pi}{\alpha^2}\int_0^{\infty} e^{-\rho^2/2}\rho\, d\rho = \frac{2\pi}{\alpha^2}\left[-e^{-\rho^2/2}\right]_0^{\infty} = \frac{2\pi}{\alpha^2}$$

Thus the inversion formula gives

$$\frac{1}{2\pi} e^{-t^2/2\alpha^2}\frac{\sqrt{2\pi}}{\alpha} = \frac{1}{\sqrt{2\pi}\,\alpha} e^{-t^2/2\alpha^2}$$

as was to be shown. Some additional properties of transforms will now be established.

Theorem 12. Let $f(t) = 0$ for $t < 0$, let $|f(t)| < Me^{ct}$ for all t, and, of course, let f be integrable on finite intervals; then the Laplace transform of $t^n f(t)$ exists for Re $p > c$ and $n > -1$. Improper behavior is not of much interest to us and hence only $n > 0$ will be discussed.

PROOF: The result follows from the fact that for any fixed $\delta > 0$, $t^n < Be^{\delta t}$ for all t if B is sufficiently large.   To see this, recall that

$$Be^{\delta t} = B\left[1 + \delta t + \frac{(\delta t)^2}{2!} + \cdots + \frac{(\delta t)^k}{k!} + \cdots\right] \geq B + B\frac{(\delta t)^k}{k!}$$

Now take $k > n$ and take $B > k!/\delta^k$ (also take $B > 1$ to cover the interval $|t| < 1$).   Then we have

$$Be^{\delta t} > B + t^k > t^n$$

Now it follows that

$$|t^n f(t)| \leq BMe^{(c+\delta)t}$$

and hence, by Theorem 10, $L[t^n f(t)]_p$ exists for all Re $p > c + \delta$.   However, δ was any number greater than zero; thus the transform exists for all Re $p > c$.

The corresponding result for two-sided transforms follows.

Corollary 3.   If

$$|f(t)| \leq \begin{cases} Me^{c_1 t} & t \geq 0 \\ Me^{c_2 t} & t < 0 \end{cases}$$

then $L[t^n f(t)]_p$ exists for $c_1 < $ Re $p < c_2$.   For n not an integer, any single "branch" of t^n will do.   Also, t^n can be replaced by $|t|^n$.

Recall that for the inversion formula, exponential bounds were not required for f.   The requirement was simply one (real) value of σ for which $f(t)e^{-\sigma t}$ was absolutely integrable.   If we have exponential bounds of order c_1 and c_2, then $f(t)e^{-\sigma t}$ is absolutely integrable for any $c_1 < \sigma < c_2$, and in this case any such σ can be used in the inversion formula.   Also, in this case the integral of the inversion formula has the same value for all such σ—a curious by-product of the work.   If f itself is absolutely integrable, $\sigma = 0$ will do and then $L(f)_{j\omega}$ is called the Fourier transform of f.   It is then common to write $F(\omega)$ in place of $F(j\omega)$, and the transform pair becomes

$$F(\omega) = \int_{-\infty}^{\infty} e^{-j\omega t} f(t)\, dt$$

and

$$f(t) = \lim_{A \to \infty} \frac{1}{2\pi} \int_{-A}^{A} e^{-j\omega t} F(\omega)\, d\omega$$

Thus, as mentioned, the Fourier transform is a special case of the two-sided Laplace transform (and vice versa, as indicated by Prob. 8).   However, in mathematical studies a different distinction is often stressed.   For Fourier transforms, the transform is usually assumed to exist on a line, i.e., for one value of σ (but all ω), while with Laplace transforms a strip (of positive width $c_2 - c_1$) of convergence is usually assumed.   Some aspects of the theory are quite delicate mathematically when only a line of convergence is assumed, and this is the case usually treated in mathematical studies of Fourier transforms (with $\sigma = 0$ for convenience).

With a strip of convergence, transforms are well-behaved functions, while with only a line of convergence they can be rather wild functions. We shall show that with exponential bounds, Laplace transforms are regular (analytic) functions of p. The theory of regular functions will be considered in detail in Sec. 2-4. For our immediate needs, $F(p)$ is regular in the strip $c_1 < \text{Re } p < c_2$ iff

$$\lim_{\Delta p \to 0} \frac{F(p + \Delta p) - F(p)}{\Delta p}$$

exists for each p in the strip. With the dominated convergence theorem available, we can give a fairly simple proof that transforms are regular.

Theorem 13. Let f have exponential bounds of order c_1 and c_2; that is, let

$$f(t) \leq \begin{cases} Me^{c_1 t} & t \geq 0 \\ Me^{c_2 t} & t < 0 \end{cases}$$

where $c_1 < c_2$, and let f be integrable on finite intervals; then $F(p) = L(f)_p$ is regular for $c_1 < \text{Re } p < c_2$, and if $F^n(p)$ denotes the nth derivative of F,

$$F^n(p) = \int_{-\infty}^{\infty} (-t)^n e^{-pt}\, dt$$

That is, we can differentiate an arbitrary number of times under the integral sign.

PROOF: As in some of the above theorems, it is simpler to treat right and left sides of the transform separately. To do this, we could define

$$f_+(t) = \begin{cases} f(t) & \text{for } t \geq 0 \\ 0 & \text{for } t < 0 \end{cases}$$

$$f_-(t) = \begin{cases} 0 & \text{for } t \geq 0 \\ f(t) & \text{for } t < 0 \end{cases}$$

Then $f = f_+ + f_-$; and if $F_+ = L(f_+)$ and $F_- = L(f_-)$, then $F = L(f) = F_+ + F_-$. We then proceed with the proofs for F_+ and F_- separately. Thus, it is adequate to consider $f(t) = 0$ for $t < 0$ since the proofs for f_+ and f_- are similar.

In this case, then,

$$F(p) = \int_0^{\infty} e^{-pt} f(t)\, dt$$

and $|f(t)| \leq Me^{c_1 t}$. Let p be a specific point in the strip and let $|\Delta p| \neq 0$ be small so that $p + \Delta p$ is always in the strip. The difference quotient is

$$\frac{F(p + \Delta p) - F(p)}{\Delta p} = \int_0^{\infty} e^{-pt} \frac{e^{-\Delta p t} - 1}{\Delta p} f(t)\, dt$$

If we could interchange the limit as $\Delta p \to 0$ and the t integration, the proof would be nearly complete. Note that

$$\frac{e^{-\Delta pt} - 1}{\Delta p} = -t + \frac{\Delta pt^2}{2!} - \frac{(\Delta p)^2 t^3}{3!} + \cdots$$

Hence,

$$\left| \frac{e^{-\Delta pt} - 1}{p} \right| \leq t + t^2 |\Delta p| \left(1 + |\Delta pt| + \frac{|\Delta pt|^2}{2!} + \cdots \right)$$

The right-hand side is

$$t + t^2 |\Delta p| e^{|\Delta p|t}$$

Thus, if $g(\Delta p, t)$ denotes the integrand for the difference quotient, we have

$$|g| \leq t|e^{-pt}f(t)| + t^2 |\Delta p|\, |e^{-(p-|\Delta p|)t}f(t)|$$

We can now obtain a dominating function for the integrand and apply the dominated convergence theorem. Suppose $p = \sigma + j\omega$, with $\sigma > c_1$. Let σ_0 be a real number between σ and c_1; that is, $\sigma > \sigma_0 > c_1$. Then, for any $|\Delta p| < \sigma - \sigma_0$,

$$|g| \leq tMe^{-(\sigma - c_1)t} + t^2(\sigma - \sigma_0)Me^{-(\sigma_0 - c_1)t}$$

The situation is depicted in Figure 2-5. This last function is independent of Δp and integrable on the infinite interval $[0, \infty)$. The formal proof of

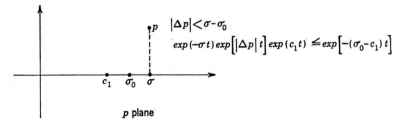

FIGURE 2-5. Choice of dominating function.

integrability uses logic similar to that in the proof of Theorem 12, but this should be clear since $\sigma - c_1$ and $\sigma_0 - c_1$ are both positive. Thus

$$\lim_{\Delta p \to 0} \int_0^\infty g(t, \Delta p)\, dt = \int_0^\infty \lim_{\Delta p \to 0} g(t, \Delta p)\, dt$$

When the limit is inside, we simply have the derivative of e^{-pt} with respect to p. Therefore,

$$F'(p) = \int_0^\infty (-t)e^{-pt}f(t)\, dt$$

We can now proceed to take the second derivative. Clearly, the dominator for this difference quotient will simply be t times the one obtained above, and multiplying by t will not destroy the integrability of this dominating function since the decaying exponential always wins out over powers of t. Continuing in this way, we obtain

$$F^n(p) = \int_0^\infty (-t)^n e^{-pt} f(t) \ dt$$

as was to be shown.   The proof for the left half of the transform is essentially the same.

While we are discussing fundamentals, one more important remark should be made.   It is obvious that Fourier transforms are a special case of Laplace transforms; less obvious but nonetheless true is the fact that Laplace transform theory follows trivially from Fourier transform theory. This is given as an important exercise in Prob. 8.   It is mathematically very simple to obtain Laplace theory from Fourier theory by a few simple manipulations.   In spite of this simplicity, the extension afforded by Laplace theory is important in many applied problems (mostly those applications discussed in Part I of the book).

Problems

5. If

$$f(t) = \begin{cases} t & \text{for } t \geq 0 \\ 0 & \text{for } t < 0 \end{cases}$$

find $F(p)$ and indicate the region in the p plane for which $L(f)$ exists.

6. If

$$f(t) = \begin{cases} e^t & \text{for } t \geq 0 \\ 0 & \text{for } t < 0 \end{cases}$$

find $F(p)$ and indicate the region of convergence.

7. For each of the following functions indicate the values of p for which the two-sided transform of the function exists.   Do not give proofs.

(a) $f(t) = \sin t$ for all real t

(b) $f(t) = \begin{cases} \sin t \text{ for } t \geq 0 \\ 0 \text{ for } t < 0 \end{cases}$

(c) $f(t) = e^t$ for all t

(d) $f(t) = e^{-t^2}$ for all t

(e) $f(t) = \begin{cases} e^{t^2} \text{ for } t > 0 \\ 0 \text{ for } t < 0 \end{cases}$

(f) $f(t) = \dfrac{\sin t}{t}$ for all t.   Let $f(t) = 1$ at $t = 0$.

(g) $f(t) = \begin{cases} 0 \text{ if } t \text{ is not an integer} \\ e^{t^2} \text{ when } t \text{ is an integer} \end{cases}$

(h) $f(t) = \cos e^{at}$ for all real t, where a is real and not zero.

8. Given the following theorem for Fourier transforms:

If

$$\int_{-\infty}^\infty |g(t)| \ dt < \infty$$

g is of bounded variation on finite intervals, and

$$G(\omega) = \int_{-\infty}^{\infty} e^{-i\omega t} g(t) \, dt$$

then

$$\tfrac{1}{2}[g(t+0) + g(t-0)] = \tfrac{1}{2} \lim_{A \to \infty} \int_{-A}^{A} e^{i\omega t} G(\omega) \, d\omega$$

Prove Theorem 11 by substitutions and changes of variables; e.g., let $f(t)e^{-\sigma t} = g(t)$ and let $p = \sigma + j\omega$.

9. Show that if f has exponential bounds of order c_1 and c_2, then

$$|F(p)| \le \frac{M}{\sigma - c_1} + \frac{M}{c_2 - \sigma}$$

in the strip determined by c_1 and c_2.

2-3 COMPUTATIONAL THEOREMS

The last section said quite a bit about the nature of Laplace transforms but it did not solve any problems.   Here we shall develop the tools used to solve problems; however, it is felt that most of the actual problem solving should be deferred until the end of Sec. 2-4, which provides the convenient method for taking inverse transforms.

Theorem 14.   Let $f(t) = 0$ for $t < 0$, let

$$\lim_{\delta \to 0} f(|\delta|)$$

exist and be denoted by $f(0+)$, let f have an exponential bound of order c, let $f'(t)$ exist for $t > 0$, and let f' be integrable on finite intervals; then $L(f')_p$ exists for Re $p > c$, and for such p

$$L(f')_p = pL(f)_p - f(0+)$$

By the way, the point $t = 0$ took on special significance only because it is the only point where f was permitted to be discontinuous (of course, f is certainly continuous for $t > 0$ since f' exists there).   The two-sided transform version with a jump discontinuity at T has the following conclusion:

$$L(f')_p = pL(f)_p - [f(T+0) - f(T-0)]e^{-Tp}$$

This version will be proved later.

PROOF: Consider

$$L(f')_p \equiv \int_0^{\infty} f'(t)e^{-pt} \, dt = \lim_{\delta \to 0+} \lim_{A \to \infty} \int_{\delta}^{A} f'(t)e^{-pt} \, dt$$

Integration by parts gives

$$e^{-pt}f(t)]_{\delta}^{A} + p \int_{\delta}^{A} f(t)e^{-pt} \, dt$$

As for the first term,

$$\lim_{A \to \infty} e^{-pA}f(A) - \lim_{\delta \to 0+} e^{-p\delta}f(\delta)$$

the part involving A goes to zero for Re $p > c$ since, for such p, $|e^{-pA}f(A)| \leq Me^{-(\sigma-c)A}$, which clearly goes to zero. The part involving δ gives $-f(0+)$. The other term obtained by integration by parts gives $pL(f)_p$, and it exists for Re $p > c$ by Theorem 10.

As a preliminary to a simple example, recall that if

$$f(t) = \begin{cases} e^{at} & t \geq 0 \\ 0 & t < 0 \end{cases}$$

then
$$L(f)_p = \int_0^\infty e^{-(p-a)t}\, dt = \frac{1}{p-a}$$

with convergence for Re $p >$ Re a.

Example 3. Consider the circuit shown in Figure 2-6. Suppose

$$f(t) = \begin{cases} E & \text{for } t \geq 0 \\ 0 & \text{for } t < 0 \end{cases}$$

Then $L(f)_p = E/p$ (special case of e^{at} where $a = 0$); the problem is to find $g(t)$ for $t > 0$. We have $g(t) = 0$ for $t < 0$ from the circuit or for mathematical convenience—in this case we have it from the circuit. The differential equation relating f and g is the following: $f - g = Ri$, but $i = Cg'$;

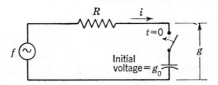

FIGURE 2-6. A simple RC circuit.

let $T = RC$; then $Tg' + g = f$. Suppose there is a solution g which is transformable for p having a sufficiently large real part, and suppose also that the solution satisfies the conditions of Theorem 14. Then, taking the transform of both sides yields $(Tp + 1)G - Tg_0 = F$ since $g_0 = g(0+)$ is equal to the initial voltage on the capacitor. For a step applied voltage we get

$$G = \frac{E}{p(Tp+1)} + \frac{Tg_0}{Tp+1}$$

Expand the first term in partial fractions thus:

$$\frac{E}{p(Tp+1)} = \frac{A}{p} + \frac{B}{Tp+1}$$

Multiply by $Tp + 1$ and let $p \to -1/T$. This gives $B = -TE$; similarly, $A = E$. Thus,

$$G = \frac{T(g_0 - E)}{Tp+1} + \frac{E}{p}$$

The inverse transform is recognized since these are special cases of the transform of $e^{at}U(t)$, where $U(t)$ denotes the unit step function, that is,

$$U(t) = \begin{cases} 1 & \text{for } t \geq 0 \\ 0 & \text{for } t < 0 \end{cases}$$

Hence, it is seen that

$$g(t) = U(t)[E + (g_0 - E)e^{-t/T}]$$

as is well known for such a circuit.

The derivation of g required the assumption that the equation had a transformable solution; however, it is now clear that we can read the derivation backward to establish g as a solution since the g found satisfies all the assumptions we made about it.

Theorem 15.   Let f be integrable on finite intervals, let $f(t) = 0$ for $t < 0$, let f have an exponential bound of order c, and let

$$g(t) = \begin{cases} \int_0^t f(\tau) \, d\tau + g_0 & \text{for } t \geq 0 \\ 0 & \text{for } t < 0 \end{cases}$$

Then $L(g)_p = G(p) = \dfrac{1}{p} L(f)_p + \dfrac{g_0}{p}$ for Re $p > \max(c, 0)$

PROOF: By the fundamental theorem of calculus, $g' = f$ at the continuity points of f. The theorem is correct as stated; however, to avoid some detailed mathematical considerations, assume that f is continuous (or at least piecewise continuous) for $t > 0$. Then, by Theorem 14, $pG = F + g(0+)$ if we can establish an exponential bound. Also $g(0+) = g_0$; hence $G = (1/p)F + g_0/p$ as expected. To obtain an exponential bound, observe that

$$|g(t)| \leq |g_0| + \int_0^t |f(\tau)| \, d\tau \leq |g_0| + M \int_0^t e^{c\tau} \, d\tau = |g_0| + \frac{M}{c}(e^{ct} - 1) \leq Be^{c't}$$

if $B > |g_0| + |M/c|$ and $c' \geq \max(0, c)$. Of course, if $c = 0$, we get $|g(t)| \leq |g_0| + Mt$, and any $c' > 0$ will serve as an exponential bound.

Example 4.   In the interest of including an example, consider the circuit shown in Figure 2-6. Suppose we wish to find the current $i(t)$ for $t > 0$. The equation to be solved is $f = iR + q/C$, but

$$q(t) = \int_0^t i(\tau) \, d\tau + Cg_0$$

and hence $f = iR + \dfrac{1}{C} \int_0^t i + g_0$

where g_0 is the initial voltage on the capacitor. Taking the transform of both sides with a step input $EU(t)$ gives

$$\frac{E}{p} = IR + \frac{1}{pC} I + \frac{g_0}{p} \qquad \text{and} \qquad I = \frac{E - g_0}{R} \frac{1}{p + 1/RC}$$

Therefore,
$$i(t) = \frac{E - g_0}{R} e^{-t/RC} U(t)$$

In the following theorem, and normally throughout the book, f^n will denote the nth derivative of f.

Theorem 16. Let $f^n(t)$ exist for $t > 0$, let $f(t) = 0$ for $t < 0$, let f^n be integrable on finite intervals, let $f^{n-1}(0+)$ exist, and let $|f^{n-1}(t)| \leq Me^{ct}$; then $L(f^n)_p = p^n L(f)_p - p^{n-1}f(0+) - p^{n-2}f'(0+) - \cdots - pf^{n-2}(0+) - f^{n-1}(0+)$ for Re $p > \max(c, 0)$.

PROOF: The existence of $f^{n-1}(0+)$ implies the existence of $f^{n-2}(0+)$, etc. This is true since for $a > 0, t > 0$,

$$f^{n-2}(t) = \int_a^t f^{n-1}(\tau)\, d\tau + f^{n-2}(a)$$

and the integral is a continuous function of its upper limit (and lower limit, for that matter). It follows that

$$\lim_{t \to 0+} \int_a^t f^{n-1}(\tau)\, d\tau = \int_a^0 f^{n-1}(\tau)\, d\tau$$

and hence
$$f^{n-2}(0+) = f^{n-2}(a) - \int_0^a f^{n-1}(\tau)\, d\tau$$

Also, as was shown for Theorem 15, the exponential bound on f^{n-1} carries over to its integrals f^{n-2}, etc. After making these observations we can carry out the formal proof by induction. Let the theorem be true for $n - 1$. We shall show it is then true for n. Also, it is known to be true for $n = 1$, which is needed to complete the logic.

Integration by parts on $L(f^n)$ gives

$$\int_\delta^A f^n(t)e^{-pt}\, dt = f^{n-1}(t)e^{-pt}\Big]_\delta^A + p \int_\delta^A f^{n-1}(t)e^{-pt}\, dt$$

In the limit we get the following if the theorem is assumed true for f^{n-1}:

$$L(f^n)_p = -f^{n-1}(0+) + p[p^{n-1}L(f)_p - p^{n-2}f(0+) - \cdots - f^{n-2}(0+)]$$
$$= p^n L(f)_p - p^{n-1}f(0+) - \cdots - f^{n-1}(0+)$$

Example 5. Suppose

$$f(t) = \begin{cases} \sin t & \text{for } t \geq 0 \\ 0 & \text{for } t < 0 \end{cases}$$

Then
$$F(p) = \frac{1}{2j} \int_0^\infty (e^{jt} - e^{-jt})e^{-pt}\, dt$$

$$= \frac{1}{2j}\left(\frac{-1}{j - p} - \frac{1}{j + p}\right) \qquad \text{for Re } p > 0$$

Thus
$$F(p) = \frac{1}{p^2 + 1}$$

Note that $f(0+) = 0$ and $f'(0+) = \cos 0 = 1$. Therefore, the transform of $f''(t) = -\sin t$ is equal to

$$p^2 F - 1 = \frac{p^2}{p^2 + 1} - 1 = \frac{-1}{p^2 + 1}$$

which is $-F$, as it should be.

Theorem 17.   Let $L[f(t)]_p = F(p)$.   Then $L[f(t + a)]_p = F(p)e^{ap}$, where a is real.

PROOF: Consider

$$\int_{-\infty}^{\infty} e^{-pt} f(t + a)\, dt$$

Let $t + a = \tau$.   Then

$$L[f(t + a)]_p = \int_{-\infty}^{\infty} e^{-p(\tau - a)} f(\tau)\, d\tau = e^{ap} L(f)_p$$

Theorem 18.   Let $L(f)_p = F(p)$ for $c_1 < \operatorname{Re} p < c_2$.   Then $L[e^{at}f(t)]_p = F(p - a)$ for $c_1 < \operatorname{Re}(p - a) < c_2$, where a may be complex.

PROOF:

$$L[e^{at}f(t)]_p = \int_{-\infty}^{\infty} e^{-(p - a)t} f(t)\, dt = F(p - a)$$

Example 6.   Suppose we wish to find the inverse transform of

$$\frac{b}{(p - a)^2 + b^2}$$

along a line $\operatorname{Re}(p - a) > 0$.   As a simple extension of Example 5, $b/(p^2 + b^2)$ is the transform of $U(t) \sin bt$.   Then, by Theorem 18, the inverse transform of $b/[(p - a)^2 + b^2]$ is $e^{at} U(t) \sin bt$.

As an application of Theorem 17, the two-sided version of Theorem 14 will be derived with a jump at $t = T$ rather than at $t = 0$.

The left-sided transform version of Theorem 14 will be assumed (it is nearly obvious):   If $f(t) = 0$ for $t > 0$, f' is integrable on finite intervals, and $|f(t)| < M e^{c_2 t}$, then for $\operatorname{Re} p < c_2$, $L(f') = pL(f) + f(0-)$.   Now let f have a jump discontinuity only at T.   Let f_s be such that $f(t) = f_s(t - T)$. Then $f_s(t)$ has a jump only at $t = 0$.   Since $f'(t) = f_s'(t - T)$, Theorem 17 gives the two-sided transform $L(f') = e^{-Tp} L(f_s')$.   Let $f_s = f_{s+} + f_{s-}$, where $f_{s+}(t) = 0$ for $t < 0$ and $f_{s-}(t) = 0$ for $t > 0$.   Then

$$L(f_s') = pL(f_{s+}) - f_s(0+) + pL(f_{s-}) + f_s(0-)$$

Finally, $L(f_{s+} + f_{s-}) = L(f_s)$, $f_s(0+) = f(T + 0)$, and $f_s(0-) = f(T - 0)$. Therefore, $L(f') = e^{-Tp} L(f_s) - e^{-Tp}[f(T + 0) - f(T - 0)]$.   But $L(f_s) = e^{pT} L(f)$, and we have $L(f') = L(f) - e^{-Tp}[f(T + 0) - f(T - 0)]$ for $c_1 < \operatorname{Re} p < c_2$.   For jumps at $T_1, \ldots, T_n$ of size $J_k = f(T_k + 0) - f(T_k - 0)$ the general conclusion is

$$L(f') = L(f) - \sum_{k=1}^{n} J_k \exp(-pT_k)$$

The above method of proof is not easily adapted to more than one jump; however, direct computation as used in the proof of Theorem 14 goes through without any difficulty.

Convolution theorems and final-value–initial-value theorems will now be given to complete this section.

Theorem 19 (A Convolution Theorem). Let $F = L(f)$ and $H = L(h)$ and let

$$\int_{-\infty}^{\infty} e^{-\sigma t}|f(t)|\, dt \quad\text{and}\quad \int_{-\infty}^{\infty} e^{-\sigma t}|h(t)|\, dt$$

exist; then

$$\int_{-\infty}^{\infty} h(t - \tau)f(\tau)\, d\tau$$

exists and will be denoted by $g(t) = h(t) * f(t)$, $L(g)_p = G(p)$ exists for Re $p = \sigma$, and $G(p) = H(p)F(p)$.

PROOF: Consider

$$H(p)F(p) = \left[\int_{-\infty}^{\infty} e^{-px}f(x)\, dx\right]\left[\int_{-\infty}^{\infty} e^{-py}h(y)\, dy\right]$$
$$= \int_{-\infty}^{\infty} f(x)\left[\int_{-\infty}^{\infty} e^{-p(x+y)}h(y)\, dy\right] dx$$

Suppose we make the following change of variable: $y = t - x$ for the y integration. Then

$$H(p)F(p) = \int_{-\infty}^{\infty} f(x)\left[\int_{-\infty}^{\infty} e^{-pt}h(t - x)\, dt\right] dx$$

We now interchange the orders of integrations; the absolute integrability assumed in the theorem (along with Fubini's theorem) can be used to justify the interchange:†

$$H(p)F(p) = \int_{-\infty}^{\infty} e^{-pt}\left[\int_{-\infty}^{\infty} h(t - x)f(x)\, dx\right] dt = G(p)$$

which completes the proof.

Theorem 20 (A Similar Convolution Theorem). Let

$$\frac{1}{2\pi j}\int_{-\infty}^{\infty}\int_{\sigma-j\infty}^{\sigma+j\infty} e^{\sigma(t-\tau)}|h(\tau)|\,|F(p)|\, dp\, d\tau$$

exist. Then

$$H(p) = \int_{-\infty}^{\infty} e^{-p\tau}h(\tau)\, d\tau \qquad f(t) = \frac{1}{2\pi j}\int_{\sigma-j\infty}^{\sigma+j\infty} e^{pt}F(p)\, dp$$

and

$$g(t) = \int_{-\infty}^{\infty} f(t - \tau)h(\tau)\, d\tau$$

† The background for Theorems 19 and 20 has not been reviewed. It develops that $g(t) = h(t) * f(t)$ may not exist for every t, and $L(g)$ may be an improper integral, as mentioned in Sec. 2-1. Problem 14 gives an example where $g(t)$ does not exist for integer t.

exist and

$$g(t) = \frac{1}{2\pi j} \int_{\sigma-j\infty}^{\sigma+j\infty} e^{pt} G(p) \, dp$$

where $G(p) = F(p)H(p)$.

PROOF: Consider

$$\frac{1}{2\pi j} \int_{-\infty}^{\infty} \int_{\sigma-j\infty}^{\sigma+j\infty} e^{p(t-\tau)} h(\tau) F(p) \, dp \, d\tau$$

The hypothesis justifies doing the integrals in either order; therefore,

$$\int_{-\infty}^{\infty} \left[\frac{1}{2\pi j} \int_{\sigma-j\infty}^{\sigma+j\infty} e^{p(t-\tau)} F(p) \, dp \right] h(\tau) \, d\tau = \int_{-\infty}^{\infty} f(t-\tau) h(\tau) \, d\tau = g(t)$$

is equal to

$$\frac{1}{2\pi j} \int_{\sigma-j\infty}^{\sigma+j\infty} e^{pt} F(p) \left[\int_{-\infty}^{\infty} e^{-p\tau} h(\tau) \, d\tau \right] dp = \frac{1}{2\pi j} \int_{\sigma-j\infty}^{\sigma+j\infty} e^{pt} F(p) H(p) \, dp$$

as was to be shown.

The importance of convolution will be discussed later. The relationship between the behavior of f at $t = 0+$ and ∞ and the behavior of its transform at $p = \infty$ and $0+$ will now be established. However, before we proceed, a simple exercise using convolutions will be given.

Example 7. Consider the simple RC circuit of Chap. 1, Prob. 3 (Figure 2-6 without the switch). An equation which relates input and output is

$$Tg' + g = f$$

The transfer function is $H(p) = 1/(Tp + 1)$ and the impulse response is the inverse transform of H, that is, $h(t) = U(t)(1/T)e^{-t/T}$. Suppose $f(t) = U(t)$. Then

$$g(t) = \int_{-\infty}^{\infty} f(t-\tau) h(\tau) \, d\tau = \int_{0}^{t} f(t-\tau) h(\tau) \, d\tau$$

$$= \frac{1}{T} \int_{0}^{t} e^{-\tau/T} \, d\tau = 1 - e^{-t/T}$$

(for $t > 0$, and $g(t) = 0$ for $t < 0$).

Either convolution theorem gives $G(p) = H(p)F(p)$ and $F(p) = 1/p$; thus $G(p) = 1/p(Tp + 1)$, the inverse transform of which is $U(t)(1 - e^{-t/T})$, as expected.

Theorem 21 (Final-value Theorem). Let $f(t) = 0$ for $t < 0$, let f be bounded on finite intervals, let

$$\lim_{t \to \infty} f(t)$$

exist in the extended numbers (i.e., let the limit be finite or infinite; in the infinite case let f be real so that the limit is either ∞ or $-\infty$), and let

$L(f)_\sigma = F(\sigma)$ exist for all $\sigma > 0$.   Then

$$\lim_{\sigma \to 0+} \sigma F(\sigma)$$

exists in the extended numbers and

$$\lim_{\sigma \to 0+} \sigma F(\sigma) = \lim_{t \to \infty} f(t)$$

PROOF: Consider

$$\sigma F(\sigma) = \int_0^\infty \sigma e^{-\sigma t} f(t) \, dt$$

Let $\sigma t = u$.   Then

$$\sigma F(\sigma) = \int_0^\infty e^{-u} f\left(\frac{u}{\sigma}\right) du$$

If

$$\lim_{t \to \infty} f(t)$$

is finite, $f(t)$ is bounded and in turn $f(u/\sigma)$ is bounded.   In this case we have $|f(u/\sigma)e^{-u}| \le Me^{-u}$, which is an integrable function of u.   Thus we can apply the dominated convergence theorem and interchange limit and integration thus:

$$\lim_{\sigma \to 0+} \int_0^\infty e^{-u} f\left(\frac{u}{\sigma}\right) du = \int_0^\infty e^{-u} \lim_{\sigma \to 0+} f\left(\frac{u}{\sigma}\right) du$$

However,

$$\lim_{\sigma \to 0+} f\left(\frac{u}{\sigma}\right) = \lim_{t \to \infty} f(t)$$

which is independent of u and will be denoted by $f(\infty)$; the exception at $u = 0$ is of no importance since the value of an integral is independent of the value of the integrand at one point.   Therefore,

$$\lim_{\sigma \to 0+} \sigma F(\sigma) = \int_0^\infty e^{-u} f(\infty) \, du = f(\infty)$$

since

$$\int_0^\infty e^{-u} \, du = 1$$

In the infinite case $f(u/\sigma)$ becomes arbitrarily large as $\sigma \to 0^+$, and in turn

$$\int_0^\infty e^{-u} f\left(\frac{u}{\sigma}\right) du$$

becomes arbitrarily large, which is what we wanted to show.   The details of the proof for this case will be given simply for completeness.   Let $a > 0$ and let

$$\lim_{t \to \infty} f(t) = \infty$$

Then for any $M > 0$, there exists a $\sigma_0 > 0$ such that $f(u/\sigma) > M$ for all $u > a$ and all $\sigma < \sigma_0$.   In turn,

$$\int_a^\infty e^{-u} f\left(\frac{u}{\sigma}\right) du > M \int_a^\infty e^{-u} \, du = Me^{-a}$$

for such σ. Let b be the minimum value of $f(t)$; of course b is finite since f is bounded on finite intervals and goes to ∞ (not $-\infty$ for the case now being treated) as t goes to ∞. Now

$$\int_0^\infty e^{-u} f\left(\frac{u}{\sigma}\right) du = \int_0^a e^{-u} f\left(\frac{u}{\sigma}\right) du + \int_a^\infty e^{-u} f\left(\frac{u}{\sigma}\right) du$$

and
$$\int_0^a e^{-u} f\left(\frac{u}{\sigma}\right) du \geq b \int_0^a e^{-u} du = b(1 - e^{-a})$$

Therefore,
$$\int_0^\infty e^{-u} f\left(\frac{u}{\sigma}\right) du \geq b(1 - e^{-a}) + Me^{-a} \qquad \text{for all } 0 < \sigma < \sigma_0$$

However, b and a are fixed and M can be made arbitrarily large. That is, by taking σ small we can make $\sigma F(\sigma)$ arbitrarily large, which is the definition of

$$\lim_{\sigma \to 0+} \sigma F(\sigma) = \infty = \lim_{t \to \infty} f(t)$$

as was to be shown. A similar proof is used if

$$\lim_{t \to \infty} f(t) = -\infty$$

By the way, if
$$\lim_{p \to 0} pF(p)$$

exists, it equals
$$\lim_{\sigma \to 0+} \sigma F(\sigma)$$

so that normally we need not restrict p to nonnegative real values when applying the theorem.

Theorem 22 (*Initial-value Theorem*).   Let $f(t) = 0$ for $t < 0$, let f have an exponential bound of order c, and let

$$\lim_{t \to 0+} f(t) = f(0+)$$

exist (infinite values will not be considered in the theorem, but will be discussed below).   Then if $F(\sigma) = L(f)_\sigma$,

$$\lim_{\sigma \to \infty} \sigma F(\sigma)$$

exists and
$$\lim_{\sigma \to \infty} \sigma F(\sigma) = \lim_{t \to 0+} f(t)$$

PROOF: As before, we have

$$\sigma F(\sigma) = \int_0^\infty e^{-u} f\left(\frac{u}{\sigma}\right) du \qquad \text{for } \sigma > c$$

Then $|e^{-u} f(u/\sigma)| \leq Me^{-u + c(u/\sigma)}$. Since only large values of σ are of interest, we can use, say, $Me^{-u/2}$ as a dominating function for all $\sigma > 2c$. Thus again we can apply the dominated convergence theorem to obtain

$$\lim_{\sigma \to \infty} \int_0^\infty e^{-u} f\left(\frac{u}{\sigma}\right) du = \int_0^\infty e^{-u} \lim_{\sigma \to \infty} f\left(\frac{u}{\sigma}\right) du = \int_0^\infty e^{-u} f(0+)\, du = f(0+)$$

as was to be shown.

We have very little need to consider improper transforms which occur if f is not bounded on finite intervals. However, Theorem 22 can be extended to cover the possibility that

$$\lim_{t \to 0+} f(t) = \infty \ (\text{or} - \infty)$$

Again, consider only real f for this extension. If $f(0+)$ is infinite, f must go to infinity slowly enough for $L(f)_p$ to exist as an improper integral. Granting this, there is no difficulty in the extension since, as before, $f(u/\sigma)$ becomes arbitrarily large as σ gets large and, in turn,

$$\sigma F(\sigma) = \int_0^\infty e^{-u} f\left(\frac{u}{\sigma}\right) du$$

becomes large.

Example 8. The use of the convolution theorem and the inversion formula will now be illustrated by deriving the conclusion of Parseval's theorem. The following strong form of the theorem is derived in Chap. 10.

Theorem 23

$$\int_{-\infty}^\infty |f(t)|^2\, dt$$

exists iff

$$\frac{1}{2\pi} \int_{-\infty}^\infty |F(\omega)|^2\, d\omega$$

exists, and when they exist they are equal.

DERIVATION: For our derivation we take $F(\omega) = L(f)_{j\omega}$. Also, we shall make use of the following lemma.

Lemma 1. If $F(\omega) = L[f(t)]_{j\omega}$, then $\bar{F}(\omega) = L[\bar{f}(-t)]_{j\omega}$, where the bar denotes complex conjugate. To see this, consider

$$L[\bar{f}(-t)]_{j\omega} = \int_{-\infty}^\infty \bar{f}(-t) e^{-j\omega t}\, dt$$

and let $-t = u$. Then we get

$$\int_{-\infty}^\infty \bar{f}(u) e^{j\omega u}\, du$$

which is clearly the complex conjugate of

$$\int_{-\infty}^\infty f(t) e^{-j\omega t}\, dt$$

as was to be shown.

By the lemma and the convolution theorem 19,

$$F(\omega)\bar{F}(\omega) = \int_{-\infty}^{\infty} e^{-j\omega t}\left\{\int_{-\infty}^{\infty} \bar{f}[-(t-\tau)]f(\tau)\,d\tau\right\}dt$$

and, by the inversion formula,

$$\int_{-\infty}^{\infty} \bar{f}[-(t-\tau)]f(\tau)\,d\tau = \frac{1}{2\pi}\int_{-\infty}^{\infty} e^{j\omega t}F(\omega)\bar{F}(\omega)\,d\omega$$

In particular, at $t = 0$ we get

$$\int_{-\infty}^{\infty} |f(\tau)|^2\,d\tau = \frac{1}{2\pi}\int_{-\infty}^{\infty} |F(\omega)|^2\,d\omega$$

If we use the lemma and Theorem 20, we get

$$\int_{-\infty}^{\infty} \bar{f}[-(t-\tau)]f(\tau)\,d\tau = \frac{1}{2\pi}\int_{-\infty}^{\infty} e^{j\omega t}F(\omega)\bar{F}(\omega)\,d\omega$$

in just one step.

Example 9. Let $f_n(t) = t^n U(t)$ for $n = 0, 1, \ldots$. Then if $F_n = L(f_n)$, $F_0(p) = 1/p$. The first problem is to find F_n for $n > 0$. There are many ways to do this; Theorem 13 will be used here. Note that

$$F_0(p) = \int_0^{\infty} e^{-pt}\,dt$$

and hence

$$F_0'(p) = \int_0^{\infty} (-t)e^{-pt}\,dt$$

by Theorem 13. However, $F_0'(p) = -1/p^2$ and hence

$$-F_0'(p) = \int_0^{\infty} te^{-pt}\,dt = F_1(p) = \frac{1}{p^2}$$

We can continue in this way to obtain

$$F_0''(p) = \int_0^{\infty} t^2 e^{-pt}\,dt = F_2(p) = \frac{2}{p^3}$$

and generally

$$F_n(p) = \frac{n!}{p^{n+1}} \quad \text{for Re } p > 0$$

Let us now use these functions f_n and their transforms to verify Theorems 21 and 22. For $n = 0$, $\sigma F_0(\sigma) = \sigma/\sigma = 1$ and

$$\lim_{\sigma \to 0+} \sigma F_0(\sigma) = 1 \qquad \lim_{\sigma \to \infty} \sigma F_0(\sigma) = 1$$

These clearly equal

$$\lim_{t \to \infty} U(t) \qquad \text{and} \qquad \lim_{t \to 0+} U(t)$$

respectively, as expected. For $n > 0$, $\sigma F_n(\sigma) = n!/\sigma^n$ and

$$\lim_{\sigma \to 0+} \sigma F_n(\sigma) = \infty \qquad \text{and} \qquad \lim_{\sigma \to \infty} \sigma F(\sigma) = 0$$

which agree with

$$\lim_{t \to \infty} f_n(t) \qquad \text{and} \qquad \lim_{t \to 0+} f_n(t)$$

In all these examples the real variable σ could be replaced by the complex variable p, and the fact that $F_n(p)$ is defined only for Re $p > 0$ could be ignored. As another example, consider $f(t) = U(t - T)$ and of course $F(p) = e^{-pT}/p$ for Re $p > 0$. Again

$$\lim_{p \to 0} pF(p) = \lim_{p \to 0} e^{-pT} = 1 = \lim_{t \to \infty} f(t)$$

Also

$$\lim_{\sigma \to \infty} e^{-\sigma T} = 0 = \lim_{t \to 0+} f(t)$$

if $T > 0$ as expected; however,

$$\lim_{p \to \infty} e^{-pT}$$

is meaningless in that as a function of the complex variable p, e^{-pT} has no limit as p goes to ∞; that is, in this case we must restrict p to nonnegative real values in applying Theorem 22.

Example 10 (*General Factorial Function*). Let $f_n(t) = U(t)t^n$, where n is any real number greater than -1. Then

$$F_n(p) = \int_0^\infty t^n e^{-pt} \, dt$$

For $p = \sigma$ and $\sigma > 0$, $F_n(\sigma)$ exists and

$$F_n(\sigma) = \int_0^\infty t^n e^{-\sigma t} \, dt$$

Let $\sigma t = u$. Then

$$F_n(\sigma) = \frac{1}{\sigma^{n+1}} \int_0^\infty u^n e^{-u} \, du$$

For integer n,

$$\int_0^\infty u^n e^{-u} \, du = n!$$

by Example 9. The definition of the factorial function $n!$ is extended to all real $n > -1$ by setting

$$n! \equiv \int_0^\infty u^n e^{-u} \, du \qquad \text{for all } n > -1$$

For other n we use the definition $(n + 1)n! = (n + 1)!$; hence the above definition for $-1 < n < 0$ can be used to obtain values of $n! = (n + 1)!/(n + 1)$ for $-2 < n < -1$, etc. In this way $n!$ is defined for all real n except the negative integers where $n!$ "blows up." Hence by definition

$(n + 1)n! = (n + 1)!$ for $n < -1$. For $n > -1$, the formula

$$n! = \int_0^\infty u^n e^{-u}\, du$$

can be integrated by parts to establish the relation thus:

$$\frac{u^{n+1}}{n+1} e^{-u}\Big]_0^\infty + \frac{1}{n+1} \int_0^\infty u^{n+1} e^{-u}\, du$$

The first term contributes zero for $n > -1$ and we are left with

$$n! = \frac{1}{n+1} (n+1)!$$

as expected. Of course there was no question for n a positive integer. Thus we have $F_n(\sigma) = n!/\sigma^{n+1}$. Also, Theorem 13 establishes that $F_n(p)$ is a regular function of p for Re $p > 0$ if $n \geq 0$. The proof can easily be modified to cover $n > -1$; hence, $F_n(p) = n!/p^{n+1}$ for Re $p > 0$ since p^{n+1} is the only regular function equal to σ^{n+1} when p is real, i.e., when $p = \sigma$. Here we draw on the theory of analytic continuation, which will be discussed briefly in the next section. It is enough here to note that p^{n+1} is well defined if we insist that p^{n+1} be regular for Re $p > 0$, that it equal σ^{n+1} when p is real and equal to σ, and that σ^{n+1} have the ordinary real meaning.

Problems

10. In the sketch let $f(t) = IU(t)$, where I is a constant. Find the current in the resistor by using Laplace transforms. Assume that $i_L(0+) = 0$.

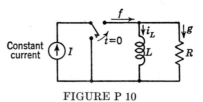

FIGURE P 10

11. (a) Show that $L[U(t) \cos \alpha t] = p/(p^2 + \alpha^2)$ for Re $p > 0$.
(b) Find $L[e^{\alpha t}t^n U(t)]$ given that $L[t^n U(t)]_p = n!/p^{n+1}$.
12. (a) Given that

$$L\left(\frac{1}{\sqrt{2\pi}\,\alpha} e^{-t^2/2\alpha^2}\right) = e^{\frac{1}{2}\alpha^2 p^2}$$

find

$$L\left[\exp \frac{(t-a)^2}{-2\alpha^2}\right]$$

(b) Use the result of (a) to find

$$g(t) = \int_{-\infty}^{\infty} \exp \frac{-(t-a-\tau)^2}{2\alpha^2} \exp \frac{-(\tau-b)^2}{2\beta^2}\, d\tau$$

in closed form.

13. (a) If $f(t) = U(t) \cos \alpha t$, then

$$F(\sigma) = \frac{\sigma}{\sigma^2 + \alpha^2} \quad \text{and} \quad \lim_{\sigma \to 0+} \sigma F(\sigma) \neq \lim_{t \to \infty} f(t)$$

In what way does f fail to satisfy the hypotheses of Theorem 21?
   (b) If $f(t) = U(t)e^t$, then

$$F(\sigma) = \frac{1}{\sigma - 1} \quad \text{and} \quad \lim_{\sigma \to 0+} \sigma F(\sigma) \neq \lim_{t \to \infty} f(t)$$

In what way does f fail to satisfy the hypotheses of Theorem 21?

14. Let

$$f(t) = \begin{cases} 0 & \text{for } |t| < \dfrac{5}{2} \\ |n| & \text{for } |t - n| < \dfrac{1}{2|n|^3} \text{ and } |t| > \dfrac{5}{2} \end{cases}$$

as shown.   Observe that

$$\int_{-\infty}^{\infty} |f(t)| \, dt < \infty$$

and hence we can use f and $h = f$ in Theorem 19 with $\sigma = 0$.   Show that

$$g(0) = \int_{-\infty}^{\infty} h(-\tau)f(\tau) \, d\tau = \int_{-\infty}^{\infty} f^2 \, d\tau = \infty$$

Thus we have an example where $h * f$ does not exist for certain values of t.

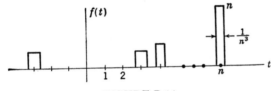

FIGURE P 14

15. Find the overall transfer function $H(p)$ for the system shown.   Assume zero initial conditions so that $G = HF$.

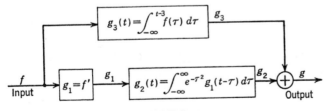

FIGURE P 15

2-4   INVERSION BY RESIDUES WITH A REVIEW† OF FUNCTIONS OF A COMPLEX VARIABLE

In the majority of applied problems the inversion formula of Theorem 11 can be evaluated by inspection if the theory of integration by residues is

† Because of the review of regular function theory, this section is rather long; however, the primary objective of the section is filled if the student can merely solve Prob. 22.

available.   The major restriction placed on functions such that they fall within the domain of applicability of the theory of integration by residues is that the functions be regular.   The term analytic is commonly used; however, here the term regular will refer to single-valued functions having certain properties, while analytic functions will be permitted to be multivalued.   We shall seldom need to consider multivalued functions.   The fact that transforms are regular was established by Theorem 13.   For reference, a brief summary of the theory of regular functions will be given here.   The material after Theorem 30 is of the most interest in our applications.   For additional material on regular function theory see Ref. 5.

THEORY OF REGULAR FUNCTIONS

The two operations which play the central role in this theory are differentiation and integration.   The functions are not always defined at every point of the complex plane; however, in the definition of regular function we insist that the domain of definition of the function be suitable for differentiation and integration.   For differentiation we need an open set such that the limit of the difference quotient can be formulated, and for integration we need a connected set such that for any two points there exists a "path" in the domain which joins these points and along which an integral can be formulated.   A set which is both open and connected is called a *region*, and one of the requirements for a function to be regular is that its domain of definition be a region.   To make the definition of region meaningful, we shall now define open and connected.

Let R be a set of complex numbers; that is, R is a subset of the complex plane.   Then R is open iff for each $z_0 \in R$, there exists a real $\delta > 0$ such that $z \in R$ whenever $|z - z_0| < \delta$.   The set R is an open, connected† set (i.e., a region) iff it is open and each pair of points of R can be joined by a polygonal line lying entirely within the set R.   Of course, a polygonal line is a finite number of joined line segments which does not intersect itself.   A path is a continuous curve of finite length which does not intersect itself.   A precise analytical definition can be given thus: An oriented set of points C of the complex plane is a *path* iff there exists a complex-valued function of a real variable $z(t)$ defined for t in some finite interval $[\alpha, \beta]$ such that (1) C is the range of $z(t)$, (2) $z(t)$ is continuous and of bounded variation, and (3) $z(t)$ is a one-to-one mapping; i.e., to each point of C there corresponds just one $t \in [\alpha, \beta]$.   The order of the points of $[\alpha, \beta]$ induces an orientation of C. A *simple closed path* is defined by replacing condition 3 in the definition of path with the following: $z(t) = z(t')$ iff t and t' are equal or one is α and the other is β.   A circle is a typical simple closed path, and any simple closed path can be obtained by drawing a circle on a sheet of rubber and then making a continuous planar distortion of the sheet.

---

† There is some simplification in avoiding the definition of a connected set which may not be open.   A set R is *connected* iff there do not exist two disjoint open sets which cover R with each open set containing points of R.

JORDAN CURVE THEOREM

A simple closed curve (curve differs from path in that it need not be of finite length; i.e., the condition that z is of bounded variation is dropped) divides the plane into two disjoint parts, one part inside the curve and one outside. This theorem is intuitively obvious, but very difficult to prove.

For this subsection we abandon the notation $F(p)$ in favor of $f(z)$, etc. Let $g(z)$ be a complex-valued function of a complex variable defined for $0 < |z - z_0| < a$. Then

$$\lim_{z \to z_0} g(z) = w$$

iff for any $\epsilon > 0$ there exists a $\delta > 0$ such that $|g(z) - w| < \epsilon$ whenever $0 < |z - z_0| < \delta$. Now let $f(z)$ be defined for $0 \le |z - z_0| < a$. Then the derivative of f at z_0 exists iff

$$\lim_{z \to z_0} \frac{f(z) - f(z_0)}{z - z_0}$$

exists. This limit is the derivative, and it is denoted by $f'(z_0)$. Finally, let f be a complex-valued function of a complex variable whose domain is R, where R is a subset of the complex plane; then f *is regular* (or regular on R) iff (1) R is a region and (2) for each $z \in R$, $f'(z)$ exists.

Theorem 24 (*Cauchy-Riemann Equations*). Let $u(x, y) = \text{Re } [f(x + jy)]$ and $v(x, y) = \text{Im } [f(x + jy)]$. Then f is regular on the region R iff $\partial u/\partial x = \partial v/\partial y$ and $\partial u/\partial y = -\partial v/\partial x$ at every point of the region. The *only if* is

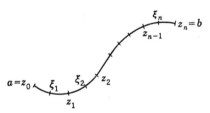

FIGURE 2-7.   Path of integration.

very easy to prove; the *if* part is deep and very difficult to prove in the strong form stated here.

Let C be a path between a and b, and partition the path as indicated in Figure 2-7. Let $f(z)$ be defined for all z on C. Then the integral of f from a to b along C is defined thus (if it exists):

$$\lim_{\substack{\max_i |z_i - z_{i-1}| \to 0}} \sum_{i=1}^{n} f(\xi_i)(z_i - z_{i-1})$$

It is denoted by

$$\int_{C_a}^{b} f \qquad \text{or} \qquad \int_{C_a}^{b} f(z)\, dz$$

Of course the definition of $\int_C f$ when C is a simple closed path goes in the same way, and such integrals will be counterclockwise unless otherwise stated. By the way, this differs from a complex-valued line integral in the plane only in that $z_i - z_{i-1}$ appears in the sum rather than $|z_i - z_{i-1}|$.

With the above definition we should now proceed to develop the theory of integration; e.g., the following can be proved:

1. Continuous functions (and hence certainly regular functions) are integrable.

2. Integration is linear.

3. If $|f| < M$ on C and L is the length of C, then

$$\left| \int_C f \right| \leq ML$$

assuming that f is integrable.

The following is the key theorem for the theory of regular functions.

Theorem 25 (Cauchy's Theorem). Let f be regular on R and let C be a simple closed path in R with the interior of C contained in R. Then

$$\int_C f = 0$$

REMARKS: A complete proof of this theorem is beyond the scope of this review; however, one method of proof will be sketched. Also, a simple "derivation" can be based on the Cauchy-Riemann equations (see Prob. 18).

A proof can be given by first proving the theorem for the special case when C is a triangle, then for C a polygon by triangulation of the polygon, and finally for an arbitrary simple closed path by approximating the path with polygons. The most pleasant part of this proof is the first, which will be given here. Let the path be T, a triangle. Divide T into four triangles T_a, T_b, T_c, and T_d with lines between the mid-points of the sides of T thus:

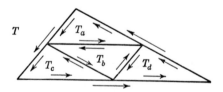

Then

$$\int_T f = \int_{T_a} f + \int_{T_b} f + \int_{T_c} f + \int_{T_d} f$$

since

$$\int_{\substack{C \\ a}}^{b} f = - \int_{\substack{C \\ b}}^{a} f$$

which provides cancellation of the integrals along the interior sides (sides of T_b). Now

$$\left| \int_T f \right| \leq 4 \left| \int_{T_1} f \right|$$

if T_1 is the triangle for which the corresponding integral has the largest absolute value. The length of the path for T_1 is $L/2$ if L is the length of the path T. We now divide T_1 in a manner similar to that for the division of T. Then

$$\left| \int_{T_1} f \right| \leq 4 \left| \int_{T_2} f \right|$$

where T_2 corresponds to the term having the largest absolute value of the four integrals which equal $\int_{T_1} f$.

Proceeding in this way, we get

$$\left| \int_{T} f \right| \leq 4^n \left| \int_{T_n} f \right|$$

where the length of the path T_n is $2^{-n}L$. Also T_{n+1} is inside T_n. Let z_0 be the cluster point of the sequence of triangles $\{T_n\}$, and write $f(z)$ thus:

$$f(z) = f(z_0) + f'(z_0)(z - z_0) + \gamma(z)(z - z_0)$$

where the equation defines $\gamma(z)$ for $z \neq z_0$. Let $\gamma(z_0) = 0$. Since $f'(z_0)$ exists, we see that $\gamma(z) = [f(z) - f(z_0)]/(z - z_0) - f'(z_0)$ goes to zero as $z \to z_0$. Now

$$\int_{T_n} f(z)\, dz = [f(z_0) - z_0 f'(z_0)] \int_{T_n} dz + f'(z_0) \int_{T_n} z\, dz + \int_{T_n} \gamma(z)(z - z_0)\, dz$$

It is easy to show that the first two terms are zero by using the definition of integral directly (see problems); therefore,

$$\left| \int_{T} f \right| \leq 4^n \left| \int_{T_n} \gamma(z)(z - z_0)\, dz \right|$$

Now for any $\epsilon > 0$ there exists an n large enough that $|\gamma(z)| < \epsilon$ on T_n since γ is continuous. For such an n, $|\gamma(z)(z - z_0)| < \epsilon 2^{-n}L/2$ since $|z - z_0|$ is not greater than half the length of T_n. In turn,

$$\left| \int_{T_n} \gamma(z)(z - z_0)\, dz \right| < \epsilon 2^{-(n+1)}L 2^{-n}L$$

and hence $$\left| \int_{T} f \right| < \frac{\epsilon L^2}{2} \qquad \text{for any } \epsilon > 0$$

The left side of this last relation is fixed; yet it is smaller than an arbitrary $\epsilon L^2/2 > 0$; clearly, then,

$$\left| \int_{T} f \right| = 0 \qquad \text{or} \qquad \int_{T} f = 0$$

as was to be shown.

A *simply connected region* R is a region such that whenever C is a simple closed path in R, the interior of C is contained in R. From Cauchy's theorem it is seen that if f is regular on the simply connected region R, then

$$\int_{C_1}^{b} {}_a f = \int_{C_2}^{b} {}_a f$$

if C_1 and C_2 are paths in R between a and b.   Then

$$\int_{C_2} f - \int_{C_1} f = 0 \qquad \text{by Cauchy's theorem}$$

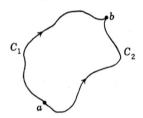

In such situations we drop the path C from the notation and write

$$\int_a^b f$$

Theorem 26 (*Near Converse to Theorem 25*).   Let f be continuous on the simply connected region R and let $\int_C f = 0$ for every simple closed path in R.   Then f is regular in R.

Theorem 27 (*Fundamental Theorem of Calculus*).   Let f be regular in the simply connected region R; then

$$F(z) = \int_a^z f(\xi)\, d\xi$$

is a regular function of z where the path of integration is in R, and $F'(z) = f(z)$.   Also, if $G'(z) = f(z)$ for each $z \in R$, then $F - G$ is constant and

$$\int_a^b f(\xi)\, d\xi = G(b) - G(a)$$

Lemma 2.   Let f' exist on the simple closed paths $C, C_1, \ldots, C_n$, and let f' exist at points which are inside C but outside $C_1, \ldots, C_n$, where $C, C_1, \ldots, C_n$ are as shown.   Then

$$\int_C f = \int_{C_1} f + \int_{C_2} f + \cdots + \int_{C_n} f$$

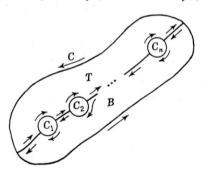

PROOF: Let T be the "top" simple closed path and B the "bottom" path. Then, by Theorem 25,

$$\int_T f = 0 \qquad \text{and} \qquad \int_B f = 0$$

However,

$$0 = \int_T f + \int_B f = \int_C f - \int_{C_1} f - \cdots - \int_{C_n} f$$

since the integrals along the connecting lines cancel one another and we get clockwise integrals around $C_1, \ldots, C_n$.

Theorem 28 (*Cauchy's Formula*). Let C be a simple closed path, let f' exist on and inside C, and let z_0 be inside C; then

$$f(z_0) = \frac{1}{2\pi j} \int_C \frac{f(z)}{z - z_0}\, dz$$

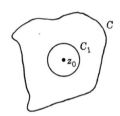

PROOF: It is easy to see that $f(z)/(z - z_0)$ is regular on and inside C except at $z = z_0$. Therefore, by Lemma 2 we can use C_1 in place of C. Let

$$\frac{1}{2\pi j} \int_{C_1} \frac{f(z)}{z - z_0} = \frac{1}{2\pi j} \int_{C_1} \frac{f(z) - f(z_0)}{z - z_0}\, dz + \frac{f(z_0)}{2\pi j} \int_{C_1} \frac{dz}{z - z_0}$$

The second term can be evaluated by integrating from the definition; however, it can also be evaluated by changing the integration variable from z to θ thus:

$$z - z_0 = \rho e^{j\theta} \qquad \text{and} \qquad dz = j\rho e^{j\theta}\, d\theta$$

We get

$$\frac{f(z_0)}{2\pi j} \int_0^{2\pi} \frac{j e^{j\theta}\, d\theta}{e^{j\theta}} = f(z_0)$$

For the first term

$$\frac{1}{2\pi j} \int_{C_1} \frac{f(z) - f(z_0)}{z - z_0}\, dz$$

let $\epsilon > 0$ and take ρ small enough so that $|f(z) - f(z_0)| < \epsilon$ for z on C_1; this can be done since $f'(z_0)$ exists and in turn f is continuous at z_0. The length of C_1 is $2\pi\rho$; hence

$$\left| \frac{1}{2\pi j} \int_{C_1} \frac{f(z) - f(z_0)}{z - z_0}\, dz \right| \leq \frac{1}{2\pi} \frac{\epsilon}{\rho} 2\pi\rho = \epsilon$$

However, ϵ is an arbitrary positive number; in turn,

$$\frac{1}{2\pi j} \int_{C_1} \frac{f(z) - f(z_0)}{z - z_0}\, dz$$

must be zero.

   Theorem 29 (One Derivative Now Implies All Derivatives).   Under the conditions of Theorem 28, all the derivatives of f exist, and if f^n denotes the nth derivative,

$$f^n(z_0) = \frac{n!}{2\pi j} \int_C \frac{f(z)}{(z - z_0)^{n+1}}\, dz$$

The proof is not very difficult.   It consists in justifying repeated interchanges of differentiation and integration.   A version of the dominated convergence theorem can be used to justify the interchange.

   We now turn to the relationship between power (and Laurent) series and regular functions.   Put loosely, all power series are regular and all regular functions can be expanded in power series.   Our interest is in expanding regular functions in series; this expansion follows from Cauchy's integral formula.   However, some facts about power series will now be mentioned.

   Theorem 30.   Let a_n be a sequence of complex numbers.   Then there exists a nonnegative r in the extended reals (that is, $0 \le r \le \infty$) such that

$$\sum_{n=0}^{\infty} a_n z^n$$

converges for $|z| < r$ and the series diverges for $|z| > r$ (almost anything can happen at $|z| = r$).   For $|z| < r$,

$$f(z) = \sum_{n=0}^{\infty} a_n z^n$$

is regular, and

$$f'(z) = \sum_{n=0}^{\infty} n a_n z^{n-1}$$

for such z.   Also, the series can be integrated termwise inside the circle $|z| = r$.   Finally, if

$$f(z) = \sum_{n=0}^{\infty} a_n z^n$$

and

$$g(z) = \sum_{n=0}^{\infty} b_n z^n$$

then

$$f(z)g(z) = \sum_{n=0}^{\infty} \left(\sum_{k=0}^{n} b_{n-k} a_k \right) z^n$$

inside the smaller circle of convergence.

Theorem 31 (*Taylor Series Expansion*). Let C be a circle having center z_0 and let f' exist on and inside C. Then, for z inside C,

$$f(z) = \sum_{n=0}^{\infty} a_n (z - z_0)^n$$

where

$$a_n = \frac{1}{2\pi j} \int_C \frac{f(z)}{(z - z_0)^{n+1}} \, dz = \frac{f^n(z_0)}{n!}$$

PROOF: By Cauchy's formula,

$$f(z) = \frac{1}{2\pi j} \int_C \frac{f(\xi)}{\xi - z} \, d\xi = \frac{1}{2\pi j} \int_C \frac{f(\xi)}{(\xi - z_0) - (z - z_0)} \, d\xi$$

$$= \frac{1}{2\pi j} \int_C \frac{f(\xi)}{\xi - z_0} \frac{1}{1 - (z - z_0)/(\xi - z_0)} \, d\xi$$

Let $\alpha = (z - z_0)/(\xi - z_0)$, and observe that

$$\frac{1}{1 - \alpha} = 1 + \alpha + \alpha^2 + \cdots + \alpha^n + \frac{\alpha^{n+1}}{1 - \alpha}$$

by, say, long division. If we integrate the corresponding finite series, we obtain

$$f(z) = \sum_{k=0}^{n} a_k (z - z_0)^k + R_n$$

where

$$R_n = \frac{1}{2\pi j} \int_C \frac{f(\xi)}{(\xi - z_0)} \frac{\alpha^{n+1}}{1 - \alpha} \, d\xi = \frac{(z - z_0)^{n+1}}{2\pi j} \int_C \frac{f(\xi)}{(\xi - z)(\xi - z_0)^{n+1}} \, d\xi$$

It only remains to be shown that R_n goes to zero as $n \to \infty$. Observe that

$$|\xi - z| \geq b > 0$$
$$|z - z_0| = a = r - b$$

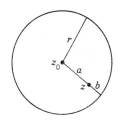

Hence

$$|R_n| \leq \frac{a^{n+1}}{2\pi} \frac{M}{br^{n+1}} 2\pi r$$

where M is the maximum value of $|f(\xi)|$ for ξ on C. Thus

$$|R_n| \leq \frac{Mr}{2\pi b} \left(\frac{a}{r}\right)^{n+1}$$

but $0 < a/r < 1$, from which it is clear that $|R_n| \to 0$. Of course this proof gives a_n in the integral form. Theorem 29 provides the other form for the coefficients.

Theorem 32 (Laurent Series).   Let $f'(z)$ exist on and between concentric circles C_1 and C_2, and let z_0 be the center of these circles.   Then

$$f(z) = \sum_{n=-\infty}^{-1} a_n(z - z_0)^n + \sum_{n=0}^{\infty} a_n(z - z_0)^n \equiv \sum_{n=-\infty}^{\infty} a_n(z - z_0)^n$$

for z between the circles and

$$a_n = \frac{1}{2\pi j} \int_C \frac{f(\xi)}{(\xi - z_0)^{n+1}} d\xi$$

where C is any simple closed path around z_0 in the closed ring determined by C_1 and C_2.

PROOF: Let z be in the ring, and then form the simple closed paths T and B thus:

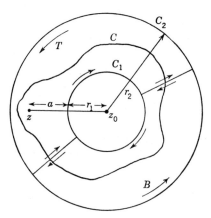

By Cauchy's formula,

$$f(z) = \frac{1}{2\pi j} \int_T \frac{f(\xi)}{\xi - z} d\xi$$

Note that for ξ on and inside B, $f(\xi)/(\xi - z)$ is regular in ξ; therefore, by Theorem 25,

$$\frac{1}{2\pi j} \int_B \frac{f(\xi)}{\xi - z} d\xi = 0$$

Adding, we get

$$f(z) = \frac{1}{2\pi j} \int_{C_2} \frac{f(\xi)}{\xi - z} d\xi - \frac{1}{2\pi j} \int_{C_1} \frac{f(\xi)}{\xi - z} d\xi$$

The first term is expanded exactly as done in Theorem 31. For the second term we have

$$-\frac{1}{2\pi j} \int_{C_1} \frac{f(\xi)}{\xi - z} d\xi = \frac{1}{2\pi j} \int_{C_1} \frac{f(\xi)}{(z - z_0) - (\xi - z_0)} d\xi$$

or

$$\frac{1}{2\pi j(z - z_0)} \int_{C_1} f(\xi) \frac{1}{1 - (\xi - z_0)/(z - z_0)} d\xi$$

As before, let

$$\alpha = \frac{\xi - z_0}{z - z_0} \quad \text{and} \quad \frac{1}{1-\alpha} = 1 + \alpha + \alpha^2 + \cdots + \alpha^n + \frac{\alpha^{n+1}}{1-\alpha}$$

Termwise integration gives

$$\sum_{k=1}^{n} b_k(z - z_0)^{-k} + R_n$$

where $b_k = \dfrac{1}{2\pi j} \displaystyle\int_{C_1} \dfrac{f(\xi)}{(\xi - z_0)^{1-k}} \, d\xi$ or $\displaystyle\sum_{k=-1}^{-n} a_k(z - z_0)^k + R_n$

Of course,

$$R_n = \frac{(z - z_0)^{-n-1}}{2\pi j} \int_{C_1} \frac{f(\xi)}{z - \xi} (\xi - z_0)^{n+1} \, d\xi$$

$$|R_n| \le \frac{M}{2\pi a} \left(\frac{r_1}{r_1 + a}\right)^{n+1} 2\pi r_1$$

which goes to zero as $n \to \infty$. Finally, by Lemma 2, the paths C_1 and C_2 of the integrals for the coefficients of the negative powers and the nonnegative powers, respectively, can be changed to any path C of the type indicated in the sketch given at the beginning of this proof.

Suppose f is such that for some fixed C_2, the radius of C_1 can be taken arbitrarily small (but positive); hence, there is a Laurent series which converges for $0 < |z - z_0| < r_2$. Then z_0 is called an isolated singularity iff the series diverges for $z = z_0$. If z_0 is an isolated singularity and there is some $m > 0$ such that $a_m \ne 0$ and $a_k = 0$ for all $k < m$, then z_0 is called a pole of f of order m. Non pole isolated singularities are called essential singularities; for example, $e^{1/z}$ has an essential singularity at $z = 0$.

Let z_0 be an isolated singularity of f and let

$$f(z) = \sum_{n=-\infty}^{\infty} a_n(z - z_0)^n$$

for $0 < |z - z_0| < r_2$. Then (and only then)

$$a_{-1} = \frac{1}{2\pi j} \int_C f(\xi) \, d\xi$$

is called the *residue of f at z_0*, where C is a simple closed path around z_0 with C inside the circle $|z - z_0| = r_2$.

Theorem 33 (Residue Theorem). Let f be regular in the region R, let C be a simple closed path in R, and let the inside of C be contained in R except for a finite number of isolated singularities; then

$$\int_C f(z) \, dz = 2\pi j(\text{sum of residues of } f \text{ inside } C)$$

PROOF: Let $C_1, \ldots, C_n$ be small circles about the singularities of f which are inside C. Then, by Lemma 2,

$$\int_C f = \sum_{k=1}^{n} \int_{C_k} f = 2\pi j (\text{sum of residues})$$

by the definition of residue.

Recall that two-sided Laplace transforms exist only on a strip. In the evaluation of the inversion formula we shall want to construct a function which is regular on, say, the entire plane (except for a finite number of poles) and which is equal to said transform on the strip of convergence. For the transforms we shall consider, this construction will be trivial; it is interesting to note that the construction is unique; however, we shall not make use of this uniqueness which follows from Theorem 34.

Theorem 34. Let f and g be regular on the region R, let $z_1, z_2, \ldots$ be a sequence of points of R such that

$$\lim_{n \to \infty} z_n = z_0 \in R$$

let $z_k \neq z_0$ for all $k \geq 1$, and let $f(z_n) = g(z_n)$ for $n = 0, 1, 2, \ldots$. Then $f(z) = g(z)$ on R. For the proof (which will not be given in detail), we expand f and g in a Taylor series as given by Theorem 31. The coefficients $f^n(z_0)/n!$ and $g^n(z_0)/n!$ can be computed by using only the values of f and g on $z_0, z_1, z_2, \ldots$. For example,

$$f'(z_0) = \lim_{n \to \infty} \frac{f(z_0) - f(z_n)}{z_0 - z_n}$$

In turn, the two series have the same coefficients and hence $f = g$ on the circle of convergence of the series. We can then expand f and g about a point inside the circle of convergence which is close to the boundary of the circle and continue in this way to get $f = g$ on R.

APPLICATION TO INVERSION

Before the residue theorem is applied to the inversion problem, a simple example of integration by residues will be given. Suppose we wish to find

$$\int_{-\infty}^{\infty} \frac{dx}{1 + x^2}$$

Of course this can be done by inspection since arctan x is an antiderivative and

$$\lim_{R \to \infty} [\arctan R - \arctan (-R)]$$

is π. This same integral will now be evaluated by using the residue theorem. Suppose we consider the function $1/(1 + z^2)$ as a function of the complex variable z. This function is regular except at $z = \pm j$. To apply the residue theorem, we need a simple closed path; for this problem we introduce the path shown. Let I_1 denote the integral along C_1, that is, from $-R$ to R

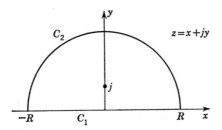

on the real axis. Let I_2 be the integral along the arc at $|z| = R$. Then, by the residue theorem,

$$I_1 + I_2 = 2\pi j(\text{residue at } z = j)$$

There are several ways to find the residue. Expansion into partial fractions will usually be used here:

$$\frac{1}{z^2 + 1} = \frac{1}{(z + j)(z - j)} = \frac{A}{z + j} + \frac{B}{z - j}$$

To find B, multiply each side by $z - j$ and then take the limit as $z \to j$. This gives $1/(j + j) = 0 + B$ or $B = 1/2j$. Now for the residue at j, we wish to expand $1/(z^2 + 1)$ in a Laurent series about $z_0 = j$. This can be done by expanding $A/(z + j)$ and $B/(z - j)$ into Laurent series about j and then adding. However, $B/(z - j)$ is its own Laurent series about j, and $A/(z + j)$ is regular inside the circle $|z - j| < 2$; hence its Laurent series about $z = j$ is a power series which does not contribute to the residue. Thus about $z = j$,

$$\frac{1}{z^2 + 1} = \frac{1/2j}{z - j} + a_0 + a_1(z - j) + a_2(z - j)^2 + \cdots$$

where
$$a_n = \frac{d^n}{dz^n} \left(\frac{A}{z + j} \right)_{z=j}$$

The residue at $z = j$ is clearly $1/2j$. In turn,

$$I_1 + I_2 = 2\pi j \frac{1}{2j} = \pi$$

However, our interest is in
$$\lim_{R \to \infty} I_1$$

not in $I_1 + I_2$. To show that

$$\lim_{R \to \infty} I_1 = \pi$$

we first show that

$$\lim_{R \to \infty} I_2 = 0$$

For this, observe that

$$|I_2| \leq \frac{1}{R^2 - 1} \pi R \qquad \text{for } R > 1$$

since

$$\left| \frac{1}{z^2 + 1} \right| \leq \frac{1}{R^2 - 1}$$

and the length of $C_2 = \pi R$. Now, clearly,

$$\lim_{R \to \infty} |I_2| = 0$$

and hence

$$\lim_{R \to \infty} I_2 = 0$$

Finally, $I_1 = (I_1 + I_2) - I_2$,

$$\lim_{R \to \infty} I_2$$

exists and is zero, and

$$\lim_{R \to \infty} (I_1 + I_2)$$

exists and is equal to π since $I_1 + I_2$ is constant with R for $R > 1$. In turn, the limit of the difference is the difference of the limits and hence

$$\lim_{R \to \infty} I_1 = \pi$$

as expected.

The attractive feature of the above example is that it clearly generalizes to any rational function for which there are no poles on the real axis and for which the degree of the denominator is at least two greater than the degree of the numerator. For example, consider

$$I = \int_{-\infty}^{\infty} \frac{1}{a^4 + x^4} \, dx$$

where a is real. Then

$$\frac{1}{z^4 + a^4} = \frac{A_1}{z - e_1 a} + \frac{A_2}{z - e_2 a} + \frac{A_3}{z - e_3 a} + \frac{A_4}{z - e_4 a}$$

where the e's are the one-fourth roots of -1; for example, $e_1 = e^{j\pi/4}$. Now

$$A_1 = \frac{1}{a^3(e_1 - e_2)(e_1 - e_3)(e_1 - e_4)}$$

and we have a similar formula for A_2. Then $I = 2\pi j(A_1 + A_2)$, which simplifies to

$$2\pi j\left[\frac{1}{a^3 2\sqrt{2}(-1+j)} + \frac{1}{a^3 2\sqrt{2}(1+j)}\right] \quad \text{or} \quad \frac{\pi}{\sqrt{2}a^3}$$

Like the above examples, the inversion formula does not involve a simple closed path, but rather an integral along a vertical line in the p plane, namely, Re $p = \sigma$. To apply the residue theorem, semicircles will be introduced. We need a theorem which shows that the contribution along the semicircles goes to zero as the radius gets large.

Theorem 35. Let $F(p)$ be integrable for large $|p|$, and let

$$M(R) = \max_{|p|\geq R} |F(p)|$$

go to zero† as $R \to \infty$; then, for any real σ,

$$\lim_{R\to\infty}\int_{C_-} e^{pt}F(p)\,dp = 0 \qquad \text{for } t < 0$$

and

$$\lim_{R\to\infty}\int_{C_+} e^{pt}F(p)\,dp = 0 \qquad \text{for } t > 0$$

where C_- is a semicircle in the right half plane and C_+ is a semicircle in the left half plane, as pictured in Figure 2-8.

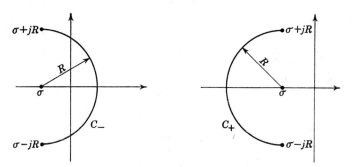

FIGURE 2-8.   Semicircles for closure of contour in Laplace inversion formula.

PROOF: The choice of C_- for $t < 0$ is made such that $|e^{pt}| = e^{\sigma t}$ will "get small" on most of C_- as $R \to \infty$; that is, with $t < 0$ we want a semicircle where $e^{\sigma t}$ will have a negative exponent; hence we want $\sigma > 0$. We pick C_+ for $t > 0$ for the same reason, i.e., to make $\sigma t < 0$ on most of the semicircle. The proofs for $t > 0$ and $t < 0$ are similar; $t < 0$ will be considered

† This is equivalent to $\lim_{p\to\infty} F(p) = 0$. Also, note that M is a function to be evaluated at $R - |\sigma|$ in the proof.

here. Let $p = \sigma + Re^{j\theta}$ on the path of integration. Of course, $dp = jRe^{j\theta}\,d\theta$, and we get

$$I = \int_{C_-} e^{pt}F(p)\,dp = \int_{C_-} F(p)e^{\sigma t}e^{Rt\cos\theta}e^{jRt\sin\theta}je^{j\theta}R\,d\theta$$

On the path of integration, $|F(p)| \leq M(R - |\sigma|)$ since $|p| \geq R - |\sigma|$ on C. Thus we get

$$|I| \leq RM(R - |\sigma|)e^{\sigma t}\int_{-\pi/2}^{\pi/2} e^{Rt\cos\theta}\,d\theta$$

or

$$|I| \leq 2RM(R - |\sigma|)e^{\sigma t}\int_{0}^{\pi/2} e^{Rt\sin\theta}\,d\theta$$

This is clear by inspection or by a simple change of integration variable. For $0 < \theta < \pi/2$, $\sin\theta > (2/\pi)\theta$; and since $Rt < 0$, this gives

$$|I| \leq 2RM(R - |\sigma|)e^{\sigma t}\int_{0}^{\pi/2} \exp\frac{2Rt\theta}{\pi}\,d\theta$$

or

$$|I| \leq 2RM(R - |\sigma|)e^{\sigma t}\frac{\pi}{2Rt}(e^{Rt} - 1)$$

Thus

$$|I| \leq \frac{\pi e^{\sigma t}}{t}M(R - |\sigma|)(e^{Rt} - 1)$$

As $R \to \infty$, $e^{Rt} \to 0$ since $Rt < 0$. Also, $M(R - |\sigma|)$ goes to 0; therefore,

$$\lim_{R\to\infty} I = 0$$

We are now in a position to apply the residue theorem to the inversion formula. Suppose

$$F(p) = \frac{A}{(p - a)^n} + \frac{B}{(p - b)^m} \qquad \text{for Re } a < \text{Re } p < \text{Re } b$$

and we wish to find

$$f(t) = \lim_{R\to\infty} \frac{1}{2\pi j}\int_{\sigma-jR}^{\sigma+jR} e^{pt}F(p)\,dp$$

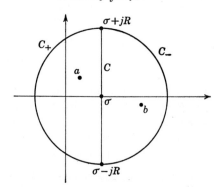

where $\text{Re } a < \sigma < \text{Re } b$. To evaluate the integral, we analytically continue the definition of F to the entire plane except for the points a and b. If $t < 0$, we consider

$$I_c \equiv \int_{\sigma-jR}^{\sigma+jR} e^{pt}F(p)\,dp \qquad \text{and} \qquad I_{c_-} \equiv \int_{C_-} e^{pt}F(p)\,dp$$

By the residue theorem, $I_c + I_{c_-} = -2\pi j$(residue at b) since the contour is clockwise rather than counterclockwise. By Theorem 35,

$$\lim_{R\to\infty} I_{c_-} = 0 \qquad \text{for } t < 0$$

In turn,

$$\lim_{R\to\infty} I_c = -2\pi j(\text{residue at } b)$$

Finally, $f(t) = -$residue of $e^{pt}F(p)$ at b for $t < 0$.

Thus we need only find the residue at b. We shall expand each term of the integrand separately in a Laurent series about $p = b$. Of course, $B/(p - b)^m$ is its own series, where it is assumed that m is a positive integer. As for $A/(p - a)^n$, this function is regular in the neighborhood of b and its Laurent series about b is a Taylor series. Finally, the series for e^{pt} is well known:

$$e^{pt} = e^{bt} + te^{bt}(p - b) + \frac{t^2e^{bt}}{2!}(p - b)^2 + \cdots + \frac{t^{n-1}e^{bt}}{(n-1)!}(p-b)^{n-1}$$
$$+ \cdots \qquad \text{by Theorem 31}$$

Now the series for the integrand consists of the power series of $A/(p - a)^n$ plus $B/(p - b)^m$ times the power series of e^{pt}. This latter product is a Laurent series which contributes the residue. The term of this product corresponding to the residue is

$$\frac{Bt^{m-1}e^{bt}}{(m-1)!}\frac{(p-b)^{m-1}}{(p-b)^m}$$

Hence

$$f(t) = \frac{-Bt^{m-1}}{(m-1)!}e^{bt} \qquad \text{for } t < 0$$

For $t > 0$ we must use C_+ to get

$$\lim_{R\to\infty} I_{c+} = 0$$

In this case the pole at $p = a$ is enclosed and the contour is in the counterclockwise direction. Thus $f(t)$ equals the residue of the integrand at a. We find the residue at a to be $A[t^{n-1}/(n-1)!]\,e^{at}$ in a manner similar to that used to find the residue at b.

Finally, the situation for $t = 0$ should be discussed. Consider the integrals separately. If n and/or m is 2 or more, the contribution of the corresponding term is zero. To see this, suppose that $m \geq 2$. Then

$$\lim_{R \to \infty} \int_{\sigma-jR}^{\sigma+jR} \frac{dp}{(p-b)^m}$$

can be seen to be zero by using the fundamental theorem of calculus or by using the residue theorem. The antiderivative is $\dfrac{1}{1-m} \dfrac{1}{(p-b)^{m-1}}$, which goes to zero when we substitute $\pm jR$ and let R go to infinity. To use the residue theorem, we know we can close the contour with C_- or C_+ since $m \geq 2$. We simply pick C_+, and no singular point is enclosed for the term $B/(p-b)^m$. If m or n is 1, the contribution is not zero. Let

$$\ln(p-b) = \ln|p-b| + j\phi(p-b)$$

where ϕ is the angle of $p-b$ and $\ln|p-b|$ is the ordinary real logarithm of the positive number $|p-b|$. Then $\ln(p-b)$ is regular on $\operatorname{Re} p = \sigma$ and its derivative is $1/(p-b)$. Thus

$$\int_{\sigma-jR}^{\sigma+jR} \frac{dp}{p-b} = \ln|\sigma+jR-b| - \ln|\sigma-jR-b| + j\phi(\sigma+jR-b)$$
$$- j\phi(\sigma-jR-b)$$

Of course

$$\lim_{R \to \infty} \ln\left|\frac{\sigma+jR-b}{\sigma-jR-b}\right| = \ln 1 = 0$$

since for large R the moduli of the numerator and the denominator are approximately R. To see the behavior of ϕ, consider the sketch. Clearly,

$$\lim_{R \to \infty} \phi = \frac{\pi}{2} \qquad \text{and} \qquad \lim_{R \to -\infty} \phi = \frac{3}{2}\pi$$

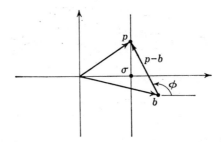

Thus the contribution of $B/(p-b)$ to $f(0)$ is

$$\frac{B}{2\pi j}\left(j\frac{\pi}{2} - j\frac{3\pi}{2}\right) = -\frac{B}{2}$$

If $n = 1$, everything goes in about the same way except that the angle ϕ

takes on different values, as shown in the sketch. Thus in this case we get a contribution of $\frac{1}{2}A$.

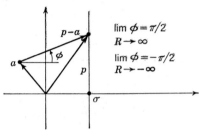

To summarize the example, if

$$F(p) = \frac{A}{(p-a)^n} + \frac{B}{(p-b)^n} \qquad \text{for Re } a < \text{Re } p < \text{Re } b$$

n and m are positive integers, Re $a < \sigma <$ Re b, and

$$f(t) = \lim_{R \to \infty} \frac{1}{2\pi j} \int_{\sigma - jR}^{\sigma + jR} e^{pt} F(p) \, dp$$

then

$$f(t) = \begin{cases} \dfrac{A t^{n-1}}{(n-1)!} e^{at} & \text{for } t > 0 \\[2mm] \dfrac{-B t^{m-1}}{(m-1)!} e^{bt} & \text{for } t < 0 \\[2mm] 0 & \text{at } t = 0 \text{ if } n \text{ and } m \geq 2 \\[2mm] \dfrac{A}{2} & \text{at } t = 0 \text{ if } n = 1 \text{ and } m \geq 2 \\[2mm] \dfrac{-B}{2} & \text{at } t = 0 \text{ if } m = 1 \text{ and } n \geq 2 \\[2mm] \dfrac{A}{2} - \dfrac{B}{2} & \text{at } t = 0 \text{ if } n \text{ and } m = 1 \end{cases}$$

This behavior at $t = 0$ is what we expect in that we get

$$f(0) = \frac{1}{2}[f(0+) + f(0-)]$$

in all cases. Observe that if F were of the same form, but for Re $p <$ Re a, we get

$$f(t) = \begin{cases} 0 & \text{for } t > 0 \\[2mm] \dfrac{-A t^{n-1}}{(n-1)!} e^{at} - \dfrac{B t^{m-1}}{(m-1)!} e^{bt} & \text{for } t < 0 \end{cases}$$

if $\sigma <$ Re $a <$ Re b. And, on the other hand, if F were of the same form but for Re $p >$ Re b, then we get

$$f(t) = \begin{cases} 0 & \text{for } t < 0 \\[2mm] \dfrac{A t^{n-1}}{(n-1)!} e^{at} + \dfrac{B t^{m-1}}{(m-1)!} e^{bt} & \text{for } t > 0 \end{cases}$$

if the inversion is with $\sigma >$ Re b.

For any proper rational function F, we simply expand F into partial fractions thus:

$$F(p) = \sum_n \sum_k \frac{A_{nk}}{(p - a_k)^n}$$

and the poles of F to the right of the line Re $p = \sigma$ contribute to $f(t)$ for $t < 0$, and the poles to the left of the inversion line contribute to $f(t)$ for $t > 0$. At $t = 0$, we always get $\frac{1}{2}[f(0+) + f(0-)]$.

An additional contour integral will be considered. One item of unfinished business in Sec. 2-2 was the evaluation of

$$I = \int_{-\infty}^{\infty} \frac{\sin x}{x} \, dx$$

Consider the following integral:

$$I(R, \delta) = \int_{-R}^{-\delta} \frac{\sin x}{x} \, dx + \int_{\delta}^{R} \frac{\sin x}{x} \, dx$$

Then
$$I = \lim_{\delta \to 0} \lim_{R \to \infty} I(R, \delta)$$

To introduce contour integration, note that

$$I(R, \delta) = \frac{1}{j} \int \frac{e^{jx}}{x} \, dx$$

since $(\cos x)/x$ is an odd function (where the same intervals of integration are used, that is, $\delta < |x| < R$). Now, analytically continue the integral with $jx = p$, and then

$$I(R, \delta) = \frac{1}{j} \int_{-jR}^{-j\delta} \frac{e^p}{p} \, dp + \frac{1}{j} \int_{j\delta}^{jR} \frac{e^p}{p} \, dp$$

where p is a complex variable. The contour can be closed as shown. Let

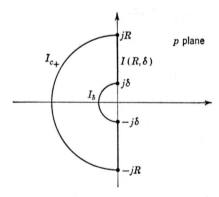

I_δ be the integral of $\dfrac{1}{j} \dfrac{e^p}{p}$ along the small semicircle about $p = 0$. Since e^p/p

is regular on and inside the contour,

$$I_{c_+} + I(R, \delta) + I_\delta = 0 \qquad \text{by Cauchy's theorem}$$

By Theorem 35,

$$\lim_{R \to \infty} I_{c_+} = 0$$

where $t = 1$ and $F(p) = 1/p$. In turn,

$$I = -\lim_{\delta \to 0^+} I_\delta = -\lim_{\delta \to 0^+} \frac{1}{j} \int \frac{e^p}{p} \, dp$$

Finally, let $p = \delta e^{j\theta}$ and $dp = j\delta e^{j\theta} \, d\theta$. Then

$$\int \frac{e^p}{p} \, dp = j \int_{-\pi/2}^{-3\pi/2} \exp(\delta e^{j\theta}) \, d\theta$$

This last integral is the integral of a complex-valued function of a real variable. The integrand is dominated by e^{δ_0} for $0 < \delta < \delta_0$; hence, by the dominated convergence theorem,

$$I = -\lim_{\delta \to 0} \frac{1}{j} j \int_{-\pi/2}^{-3\pi/2} \exp(\delta e^{j\theta}) \, d\theta$$

$$= -\int_{-\pi/2}^{-3\pi/2} \lim_{\delta \to 0} \exp(\delta e^{j\theta}) \, d\theta = -\int_{-\pi/2}^{-3\pi/2} d\theta = \pi$$

as was to be shown.

Problems

16. Use the definition of the integral to show that if $f(z) = 1$ for all z, then

$$\int_b^a f = b - a$$

along any path between a and b.

17. Suppose $f(z) = z$. Show that

$$\int_a^b z \, dz = \frac{b^2}{2} - \frac{a^2}{2}$$

directly from the definition of the integral. Assume that the path is a straight line between a and b and assume that f is an integrable function.

18. Starting with the conclusion of Green's theorem (P and Q real-valued functions of x and y),

$$\int_C P \, dx + Q \, dy = \iint_{\substack{\text{interior} \\ \text{of } C}} \left(\frac{\partial Q}{\partial x} - \frac{\partial P}{\partial y} \right) dx \, dy$$

and with

$$\int_C f(z) \, dz = \int_C (u + jv)(dx + j \, dy)$$

derive the conclusion of Cauchy's theorem.

19. Show that if z_0 is a pole of order k of $f(z)$, then the residue of f at z_0 is

$$\frac{1}{(k-1)!} \lim_{z \to z_0} \left[\frac{d^{k-1}}{dz^{k-1}} (z - z_0)^k f(z) \right]$$

20. Evaluate the inversion formula with $\sigma = 0$ with $F(p) = 1/(p^2 - 1)$.

21. Evaluate the inversion formula along the line Re $p = -1$ with $F(p) = 1/(p^2 + 1)$.

22. Find four functions of t such that the analytic continuation of each of their transforms is

$$F(p) = \frac{5p^2 - 2p - 4}{p^3 - p^2 - 2p}$$

23. Suppose $F(p) = e^p/p$. Show that F does not satisfy the conditions of Theorem 35. Find two functions of t such that the analytic continuation of each of their transforms is e^p/p.

2-5 SOME APPLIED PROBLEMS

Mostly for illustrative purposes, an assortment of rather specific problems will now be considered.   Some new points are introduced in these examples; however, they are not points to be used to any large extent in later sections. Examples 12, 14, and 15 are of considerable importance.

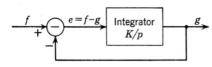

Example 11.   An Application of the Final-value Theorem. Consider the simple feedback system shown in Figure 2-9.   Here

FIGURE 2-9.   A simple feedback system.

$$g(t) = K \int_0^t [f(\tau) - g(\tau)] \, d\tau$$

(assuming that the output of the integrator is zero at $t = 0$); in turn, $G = K/p(F - G)$, or $G + (p/K)G = F$.   By the way, this is the same as the equation for the networks of Figure 2-10.   Suppose $f(t) = Ct^n U(t)$, where we shall consider $n = 0$ (step input), $n = 1$ (ramp or constant-velocity

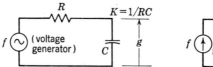 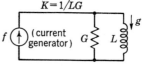

FIGURE 2-10.   Simple "equivalent" systems.

input), and $n = 2$ (quadratic or constant-acceleration input).   The problem is to find

$$\lim_{t \to \infty} [f(t) - g(t)]$$

by the final-value theorem.   Since F is known and $E = L(f - g)$ is of interest, consider $G = (K/p)E$ and $G = F - E$; therefore, $E = pF/(K + p)$. Of course, $F = Cn!/p^{n+1}$ and $pE(p) = Cn!/(p + K)p^{n-1}$.   Now, by the final-value theorem, if $n = 0$,

$$\lim_{t \to \infty} e(t) = \lim_{p \to 0} pE(p) = \lim_{p \to 0} \frac{Cp}{p + K} = 0$$

as expected.   If $n = 1$,

$$\lim_{t \to \infty} e(t) = \lim_{p \to 0} \frac{C}{p + K} = \frac{C}{K}$$

If $n \geq 2$, $$\lim_{t \to \infty} e(t) = \lim_{\sigma \to 0+} \frac{Cn!}{(\sigma + K)\sigma^{n-1}} = \infty$$

These results could easily have been guessed; e.g., with a ramp input, a constant error will be needed to keep the output growing linearly.   Since the slope is C, $C = Ke_v$ if e_v denotes a constant-velocity error; that is

$$\lim_{t \to \infty} e(t) = e_v = \frac{C}{K} \qquad \text{for } n = 1$$

Let us now modify the system to obtain one for which the velocity error is zero.   If we had two integrators in cascade, it would be possible for the output to grow linearly with the input to the first integrator zero (i.e., with the error zero).   The system now takes the form shown in Figure 2-11.

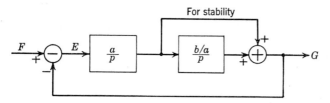

FIGURE 2-11.   Feedback system.

Without the forward loop around the second integrator, we get $p^2G + bG = bF$, which does not have desired stability features.   As matters are, we have $G = (a/p + b/p^2)E$, and $G = F - E$.   Hence

$$pE = \frac{p^3}{p^2 + ap + b} F(p)$$

Now if $F = Cn!/p^{n+1}$,

$$pE(p) = \frac{Cn!}{p^2 + ap + b} p^{2-n}$$

If $n = 0$ or 1,

$$\lim_{p \to 0} pE(p) = 0$$

That is, the position error and the velocity errors are zero.   The acceleration error is $2C/b$, where $2C$ is the acceleration corresponding to the input $Ct^2U(t)$.   The jerk ($n = 3$) and snap ($n = 4$) errors, etc., are ∞ in this case.

Finally, we shall look at the ramp response ($n = 1$) in detail as a function of t.   Let the output of the first integrator at $t = 0$ be α and the output of the second integrator at $t = 0$ be β.   Let $g(t) = 0$ for $t < 0$, and of course for $t > 0$ we have

$$g(t) = \frac{b}{a} \int_0^t \left[a \int_0^\tau e(u)\, du + \alpha \right] d\tau + \beta + a \int_0^t e(u)\, du + \alpha$$

Taking the transform of both sides gives

$$G = \frac{b}{a} \frac{1}{p} \left(a \frac{E}{p} + \frac{\alpha}{p} \right) + \frac{\beta}{p} + \frac{aE}{p} + \frac{\alpha}{p}$$

or

$$G = \frac{ap + b}{p^2 + ap + b} F + \frac{(\alpha + \beta)p + \alpha b/a}{p^2 + ap + b}$$

For a ramp input $f(t) = vtU(t)$, $F(p) = v/p^2$. The two terms will be handled separately by somewhat different methods.

Let q and $\bar{q}$ be the zeros of $p^2 + ap + b = (p - q)(p - \bar{q})$. To find the inverse transform of the first term, we shall use inversion by residues. The residues will be computed by partial-fraction expansion (Problem 19 provided another method for finding the residues). Let

$$\frac{v(ap + b)}{p^2(p - q)(p - \bar{q})} = \frac{A}{p^2} + \frac{B}{p} + \frac{C}{p - q} + \frac{D}{p - \bar{q}}$$

Then

1. $A = \dfrac{vb}{q\bar{q}} = \dfrac{vb}{b} = v$

2. $C = \dfrac{v(aq + b)}{q^2(q - \bar{q})}$

3. $D = \dfrac{v(a\bar{q} + b)}{(\bar{q})^2(\bar{q} - q)}$

Several methods can be used to compute B. A tricky method is to observe that as $p \to \infty$, the left side goes to zero as $1/p^3$ while the right side seems to go to zero more slowly—apparently as $1/p$. For the identity to hold, the right side must go faster than $1/p$; this is possible only if the last three terms tend to cancel one another for large $|p|$. This will occur iff $B = -(C + D)$. To obtain a solution to the original equation, the inversion formula must be applied in the strip of convergence of the transform of the input, for it is only in that strip that the equation relating F and G is valid. The domain for F is Re $p > 0$; thus, if Re $q < 0$ and Re $\bar{q} < 0$, the inversion will be unique,† namely,

$$(vt + B + Ce^{qt} + De^{\bar{q}t})U(t)$$

For example,

$$\frac{1}{2\pi j} \int_{\sigma - j\infty}^{\sigma + j\infty} \frac{C}{p - q} e^{pt}\, dt = \begin{cases} Ce^{qt} & \text{for } t > 0 \\ 0 & \text{for } t < 0 \end{cases}$$

if Re $q <$ Re σ.

---

† The possible lack of uniqueness is discussed in Sec. 2-6.

To simplify the results, suppose $a^2 - 4b < 0$, so that $q = -a/2 + j\sqrt{b - (a/2)^2}$ and $\bar{q}$ must now denote the complex conjugate of q. In this case $D = \bar{C}$ (from here on, the bar necessarily denotes the conjugate) and the exponential terms can be combined. Let $C = |C|e^{j\gamma}$, and $\omega_0 = \sqrt{b - (a/2)^2}$. Then we have

$$|C|e^{-(a/2)t}\left(e^{j(\omega_0 t + \gamma)} + e^{-j(\omega_0 t + \gamma)}\right) = 2|C|e^{-(a/2)t}\cos(\omega_0 t + \gamma)$$

for the exponential terms. Observe that

$$C = v\frac{-a^2/2 + b + ja\omega_0}{2j\omega_0(a^2/4 - ja\omega_0 - b + a^2/4)} = -\frac{v}{2\omega_0 j}$$

and hence, $2|C| = v/\omega_0$ and $\gamma = \pi/2$. Thus, the contribution of the exponential terms is $-v/\omega_0 e^{-(a/2)t}\sin \omega_0 t$. Of course, $D = \bar{C} = -j(v/2\omega_0)$. In turn, $B = C + D = 0$. Thus, we finally have

$$U(t)\left(vt - \frac{v}{\omega_0}e^{-(a/2)t}\sin \omega_0 t\right)$$

for the inverse transform of the first rational function.

The second term can be handled in the same way with considerably less trouble since there is no p^2 factor in the denominator; however, suppose we recall that

$$L(\sin \omega_0 t)_p = \frac{\omega_0}{p^2 + \omega_0^2} \quad \text{and} \quad L(\cos \omega_0 t)_p = \frac{p}{p^2 + \omega_0^2}$$

Then consider

$$
\begin{aligned}
\frac{(\alpha + \beta)p + (b/a)\alpha}{p^2 + ap + b} &= \frac{(\alpha + \beta)p + (b/a)\alpha}{(p + a/2)^2 + (b - a^2/4)} \\
&= \frac{(\alpha + \beta)(p + a/2)}{(p + a/2)^2 + \omega_0^2} + \frac{(b/a)\alpha - (a/2)(\alpha + \beta)}{(p + a/2)^2 + \omega_0^2}
\end{aligned}
$$

Now, by the shift theorem (18), the inverse transform (taken in the right half plane) is

$$U(t)\left\{(\alpha + \beta)e^{-(a/2)t}\cos \omega_0 t + \left[\frac{1}{\omega_0}\frac{b\alpha}{a} - \frac{a}{2\omega_0}(\alpha + \beta)\right]e^{-(a/2)t}\sin \omega_0 t\right\}$$

If $b - a^2/4 < 0$, a similar approach involving hyperbolic functions can be used. Of course if $a > 0$, it is seen that

$$\lim_{t \to \infty}[f(t) - g(t)] = 0$$

as predicted by the final-value theorem. If we let $a \to 0+$, the stabilizing link around the second integrator loses its effect and the transient terms become sinusoidal oscillations rather than damped oscillations. By the

way, with $a > 0$, the system is called underdamped when $b > a^2/4$, overdamped when $b < a^2/4$, and critically damped when $b = a^2/4$.

   Example 12.   Tilt, an Application of the Initial-value Theorem.   When
long rectangular pulses are passed through an a-c-coupled amplifier, the
rising and falling edges of the pulses
are distorted because of limited high-
frequency response, and the top of
the pulse is tilted because of limited
low-frequency response.   The tilt introduced will be computed here; Chap.
5 covers the high-frequency-response

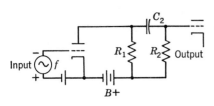

FIGURE 2-12. Simple amplifier circuit.

problem.
   Consider the amplifier shown in Figure 2-12.   High-frequency distortion
is caused by shunt capacitance, principally by the input capacitance of the
next stage which is in parallel with R_2.   This small capacitance has very
little effect on the tilt of the top of the output pulse when the input is a
long rectangular pulse; however, if shunt capacitance is included, the analysis
is considerably more complicated.   A low-frequency equivalent circuit for

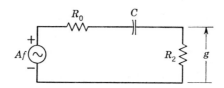

the amplifier is also shown.   A similar equivalent circuit is applicable if a
transistor amplifier is considered.
   To calculate the low-frequency distortion, f will be taken as a step function
$U(t)$, and the initial charge on the capacitor is assumed to be zero.   Note
that

$$G = \frac{AR_2}{R_0 + R_2} \frac{pT}{1 + pT} F$$

where $T = C(R_0 + R_2)$ is the time constant of the circuit.   If $F(p) = 1/p$,

$$g(t) = \frac{AR_2}{R_0 + R_2} e^{-t/T} U(t)$$

If T is large compared with the duration of the pulse† (as it should be for
good coupling), then over the duration of the pulse $e^{-t/T} \cong 1 - t/T$, as
illustrated in Figure 2-13.

   † For $0 < t < a$ (pulse duration), the circuit behaves as though the input is $U(t)$.

The tilt Q will be defined thus:

$$Q = \frac{|\text{slope of output pulse}|\, a}{\text{peak value of output pulse}}$$

For the case at hand,

$$Q = a\,\frac{(1/T)\,AR_2/(R_0 + R_2)}{AR_2/(R_0 + R_2)} = a\,\frac{1}{T}$$

The above can easily be generalized. Let $G = HF$, where H is the transfer function of the amplifier. Let the peak output for a step input occur at $t = 0+$. Then the peak output is

$$\lim_{p \to \infty} pH(p)\,\frac{1}{p}$$

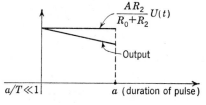

where we use the initial-value theorem and the fact that $F(p) = 1/p$ when a step input is present. Let

$$\lim_{p \to \infty} H(p) = H(\infty)$$

FIGURE 2-13.   Tilt of top of rectangular pulse.

which equals the peak output. Suppose, further, that $g(t)$ can be expanded into a power series for $0 < t < a$:

$$g(t) = g(0+) + g'(0+)t + \frac{g''(0+)}{2!}\,t^2 + \cdots$$

With good coupling the first two (nonzero) terms will be used as an approximation to g. Recall that

$$L(g')_p = pG - g(0+) = pHF - H(\infty)$$

In turn, by the initial-value theorem,

$$g'(0+) = \lim_{p \to \infty} p[pH(p)\,\frac{1}{p} - H(\infty)] = \lim_{p \to \infty} p[H(p) - H(\infty)]$$

Finally, in this case the tilt is

$$Q = a\left|\frac{\lim\limits_{p \to \infty} p[H(p) - H(\infty)]}{H(\infty)}\right|$$

For the simple RC coupling network we had

$$H(p) = H(\infty)\,\frac{pT}{pT + 1}$$

which gives a tilt of

$$Q = a\left|\lim_{p \to \infty}\left[p\left(\frac{pT}{pT + 1} - 1\right)\right]\right| = a\left|\lim_{p \to \infty}\left(p\,\frac{-1}{pT + 1}\right)\right| = \frac{a}{T}$$

as found before.

One way to compensate for tilt is to modify the circuit so as to obtain $g'(0+) = 0$. Then the output pulse can be approximated by a quadratic thus:

$$g(t) \cong g(0+) + \frac{g''(0)t^2}{2}$$

In this case, the tilt should be defined thus:

$$Q = \frac{\frac{1}{2}a^2|g''(0+)|}{|g(0+)|}$$

and $\qquad g''(0+) = \lim_{p \to \infty} p[p^2 H(p)F(p) - pg(0+) - g'(0+)]$

In this case $g'(0+) = 0$, $g(0+) = H(\infty)$, and $F(p) = 1/p$. The tilt formula becomes

$$Q = \frac{1}{2} a^2 \left| \frac{\lim\limits_{p \to \infty} p^2[H(p) - H(\infty)]}{H(\infty)} \right|$$

Two results concerning low-frequency distortion of a flat-top pulse can now be derived. Suppose the amplifier consists of n identical cascaded stages each of which has linear tilt Q_0: $f \to \boxed{H} \to \boxed{H} \to \cdots \to \boxed{H} \xrightarrow{g}$. Of course, $G = H^n F$, and the overall tilt is

$$Q = a \left| \lim_{p \to \infty} \frac{p[H^n(p) - H^n(\infty)]}{H^n(\infty)} \right| = a \left| \lim_{p \to \infty} p\left[\frac{H^n(p)}{H^n(\infty)} - 1 \right] \right|$$

$$= a \lim_{p \to \infty} \left| p\left[\frac{H(p)}{H(\infty)} - 1 \right] \right| \left| 1 + \frac{H(p)}{H(\infty)} + \left[\frac{H(p)}{H(\infty)}\right]^2 + \cdots + \left[\frac{H(p)}{H(\infty)}\right]^{n-1} \right|$$

However,

$$\lim_{p \to \infty} \left| p\left[\frac{H(p)}{H(\infty)} - 1 \right] \right| = Q_0$$

and $\qquad \lim_{p \to \infty} \left| 1 + \frac{H(p)}{H(\infty)} + \cdots + \left[\frac{H(p)}{H(\infty)}\right]^{n-1} \right| = n$

Thus, $Q = nQ_0$, that is, the tilt for n identical stages is n times the tilt of a single stage. Note that the derivation goes in the same way (except that p^2 replaces p) if the stages have quadratic tilt instead of linear tilt.

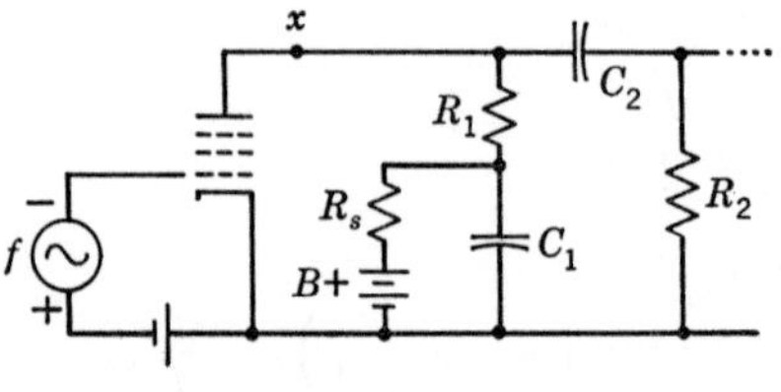

The second result is concerned with compensation for linear tilt. The original circuit is modified as shown in Figure 2-14. The problem is to choose the network parameters such that the linear tilt is zero.

Here we shall consider a pentode (or

FIGURE 2-14.   Compensation for low-frequency distortion.

a collector output transistor circuit), in which case the device looking back from x can be approximated by a current source. The equivalent circuit becomes

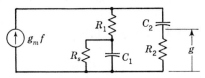

Simple manipulation gives

$$G = Fg_m \frac{p^2 C_1 C_2 R_1 R_2 + (R_1/R_s)C_2 R_2 p + C_2 R_2 p}{p^2 C_1 C_2 (R_1 + R_2) + (1 + R_1/R_s + R_2/R_s)C_2 p + pC_1 + 1/R_s}$$

Let $C_1 R_1 = T_1$, $C_2 R_2 = T_2$, and $R_s/R_1 = n$.   Then

$$G = \left(Fg_m \frac{R_1 R_2}{R_1 + R_2} \right)$$

$$\times \frac{p^2 T_1 T_2 + (1 + 1/n) T_2 p}{p^2 T_1 T_2 + \left(\dfrac{R_1}{R_1 + R_2} + \dfrac{1}{n} \right) T_2 p + \dfrac{p R_2 T_1}{R_1 + R_2} + \dfrac{R_1 R_2}{R_s (R_1 + R_2)}}$$

The last factor is $H(p)/H(\infty)$, and hence $g'(0+) = 0$ iff $H(p)/H(\infty) - 1$ has a numerator having zero for the coefficient of the linear term (clearly, the coefficient of p^2 is zero, namely, $T_1 T_2 - T_1 T_2$).   Thus to obtain linear compensation we need

$$\left(1 + \frac{1}{n} \right) T_2 = \left(\frac{R_1}{R_1 + R_2} + \frac{1}{n} \right) T_2 + \frac{R_2 T_1}{R_1 + R_2}$$

This gives the condition

$$\left(1 - \frac{R_1}{R_1 + R_2} \right) T_2 = \frac{R_2}{R_1 + R_2} T_1 \qquad \text{or} \qquad T_1 = T_2$$

Thus the condition for linear compensation is $R_1 C_1 = R_2 C_2$, which except for R_s makes the plate circuit a balanced bridge.   Under this compensated condition let $T_1 = T_2 = T$, and

$$\frac{H(p)}{H(\infty)} = \frac{(pT)^2 + (1 + 1/n)Tp}{(pT)^2 + (1 + 1/n)Tp + R_1 R_2/(R_1 + R_2)R_s}$$

Clearly,

$$\lim_{p \to \infty} p^2 \left[\frac{H(p)}{H(\infty)} - 1 \right] = \frac{-R_1 R_2}{T^2 R_s (R_1 + R_2)}$$

or

$$\frac{-R_2}{R_1 + R_2} \frac{1}{nT^2}$$

The tilt is

$$Q = \frac{1}{2n} \frac{R_2}{R_1 + R_2} \left(\frac{a}{T} \right)^2$$

if the pulse duration is a.   Suppose

$$\frac{R_2}{R_1 + R_2} \cong 1 \qquad \frac{a}{T} = 0.1 \qquad n = 5$$

Then $Q = 0.001$ compared with $Q = 0.1$ if the compensating network were not present.

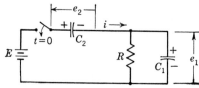

FIGURE 2-15. Simple circuit with impulsive adjustment.

Example 13.   Typical Circuit Involving "Impulsive Adjustment."   Consider the circuit in Figure 2-15. At $t = 0$, let the voltage on C_1 be A_1 and that on C_2 be A_2. Note that if $A_1 + A_2 \neq E$, the voltage around the loop $E = e_1 + e_2$ is contradicted just after the switch is closed.   Suppose we ignore the contradiction and solve for $e_1(t)$ in the usual way.   For $t > 0$,

$$E = e_2 + e_1 \qquad i = C_2 e_2' = \frac{e_1}{R} + C_1 e_1'$$

Transforming both equations gives

$$\frac{E}{p} = E_2 + E_1 \qquad C_2 p E_2 - C_2 A_2 = \frac{E_1}{R} + C_1 p E_1 - C_1 A_1$$

or, if $T = R\,(C_1 + C_2)$,

$$E_1\left(p + \frac{1}{T}\right) = \frac{E C_2}{C_1 + C_2} + \frac{C_1}{C_1 + C_2} A_1 - \frac{C_2}{C_1 + C_2} A_2$$

Let E_0 denote the voltage on the right-hand side.   Then $e_1(t) = E_0 e^{-t/T}$ for $t > 0$.   Note that when we started the problem, $e_1(0+)$ was assumed equal to A_1; yet the solution gives E_0 as $e_1(0+)$.   Also, we get $e_2(t) = E - e_1(t)$, and the contradiction has been removed.   When the equation $C_2 e_2' = e_1/R + C_1 e'$ is transformed it is seen that as far as initial conditions are concerned only $C_2 e_2(0+) - C_1 e_1(0+)$ is of importance.   This is simply the difference of the initial charges on the capacitors.   Thus we shall always get the same solution if the correct value of this difference in charges is used.

When the switch is closed, with $A_1 + A_2 \neq E$, there is an impulsive redistribution of the charges on the capacitors such that the equation $E = e_1 + e_2$ will not be contradicted after the adjustment.   This adjustment changes $e_1(0+)$ and $e_2(0+)$, but it leaves the difference $C_2 e_2(0+) - C_1 e_2(0+)$ unchanged.   The time required for this redistribution is determined by very small (second-order) circuit effects such as lead resistance and inductance (e.g., in series with C_2); these effects are negligible after the impulsive adjustment.   Since the solution using Laplace transforms involves only the difference of the initial charges, we can ride roughshod over the contradiction which exists just after the switch is closed, because the use of the correct adjusted values would not change our solution.

The adjusted values can easily be computed without resorting to the solution found by transforms. This will now be done to check $e_1(0+) = E_0$. During the brief duration of the adjustment, the capacitors short out any effects of the parallel resistors. The circuit can then be viewed as shown in Figure 2-16.

The equations to be solved for $e_1(0+)$ and $e_2(0+)$ are the following: $E = e_1(0+) + e_2(0+)$; $C_2 e_2(0+) - C_2 A_2 = C_1 e_1(0+) - C_1 A_1$. The second equation follows from continuity of current flow during the adjustment. Solving for $e_1(0+)$ gives

$$e_1(0+) = \frac{C_2}{C_1 + C_2}(E - A_2)$$
$$+ \frac{C_1}{C_1 + C_2} A_1$$

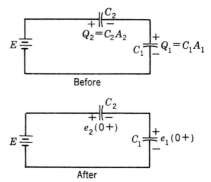

FIGURE 2-16. Conditions before and after impulsive adjustment.

as predicted. If there is a very small lead resistance r in series with C_2, the change from A_1 to E_0 takes place with the usual exponential curve with a time constant of $r\, C_1 C_2/(C_1 + C_2)$.

Only one simple circuit was discussed here; however, the same general situation prevails in all circuits involving initial conditions which contradict Kirchhoff's laws and for which there is a sudden redistribution of initial charges on capacitors and initial currents in the inductors. As far as obtaining the transient solution is concerned (neglecting fine structure during the short time involved in the adjustment), one can apply Laplace transforms in the usual way and ignore the contradictory nature of the initial conditions. The solution obtained will possess the adjusted initial conditions.

Example 14. Simple Problem Using the Two-sided Transform. Let the input to the simple RC circuit shown be $e^{-|t|}$ for all real t. Let the problem

$$2g' + g = f$$

be to find a solution g which does not have jumps (such as the jump at zero involved when a nonzero initial condition is used in a "one-sided problem"). Then if $F = L(f)$ and $G = L(g)$, the two-sided transform of both sides of the equation gives

$$2pG + G = F \qquad \text{or} \qquad G = \frac{F}{2p + 1}$$

It is easy to show that if $f(t) = e^{-|t|}$,

$$F(p) = \frac{1}{p+1} - \frac{1}{p-1} \qquad \text{for } -1 < \text{Re } p < 1$$

Hence,
$$G(p) = \frac{1}{(p+1)(2p+1)} - \frac{1}{(p-1)(2p+1)}$$

and, in terms of partial fractions,

$$G(p) = \frac{-1}{p+1} + \frac{2}{2p+1} + \frac{-\frac{1}{3}}{p-1} + \frac{\frac{2}{3}}{2p+1} = \frac{\frac{4}{3}}{p+\frac{1}{2}} - \frac{1}{p+1} - \frac{\frac{1}{3}}{p-1}$$

To obtain g we simply take the inverse transform. In order to show that the g obtained is actually a solution by reading the derivation backward (as done in Example 3), we must invert in the strip of convergence of $L(f)$. Thus we take

$$g(t) = \frac{1}{2\pi j} \int_{\sigma-j\infty}^{\sigma+j\infty} e^{pt} G(p) \, dp$$

where $-1 < \sigma < 1$. In previous examples, g was unique; however, here we get one solution if $-1 < \sigma < -\frac{1}{2}$ and a different solution if $-\frac{1}{2} < \sigma < 1$. Specifically, if $-\frac{1}{2} < \sigma < 1$,

$$g(t) = \begin{cases} \frac{1}{3}e^t & \text{for } t < 0 \\ \frac{4}{3}e^{-\frac{1}{2}t} - e^{-t} & \text{for } t > 0 \end{cases}$$

and if $-1 < \sigma < -\frac{1}{2}$,

$$g(t) = \begin{cases} \frac{1}{3}e^t - \frac{4}{3}e^{-\frac{1}{2}t} & \text{for } t < 0 \\ -e^{-t} & \text{for } t > 0 \end{cases}$$

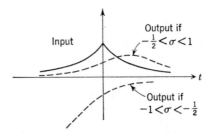

We can easily show that the two g's found are solutions to $2g' + g = f$, either by direct substitution or by reading the derivation backward. As is well known, these two solutions must differ by only a homogeneous solution; such is the case since they differ by $\frac{4}{3}e^{-\frac{1}{2}t}$ for all t, which is a homogeneous solution. Of course, the general solution can be obtained by taking either solution and adding $Ae^{-\frac{1}{2}t}$.

There is a distinction between the two solutions in terms of realizability. This is discussed in Chap. 3; however, the basic idea will be mentioned here. Since $G = (2p + 1)^{-1}F$, we could use the convolution theorem to express g explicitly in terms of f for an arbitrary (save for general mathematical conditions) input. Let $h(t)$ be an inverse transform of $(2p + 1)^{-1}$. Then

$$g(t) = \int_{-\infty}^{\infty} f(t - \tau)h(\tau) \, d\tau$$

provided that the strips of convergence for $L(h)$ and for $L(f)$ overlap. For the case at hand there are two functions h such that $L(h)_p = (2p + 1)^{-1}$, where each function involves a different strip of convergence. If we take

$$h_r = L^{-1}\left(\frac{1}{2p + 1}\right)$$

with $\sigma > -\frac{1}{2}$, we get

$$h_r(t) = \begin{cases} 0 & \text{for } t < 0 \\ \frac{1}{2}e^{-\frac{1}{2}t} & \text{for } t > 0 \end{cases}$$

and

$$g(t) = \frac{1}{2} \int_0^{\infty} f(t - \tau)e^{-\frac{1}{2}\tau} \, d\tau$$

If we take h_L as the inverse transform of $(2p + 1)^{-1}$ with $\sigma < -\frac{1}{2}$,

$$h_L(t) = \begin{cases} -\frac{1}{2}e^{-\frac{1}{2}t} & \text{for } t < 0 \\ 0 & \text{for } t > 0 \end{cases}$$

and

$$g(t) = -\frac{1}{2} \int_{-\infty}^{0} f(t - \tau)e^{-\frac{1}{2}\tau} \, d\tau$$

If the strip of $L(f)$ is entirely to the right of Re $p = -\frac{1}{2}$ [for example, $f(t) = U(t)e^t$], only $h_r * f$ can be shown to be a solution;† and if to the left of Re $p = -\frac{1}{2}$, only $h_L * f$ can be shown to be a solution. If Re $p = -\frac{1}{2}$ is inside the strip of convergence of $L(f)$, both provide solutions and $f(t) = e^{-|t|}$ is an example of such an f. For this input, it is easy to see that

$$h_r(t) * f(t) = \begin{cases} \frac{1}{3}e^t & \text{for } t < 0 \\ \frac{4}{3}e^{-\frac{1}{2}t} - e^{-t} & \text{for } t > 0 \end{cases}$$

$$h_L(t) * f(t) = \begin{cases} \frac{1}{3}e^t - \frac{4}{3}e^{-\frac{1}{2}t} & \text{for } t < 0 \\ -e^{-t} & \text{for } t > 0 \end{cases}$$

as found before.

From the viewpoint of realizability the important distinction between $h_r * f$ and $h_L * f$ (and hence the distinction between the two solutions found for $e^{-|t|}$) is that $h_r * f$ evaluated at t involves only values of f which occur before (or at) time t, while $h_L * f$ at time t involves values of f which occur after time t. With t given the physical meaning of time, it is unreasonable

† Generally, $h_L * f$ will not exist if $L(f)_p$ exists only for certain Re $p > -\frac{1}{2}$.

for a circuit to be able to produce $h_L * f$ for all f since at any time t this involves the use of future (not yet available) data about the input. Note also that for the specific case discussed, $h_L * e^{-|t|}$ provides an output which is not a reasonable output of an RC circuit for this input. It should be nearly obvious as to how the above discussion generalizes to a system for which $G = HF$ and H is an arbitrary proper rational function of p.

Example 15. A Sampling Theorem, An Application of Fourier Transforms. Under various very restricting conditions a function of a real variable can be reconstructed from periodic samples of its values. The most popular theorem of this sort normally considers functions which are Fourier-transformable and which are bandwidth-limited in that if $F(\omega) = L(f)_{j\omega}$, $F(\omega) = 0$ for $|\omega| > B$. If, in addition, f is integrable, of bounded variation on finite intervals, and $f(t) = \frac{1}{2}[f(t + 0) + f(t - 0)]$ for all t, then of course

$$f(t) = \frac{1}{2\pi} \int_{-B}^{B} e^{j\omega t} F(\omega)\, d\omega$$

which is the major hypothesis of Theorem 36. A simple generalization of this theorem is given in Prob. 30.

Theorem 36 (Popular Sampling Theorem). Let

$$f(t) = \frac{1}{2\pi} \int_{-B}^{B} e^{j\omega t} F(\omega)\, d\omega$$

let F be expressible (at least within a null function) as its Fourier series

$$F(\omega) = \sum_{n=-\infty}^{\infty} C_n \exp\left(-j\frac{n\pi}{B}\omega\right)$$

on $[-B, B]$, and let†

$$\int_{-B}^{B} e^{j\omega t} \sum_{n=-\infty}^{\infty} C_n \exp\left(-j\frac{n\pi}{B}\omega\right) d\omega = \sum_{n=-\infty}^{\infty} C_n \int_{-B}^{B} e^{j\omega t} \exp\left(-j\frac{n\pi}{B}\omega\right) d\omega$$

Then

$$f(t) = \sum_{n=-\infty}^{\infty} f\left(\frac{n\pi}{B}\right) \frac{\sin(Bt - n\pi)}{Bt - n\pi}$$

PROOF: The way we have stated the theorem leaves little work for the

† A sufficient condition for this interchange is that

$$\sum_{n=-\infty}^{\infty} |C_n| < \infty$$

This can readily be shown to be sufficient by use of Theorem 7 (the dominated convergence theorem).

proof. For it is seen that

$$f(t) = \frac{1}{2\pi} \sum_{n=-\infty}^{\infty} C_n \int_{-B}^{B} e^{j\omega t} \exp\left(-j\frac{n\pi}{B}\omega\right) d\omega$$

$$f(t) = \frac{1}{\pi} \sum_{n=-\infty}^{\infty} C_n \frac{\sin(Bt - n\pi)}{t - n\pi/B}$$

Finally, *F expressible as its Fourier series* implies that the C_n's are the Fourier coefficients:

$$C_n = \frac{1}{2B} \int_{-B}^{B} \exp\left(j\frac{n\pi}{B}\omega\right) F(\omega) d\omega$$

which is seen to equal $(\pi/B) f(n/B)$; thus

$$f(t) = \sum_{n=-\infty}^{\infty} f\left(\frac{n\pi}{B}\right) \frac{\sin(Bt - n\pi)}{Bt - n\pi}$$

as was to be shown.

Problems

24. In the sketch, let the initial current in L and the initial voltage on C be zero. Find g when

$$f(t) = \begin{cases} 1 & \text{for } t > 0 \\ 0 & \text{for } t < 0 \end{cases}$$

that is, when $f = U$. Consider all three cases: overdamped, $R/2L > 1/LC$; critically damped, $R/2L = 1/LC$; and underdamped, $R/2L < 1/LC$. Express the solution in

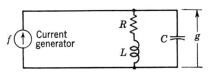

FIGURE P 24

terms of "damped" hyperbolic functions in the overdamped case and in terms of damped sinusoidal (circular) functions in the underdamped case.

25. The circuit of Prob. 24 is the high-frequency equivalent circuit of the plate (or collector) circuit of a shunt-compensated amplifier. In this application C accounts for stray capacitance and the input capacitance of the next stage, R is the load resistance (the value of which is determined by gain and bandwidth requirements), and L is present to improve the rise time of the amplifier. Show that if $L = 0$, the time required for the output to go from 0.1 to 0.9 of its final value is $2.3RC$. Then show that if L is such that the circuit is critically damped, this time is reduced to $1.6RC$.

26. Consider a simple feedback control system consisting of an "ideal" amplifier-motor combination for which the torque developed in the motor is proportional to the amplifier input. If the output of the system is the angular position of the motor shaft, then since torque is proportional to angular acceleration, the second derivative of the output of the amplifier-motor combination is proportional to the input to the amplifier.   The shaft of

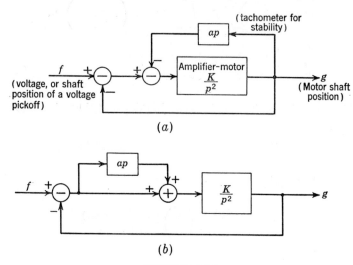

(a)

(b)

FIGURE P 26

the motor can now be made to "follow" the input to the amplifier if feedback is used, as shown in Figure P 26a.   In addition to g, the feedback includes g' to provide system stability and damping.
  (a) Find

$$\lim_{t \to \infty} [f(t) - g(t)]$$

with $f(t) = U(t)t^n$ for $n = 0, 1, 2$.
  (b) In place of using g' for stability, suppose $f' - g'$ is used, as in Figure P 26b.   Find

$$\lim_{t \to \infty} [f(t) - g(t)]$$

when $f(t) = U(t)t^n$ for $n = 0, 1, 2$.   Also find $f(t) - g(t)$ in detail as a function of t if the system starts dead and

$$f(t) = \begin{cases} 0 & \text{for } t < 0 \\ vt & \text{for } t > 0 \end{cases}$$

27. Suppose two networks having nonequal linear tilts are cascaded as shown.   Find

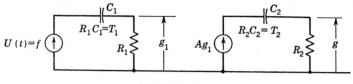

FIGURE P 27

the overall tilt coefficient, that is,

$$\lim_{t \to 0+} \left| \frac{g'(t)}{AR_1R_2} \right|$$

in terms of T_1 and T_2.

28. In the sketch, for $t < 0$, $i_2(t) = 0$ and the current in L_1 is E/R. At $t = 0$, the switch (make before break) puts L_2 in the circuit with zero initial current in L_2. These

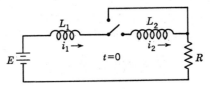

FIGURE P 28

initial conditions are not compatible; however, solve for $i = i_1 = i_2$ (for $t > 0$), overlooking the contradiction. Also, find the adjusted initial conditions.

29. Let the input to the circuit shown in Figure P 29 be

$$f(t) = \begin{cases} e^{-4t} & \text{for } t > 0 \\ 1 & \text{for } t \leq 0 \end{cases}$$

Find three continuous solutions of the differential equation relating the voltage f and the current g (use two-sided Laplace transforms).

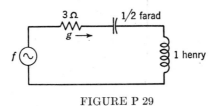

FIGURE P 29

30. Suppose

$$\int_{-\infty}^{\infty} |f(t)| e^{-\sigma t}\, dt < \infty$$

and $F(\sigma + j\omega) = L(f)_p$ is band-limited in the sense that $F(\sigma + j\omega) = 0$ for $|\omega| > B$. Then, granting similar mathematical assumptions as used in Example 15, show that

$$f(t) = \sum_{n=-\infty}^{\infty} f\left(\frac{n\pi}{B}\right) \frac{\exp\left[(\sigma/B)(tB - n\pi)\right] \sin\,(Bt - n\pi)}{Bt - n\pi}$$

2-6 PARTICULAR, HOMOGENEOUS, AND GENERAL SOLUTIONS TO DIFFERENTIAL EQUATIONS

The application† of Laplace transforms to the problem of solving linear differential equations with constant coefficients will be summarized in this section. In view of previous examples and theorems, the points discussed in this section either have been covered before or are obvious. Thus the discussion simply serves to emphasize this application of the theory.

† Often this is the only application considered for Laplace transforms; however, many other applications (e.g., Examples 12 and 15 and applications in Part II) are considered to be at least as interesting in the book.

PARTICULAR SOLUTION

Both differential and integral operators could be considered; however, to avoid cumbersome equations, only differential operators will be used. Suppose f is a known function and a g is to be found such that

$$\sum_{k=0}^{m} b_k g^k(t) = \sum_{i=0}^{n} a_i f^i(t)$$

where the superscripts denote orders of differentiation.   There is an annoying mathematical question as to whether or not the equation is to be satisfied for all t.   If f is very smooth, the equation can be satisfied for all t; however, for certain f's it is impossible to find a g which satisfies the equation for all t.   As a simple example, let $f(t) = U(t)$ and $g'(t) = U(t)$ for all t; then an obvious candidate for the solution is $g(t) = tU(t) + C$ for all t.   Note that $g'(0)$ does not exist; i.e., there is a "corner" at $t = 0$ on the graph of g.

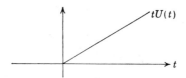

Thus, the equation is not satisfied at $t = 0$.   If inequality of g' and U is permitted at $t = 0$, we could just as well use $g(t) = tU(t) + C + AU(t)$ (where A and C are constants) as the solution.   We can settle on the "most attractive" solution $tU(t) + C$ by insisting that g be continuous at zero. For an mth-order differential equation, we settle on the attractive solution by insisting that g^{m-1} be continuous at points where

$$\sum_{i=0}^{n} a_i f^i$$

is discontinuous (the differential equation is satisfied for all other t)—enough for this mathematical detail.

To simplify matters, let f^{n-1} be continuous so that the jump contributions in Theorem 16 will be zero.   One particular solution to the differential equation can be found by taking g^{m-1} continuous.   Assuming that the other conditions for Theorem 16 are satisfied, we get

$$\sum_{k=0}^{m} b_k p^k G(p) = \sum_{i=0}^{n} a_i p^i F(p)$$

or

$$G(p) = \frac{\displaystyle\sum_{i=0}^{n} a_i p^i}{\displaystyle\sum_{k=0}^{m} b_k p^k} F(p)$$

in the strip of convergence of $L(f)_p$.   In this case, two-sided transforms can be used.   Let

$$P(p) \equiv \sum_{i=0}^{n} a_i p^i \qquad Q(p) = \sum_{k=0}^{m} b_k p^k \qquad H(p) = \frac{P(p)}{Q(p)}$$

Now we take

$$g(t) = \frac{1}{2\pi j} \int_{\sigma-j\infty}^{\sigma+j\infty} e^{pt} F(p) H(p) \, dp$$

with σ in the strip of convergence of F.   Generally, this can be seen to be a solution to the differential equation by reading the steps backward; i.e., with said g, $G = HF$.   In turn, if the g found satisfies the conditions of Theorem 16,

$$\sum_{k=0}^{m} b_k g^k = \sum_{i=0}^{n} a_i f^i$$

Of course, if the line Re $p = \sigma$ can be taken in more than one way to divide the poles of H to the right and left of said inversion line (with σ in the strip of convergence of F), then more than one particular solution can be found.

   To carry out the above program, a specific function f must be under consideration.   What are the prospects for obtaining an explicit formulation for a solution g in terms of f?   The convolution theorem provides such a formulation.   If H is a proper rational function, let $h = L^{-1}(H)$ along a line in the strip of convergence of F.   Then, by the convolution theorem, $g = h * f$, that is,

$$g(t) = \int_{-\infty}^{\infty} h(t - \tau) f(\tau) \, d\tau$$

(Chapter 1, Prob. 3, verified that such a formulation provides a solution for a specific case.)   If $L^{-1}(H)$ is taken to the right of all the poles of H, as it always can be if $f(t) = 0$ for $t < 0$, then $h(t) = 0$ for $t < 0$.   The conclusion that a general solution to any linear differential equation with constant coefficients can be expressed as a convolution is very important (another derivation of this conclusion is given in Sec. 2-7).   In connection with the analysis of various systems, this conclusion implies that the behavior of the system could be described explicitly in terms of a convolution rather than implicitly by a differential equation.

   If H is an improper rational function, we can expand H into a polynomial of degree $n - m = r$ plus a remainder which is a proper rational function.   Thus

$$H(p) = \sum_{k=0}^{r} C_k p^k + R(p)$$

where $C_r = a_n/b_m$, etc.   In this case let $h = L^{-1}(R)$ and then

$$g = \sum_{k=0}^{r} C_k f^r + f * h$$

HOMOGENEOUS SOLUTIONS

If $f(t) = 0$ for all t, the equation to be solved is

$$\sum_{k=0}^{m} b_k g^k = 0$$

If, again, we take g^{m-1} continuous, we get $Q(p)G(p) = 0$ and in turn $G = 0$ and $g = 0$, which is a solution—the trivial one.   The way to obtain non-trivial solutions is clear; namely, we let g^{m-1}, g^{m-2}, . . . , g have discontinuities.   It is well known that there are m *linearly independent* homogeneous solutions to an mth-order differential equation and that any set of solutions numbering more than m is linearly dependent.   We shall now show that all homogeneous solutions can be obtained by considering jumps at $t = 0$, the position of the jumps in most transient problems.   Of course, there is no need to restrict the jumps to $t = 0$, but it is convenient here.

Let $g(t) = 0$ for $t < 0$ and let $g^{m-1}(0+)$, . . . , $g(0+)$ denote the jumps in g at $t = 0$.   Then when the differential equation is transformed we get

$$Q(p)G(p) = \sum_{k=0}^{m-1} d_k p^k = Y(p)$$

where each d_k is a fixed linear combination of the jumps thus:

$$d_{m-1} = b_m g(0+)$$
$$d_{m-2} = b_m g^1(0+) + b_{m-1} g(0+)$$
$$\cdot \cdot \cdot \cdot \cdot \cdot \cdot \cdot \cdot \cdot \cdot \cdot \cdot \cdot \cdot \cdot \cdot \cdot \cdot \cdot \cdot$$
$$d_0 = b_m g^{m-1}(0+) + b_{m-1} g^{m-2}(0+) + \cdot \cdot \cdot + b_1 g(0+)$$

Since $b_m \neq 0$, d_{m-1} can be made to take on any value by selecting $g(0+)$. With said $g(0+)$, $g'(0+)$ can now be selected to make d_{m-2} take on any desired value, etc.   Thus, as the values of the jumps are varied over all possible values, $Y(p)$ goes over all possible polynominals of degree $m - 1$ (or lower).

Consider the homogeneous solution

$$G(p) = \frac{Y(p)}{Q(p)}$$

This is a proper rational function which we can expand in partial fractions. Since Q is a degree m, there are m terms in the expansion.   Each term† is

† Recall that if Q has a factor $(p - a_s)^n$, then corresponding to this factor there are the following terms in the partial-fraction expansion:

$$\frac{A_{1s}}{p - a_s} + \frac{A_{2s}}{(p - a_s)^2} + \cdot \cdot \cdot + \frac{A_{ns}}{(p - a_s)^n}$$

of the form $A/(p - a)^k$, which contributes

$$\frac{A t^{k-1}}{(k - 1)!}\, e^{at} U(t)$$

to the inverse transform g. Thus if $\{a_s\}$ are the zeros of Q, we get the general homogeneous solution

$$\sum_k \sum_s \frac{A_{ks} t^{k-1}}{(k - 1)!} \exp\,(a_s t) U(t)$$

where there are exactly m terms in the summation.† From the theory of partial-fraction expansion we know that as Y goes over all polynomials of degree $m - 1$ (or less), the m coefficients $\{A_{ks}\}$ go over all (complex) values. Since there is a maximum of m linearly independent solutions, we have found the general homogeneous solution. Of course

$$\left\{ \frac{t^{k-1}}{(k - 1)!} \exp a_s t \right\}$$

serves as a maximal set of independent solutions if k and a_s run over the appropriate values.

Finally, we note that the jumps $g^{m-1}(0+), \ldots, g(0+)$ uniquely determine the homogeneous solution, and the solution is a linear function of these jumps. That is, if $g_1(t)$ is the solution corresponding to $g_1^{m-1}(0+),$ $\ldots, g_1(0+)$ and $g_2(t)$ is the solution corresponding to $g_2^{m-1}(0+), \ldots,$ $g_2(0+)$, then $k_1 g_1 + k_2 g_2$ is the solution corresponding to $k_1 g_1^{m-1}(0+) +$ $k_2 g_2^{m-1}(0+), \ldots, k_1 g_1(0+) + k_2 g_2(0+)$. This linearity can be seen simply by appealing directly to the differential equation. Also, it can be seen by noting that since the coefficients of Y are linear functions of the jumps, it follows that if Y_1 corresponds to the first set of jumps and Y_2 corresponds to the second set, then $k_1 Y_1 + k_2 Y_2$ corresponds to the linear combination of the sets of jumps. In turn,

$$G = \frac{k_1 Y_1 + k_2 Y_2}{Q} = k_1 \frac{Y_1}{Q} + k_2 \frac{Y_2}{Q}$$

Hence $g = k_1 g_1 + k_2 g_2$ by the linearity of the inverse transform.

GENERAL SOLUTION

The combination of particular and homogeneous solutions will now be considered. The classical problem is as follows: Given the differential equation, given $f(t)$ with $f(t) = 0$ for $t < 0$ (and we shall retain the condition f^{n-1} is continuous), given $g(t) = 0$ for $t < 0$, and given $g^{m-1}(0+), \ldots,$ $g(0+)$, find $g(t)$ which satisfies the differential equation. In this case we

† At this point we can drop the condition $g(t) = 0$ for $t < 0$ and the solution with $U(t)$ replaced by 1 holds for all t.

take the Laplace transform and obtain

$$G(p) = \frac{P(p)}{Q(p)} F(p) + \frac{Y(p)}{Q(p)}$$

An important property of the Laplace-transform method is that $g = L^{-1}(G)$ will automatically satisfy the initial conditions. Let $g_0(t) = L^{-1}(Y/Q)$. Then the solution is

$$g = \sum_{k=0}^{n-m} C_k f^k + f * h + g_0$$

if $H = P/Q$ is an improper rational function.

In the more general two-sided case we can take† $h = L^{-1}(H)$ in the strip of convergence of $L(f)$, and the general solution is

$$g = f * h + \sum_{k=0}^{n-m} C_k f^k + \sum_k \sum_s \frac{A_{ks} t^{k-1}}{(k-1)!} \exp a_s t$$

where the $\{A_{ks}\}$ can be varied to meet any constraints placed on the solution; e.g., the value of g might be specified at m times.

As a final point, linearity for the classical case will be considered. Implicit in the definition of linear transformation is the fact that the transformation of zero is zero. This follows from the fact that if K is a linear transformation, $K(ax) = aK(x)$, and with $a = 0$ this gives $K(0) = 0K(x) = 0$. Thus if

$$g = \sum_{k=0}^{n-m} C_k f^k + f * h + g_0$$

g is not a linear transformation of f unless $g_0 = 0$. In fact, the equation of a straight line in the plane $y = ax + b$ is not a linear transformation between x and y unless $b = 0$. This is a slightly annoying feature of the definition of linearity; it is present simply because the additive term g_0 is not very exciting when we consider the relationship between f and g with g_0 fixed. The interesting terms do define a linear transformation between f and g. If the jumps (and hence g_0) are not fixed, we must think of g as a transformation of f and the jumps. In this context, g is a linear transformation of the ordered $(m + 1)$-tuple $[f, g^{m-1}(0+), \ldots, g(0)]$, where the first term is a function and the other terms are numbers. The linearity follows simply from the linear dependence of g_0 on the jumps and the linear dependence of the other terms, $\Sigma C_k f^k + f * h$, on f. Now if this ordered $(m + 1)$-tuple is zero, clearly $g = 0$, as required.

† Or of the remainder if H is not proper.

Problems

31. Use two-sided Laplace transforms to find four solutions to

$$\frac{d^3g}{dt^3} - \frac{dg}{dt} = e^{-2|t|} = f(t)$$

Specifically, find the solutions corresponding to four different inversion lines in

$$g(t) = \frac{1}{2\pi j} \int_{\sigma-j\infty}^{\sigma+j\infty} F(p)\, \frac{1}{p^3 - p}\, dp$$

32. Find the explicit particular solution of $g' + 2g = f'' - f$ (g in terms of f as a convolution plus a linear combination of derivatives of f).

2-7 IMPULSE RESPONSE AND DELTA FUNCTIONS

A number of useful concepts as well as some sins are usually included under topics such as impulse response and delta functions. Some of the relevant ideas will be discussed here.

IMPULSE RESPONSE

Let $f(t)$ be the input to a linear system. Suppose we approximate f by a sequence of narrow rectangular pulses thus:

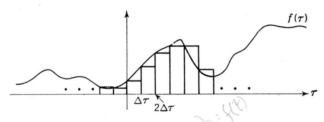

Let the pulses have width $\Delta\tau$ and height $f(n\,\Delta\tau)$. If we define

$$\delta_\Delta(t) = \begin{cases} \dfrac{1}{\Delta\tau} & \text{for } 0 < t < \Delta\tau \\ 0 & \text{for other } t \end{cases}$$

then
$$\tilde{f}(t) = \sum_{n=-\infty}^{\infty} f(n\,\Delta\tau)\delta_\Delta(t - n\,\Delta\tau)\,\Delta\tau$$

is an approximation for the actual input $f(t)$. Let the output of the system produced by the input $\delta_\Delta(t - \tau)$ be $h_\Delta(t, \tau)$, where $\delta_\Delta(t - \tau)$ is considered a function of t. That is, $h_\Delta(t, \tau)$ is the output at time t due to a narrow input pulse applied at time τ. Then the output produced by the input $\tilde{f}$ is

$$\sum_{n=-\infty}^{\infty} f(n\,\Delta\tau)h_\Delta(t, n\,\Delta\tau)\,\Delta\tau$$

where the superposition permitted by linearity has been used and we have assumed that the superposition extends to the infinite sum.   Assume also that

$$\lim_{\Delta\tau \to 0+} h_\Delta(t, \tau) = h(t, \tau)$$

exists.   Also

$$\lim_{\Delta\tau \to 0} \tilde{f} = f$$

if f is a reasonable function.   If $\Delta\tau$ is small, the output produced by f is approximately

$$\sum_{n=-\infty}^{\infty} f(n\,\Delta\tau)h(t, n\,\Delta\tau)\,\Delta\tau$$

Finally, as $\Delta\tau \to 0$, this sum approaches

$$\int_{-\infty}^{\infty} f(\tau)h(t, \tau)\,d\tau$$

if this integral exists.   One can hope (not always in vain) that since $\tilde{f}$ approaches f as $\Delta\tau \to 0$, the output due to $\tilde{f}$ will approach the output due to f as $\Delta\tau \to 0$.   Thus we now assume that if g is the output produced by f,

$$g(t) = \int_{-\infty}^{\infty} h(t, \tau)f(\tau)\,d\tau$$

A system is called time-invariant iff shifting the input in time causes the output to be shifted in time by the same amount.   That is, if the input $f(t)$ produces the output $g(t)$, the input $f(t + a)$ produces the output $g(t + a)$ for any fixed a.

If the system considered above is time-invariant, it can be shown that $h(t, \tau)$ depends only on $t - \tau$.   To see this, note that for any f,

$$\int_{-\infty}^{\infty} h(t, \tau)f(\tau + a)\,d\tau$$

[the output if $f(t + a)$ is the input] must equal

$$\int_{-\infty}^{\infty} h(t + a, \tau)f(\tau)\,d\tau$$

(the output produced by f, but translated by an amount a).   Of course,

$$\int_{-\infty}^{\infty} h(t, \tau)f(\tau + a)\,d\tau = \int_{-\infty}^{\infty} h(t, \tau - a)f(\tau)\,d\tau$$

Hence

$$\int_{-\infty}^{\infty} [h(t, \tau - a) - h(t + a, \tau)]f(\tau)\,d\tau = 0 \qquad \text{for all } f$$

For this to be the case, the bracket involving h must be zero; that is, $h(t, \tau - a) = h(t + a, \tau)$ for all τ (and for arbitrary t and a).   Specifically, for $t = 0$, $h(a, \tau) = h(0, \tau - a)$ for all τ and all a; that is, $h(a, \tau)$ is a function only of $\tau - a$ (or $a - \tau$), which was to be shown. Thus in the time-invariant case we write $\hat{h}(a - \tau)$ in place of $h(a, \tau)$, where $\hat{h}(a - \tau) = h(0, \tau - a) = h(a, \tau)$. Note that $\hat{h}(a) = h(a, 0)$, which is the (limit of the) output at time a when a narrow (limit as width goes to zero) pulse is applied at time 0. That is, $\hat{h}(t)$ is the response (in the limit) if a narrow pulse of area 1 is applied at time zero. From now on, $h(t)$ will be written in place of $\hat{h}(t)$. Thus for the time-invariant case we have

$$\int_{-\infty}^{\infty} h(t - \tau) f(\tau) \, d\tau$$

in place of

$$\int_{-\infty}^{\infty} h(t, \tau) f(\tau) \, d\tau$$

Without reference to transforms (in particular, without reference to the convolution theorem) we have been led to conclude that linear time-invariant systems can be described mathematically by a convolution integral thus:

$$g(t) = \int_{-\infty}^{\infty} h(t - \tau) f(\tau) \, d\tau$$

where $h(t)$ is the limit of the response of the system to a narrow pulse of fixed area 1 as the width of the pulse goes to zero. This limiting response

is called the *impulse response*. The importance of this observation is that if we know the response of the system to this "one input" (narrow pulse), the response to any input can be computed; also, the formulation of the output in terms of the input is explicit. Recall that in Sec. 2-6 the same formulation was obtained under the assumption that the input and output were related by a linear differential equation having constant (time-invariant) coefficients; in the case of such a differential equation the transfer function $H(p)$ is necessarily a rational function. The derivation of Sec. 2-6 gave $h(t)$ as the inverse transform of $H(p)$. However, having now derived $g = h * f$ with h the impulse response, we see that $G = HF$ by the convolution theorem, and hence it follows that the transform of the impulse response is the transfer function.

Alternatively, having derived (in Sec. 2-6) that $g = h * f$, where h is defined as the inverse transform of the transfer function, we could compute the impulse response by letting $f = \delta_\Delta$. The corresponding output is

$$\int_{-\infty}^{\infty} h(t - \tau) \delta_\Delta(\tau) \, d\tau$$

If h is continuous, it should be clear that

$$\lim_{\Delta\tau \to 0} \int_{-\infty}^{\infty} h(t - \tau) \delta_\Delta(\tau) \, d\tau = h(t)$$

which establishes h as the impulse response.
(proof follows)

which establishes h as the impulse response. As for a detailed proof, we could use the integral mean-valued theorem

$$\int_0^{\Delta\tau} h(t-\tau)\,\delta_\Delta(\tau)\,d\tau = \frac{1}{\Delta\tau}\int_0^{\Delta\tau} h(t-\tau)\,d\tau = \frac{1}{\Delta\tau}\,h(t-\theta\,\Delta\tau)\,\Delta\tau$$

where $0 \le \theta \le 1$. Now as $\Delta\tau$ goes to zero, $h(t-\theta\,\Delta\tau)$ goes to $h(t)$.

The use of a rectangular pulse is rather arbitrary in the above discussion. For example, suppose $f(t) = (\sin At)/\pi t$. This will play the role of a narrow pulse if A is large. Specifically, if

$$\int_{-\infty}^{\infty} |h(t)|\,dt < \infty$$

and h is of bounded variation with $h(t) = \frac{1}{2}[h(t+0) + h(t-0)]$, we know that

$$\lim_{A\to\infty}\int_{-\infty}^{\infty} h(t-\tau)\,\frac{\sin a\tau}{\pi\tau}\,d\tau = h(t)$$

As another pulse, we could use a Gaussian pulse

$$f(t) = \frac{1}{\sqrt{2\pi}\,\alpha}\,e^{-t^2/2\alpha^2}$$

and let α go to zero. For reasonable h's,

$$\lim_{\alpha\to 0+}\int_{-\infty}^{\infty} h(t-\tau)\,\frac{1}{\sqrt{2\pi}\,\alpha}\,e^{-\tau^2/2\alpha^2}\,d\tau = h(t)$$

DELTA FUNCTIONS

Functions such as

$$\delta_\Delta(t) \qquad \frac{\sin(t/\Delta\tau)}{\pi t} \qquad \text{and} \qquad \frac{1}{\sqrt{2\pi}\,\Delta\tau}\,e^{-t^2/2(\Delta\tau)^2}$$

have the property that when they appear in an integrand the limit of the integral is simply the rest of the integrand evaluated with the integration variable zero, e.g.,

$$\lim_{\Delta\tau\to 0}\int_{-\infty}^{\infty} h(t-\tau)\,\delta_\Delta(\tau)\,d\tau = h(t)$$

It is interesting to note that for such limiting operations we cannot interchange the limit and the integral, for example,

$$\lim_{\Delta\tau\to 0}\int_{-\infty}^{\infty} h(t-\tau)\,\delta_\Delta(\tau)\,d\tau \ne \int_{-\infty}^{\infty} h(t-\tau)[\lim_{\Delta\tau\to 0}\delta_\Delta(\tau)]\,d\tau$$

The inequality is clear since

$$\lim_{\Delta\tau\to 0}\delta_\Delta(\tau) = 0$$

and hence the right-hand side is zero.

The definition of $\delta_\Delta(\tau)$ at $\tau = 0$ or at $\tau = \Delta\tau$ is unimportant; however, by various choices of $\delta_\Delta(0)$,

$$\lim_{\Delta\tau\to 0} \delta_\Delta(0)$$

can be made to take on any value between $-\infty$ and ∞. In turn, the integrand for the right-hand side above is zero for all τ save possibly at $\tau = 0$. Even if the value of the integrand is ∞ at $\tau = 0$ (and 0 elsewhere), the definition for such an integral is zero (see Sec. 2-1).

Without regard for the fact that

$$\int_{-\infty}^{\infty} \delta(t)\, dt = 0$$

$$\delta(t) = \begin{cases} 0 & \text{for } t \neq 0 \\ \infty & \text{for } t = 0 \end{cases}$$

some people pretend that $\lim \int = \int \lim$ when faced with problems of the type discussed above. In essence, $\delta(t)$, called the delta function, is the symbol used to depict this pretense, and one writes (for example)

$$\int_{-\infty}^{\infty} h(t - \tau)\delta(\tau)\, d\tau = h(t)$$

Such an equation can correctly be viewed as a shorthand for

$$\lim_{\Delta\tau\to 0} \int_{-\infty}^{\infty} h(t - \tau)\delta_\Delta(\tau)\, d\tau$$

(other narrow pulses could be used in place of δ_Δ). It can also be viewed as a shorthand for a Stieltjes integral

$$\int_{-\infty}^{\infty} h(t - \tau)\, dU(\tau) = h(t)$$

which is defined in Chap. 10. Of course, if $h(t) = 1$, one would write

$$\int_{-\infty}^{\infty} \delta(t)\, dt = 1$$

Also, we have

$$\int_{-\infty}^{\infty} e^{-pt}\delta(t)\, dt = e^{-p0} = 1$$

which means

$$\lim_{\Delta\tau\to 0} \int_{-\infty}^{\infty} e^{-pt}\delta_\Delta(t)\, dt = 1$$

Hence it is sometimes said that the Laplace transform of the δ function is 1. It is correct to say that if one considers narrow pulses of unit area, their transforms approach 1 as their widths approach zero.

Certain respectable mathematical theories (theory of distributions and generalized functions, Refs. 6 and 7) have received some motivation from the early use of δ functions; however, inconsistencies in logic often result from such use. The following is a typical example. Note that if U is the unit step function,

$$U'(t) = \lim_{\Delta\tau\to 0} \frac{U(t) - U(t - \Delta\tau)}{\Delta\tau}$$

but

$$\frac{U(t) - U(t - \Delta\tau)}{\Delta\tau} = \delta_\Delta(t)$$

and hence

$$U'(t) = \lim_{\Delta\tau\to 0} \delta_\Delta(t) = \delta(t)$$

The user writes $L(\delta) = 1$; however, Theorem 14 gives $L(\delta) = L(U') = pL(U) - U(0+) = p(1/p) - 1 = 0$. Thus it is seen that $L(\delta)$ is equal to both 0 and 1, and hence $0 = 1$. Typically, people who use δ functions want both answers for $L(\delta)$, depending on the context.

In spite of the nonsense, δ-function notation will occasionally be used in the book. Specifically, as described in Prob. 49, such notation permits us to condense

$$h * f + \sum_n a_n f^n$$

into a single convolution. Also, in Chap. 3 the superposition of signals of various frequencies is of interest, and δ-function notation permits us to include discrete frequencies in what properly denotes only a continuous weighting over frequencies.

Problems

33. Consider a linear (not necessarily time-invariant) system. Let $S_\tau(t)$ be the step response for a unit step applied at time τ; that is, $S_\tau(t)$ is the output when $U(t - \tau)$ is the input. Using only the assumption of linearity, prove that if $h_\Delta(t, \tau)$ is the output when $\delta_\Delta(t - \tau)$ is the input, then

$$\lim_{\Delta\tau\to 0} h_\Delta(t, \tau) = S_\tau'(t)$$

if the limit exists. That is, prove that if the step response exists, then the response to $\delta_\Delta(t - \tau)$ exists; and if the impulse response exists, it equals the derivative of the step response.

34. Let $k(t, \Delta\tau)$ be a function (called a kernel) which satisfies the following conditions:
1. For all $\Delta\tau > 0$,

$$\int_{-\infty}^{\infty} k(t, \Delta\tau) \, dt = 1$$

2. For all $\Delta\tau > 0$,

$$\int_{-\infty}^{\infty} |k(t, \Delta\tau)| \, dt < M$$

3. If $\epsilon > 0$, then

$$\lim_{\Delta\tau\to 0} \left[\int_{-\infty}^{-\epsilon} |k(t, \Delta\tau)| \, dt + \int_{\epsilon}^{\infty} |k(t, \Delta\tau)| \, dt \right] = 0$$

Prove: If $f(t)$ is continuous and bounded, then

$$\lim_{\Delta\tau\to 0+} \int_{-\infty}^{\infty} f(t - \tau)k(\tau, \Delta\tau)\, d\tau = f(t)$$

Such a kernel can be viewed as a rather general pulse which is acceptable in defining impulse response or in defining δ functions.

35. (*a*) Which of the properties for k in Prob. 34 are satisfied if

$$k(t, \Delta\tau) = \frac{\sin (t/\Delta\tau)}{\pi t}$$

(*b*) Which properties are satisfied by

$$k(t, \Delta\tau) = \frac{\Delta\tau\, [\sin (t/\Delta\tau)]^2}{\pi t^2}$$

36. Consider the circuit shown in the sketch. By direct calculation, find the impulse

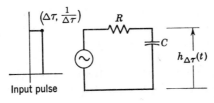

FIGURE P 36

response. The easy way is to assume that C acts nearly as a short circuit during the short duration of the pulse.

2-8 SIMULTANEOUS DIFFERENTIAL EQUATIONS

In connection with the application of Laplace transforms to differential equations, we discussed the situation for a single differential equation in detail (Sec. 2-6). It is more or less obvious that the discussion generalizes to a system of differential equations. This generalization will be described briefly here.

Let $f_1, \ldots, f_n$ be the n known driving functions for a system of n ordinary linear differential equations with constant coefficients, and let $g_1, \ldots, g_n$ be the response functions. Let the highest-order derivative to appear in any of the equations be m. Then the n equations can be written thus:

$$\sum_{k=0}^{m} b_{i1k}g_1{}^k + \sum_{k=0}^{m} b_{i2k}g_2{}^k + \cdots + \sum_{k=0}^{m} b_{ink}g_n{}^k$$
$$= \sum_{k=0}^{r} a_{i1k}f_1{}^k + \cdots + \sum_{k=0}^{r} a_{ink}f_n{}^k \qquad \text{for } i = 1, 2, \ldots, n$$

Suppose initial conditions are known for the f's and the g's; and to be specific, consider the one-sided case where the functions are zero for negative arguments.   If the above equations are transformed, we obtain

$$Q_{i1}G_1 + \cdots + Q_{in}G_n = P_{i1}F_1 + \cdots + P_{in}F_n + Y_i$$

where

$$Q_{ij}(p) = \sum_{k=0}^{m} b_{ijk}p^k \qquad P_{ij}(p) = \sum_{k=0}^{r} a_{ijk}p^k$$

and Y_i is determined by initial conditions.   If the f's and g's are smooth and the two-sided case is considered, the same equations result with $Y_i = 0$.

Before any elaborate applications of simultaneous differential equations are treated, it is advantageous to introduce convenient manageable notation.   Specifically, matrix algebra should be available.   However, for the immediate problem it is seen that solving the differential equations has been reduced to the problem of solving the following system of algebraic equations:

$$Q_{11}G_1 + \cdots + Q_{1n}G_n = \tilde{F}_1 + Y_1$$
$$\cdots \cdots \cdots \cdots \cdots \cdots \cdots \cdots \cdots$$
$$Q_{n1}G_1 + \cdots + Q_{nn}G_n = \tilde{F}_n + Y_n$$

where $\tilde{F}_i = P_{i1}F_1 + \cdots + P_{in}F_n$.   If we assume that the determinant of the coefficient is not zero (for, say, a strip in the p plane), then the G's can be found by Cramer's rule.   Specifically, if A is the determinant of the Q_{ik} coefficients and A_{ik} is the cofactor for position (i, k), then

$$G_k = \sum_{i=1}^{n} \frac{A_{ik}}{A} (\tilde{F}_i + Y_i)$$

from which g_k can be determined.

One additional observation will be made.   For simplicity, let each $Y_i = 0$, and note that

$$G_k = \sum_{i=1}^{n} \frac{A_{ik}}{A} \left(\sum_{q=1}^{n} P_{iq}F_q \right) \qquad \text{or} \qquad G_k = \sum_{q=1}^{n} \frac{\sum_{i=1}^{n} A_{ik}P_{iq}}{A} F_q$$

which gives each G_k in terms of the original driving functions.   If each

$$H_{kq} \equiv \frac{\sum_{i=1}^{n} A_{ik}P_{iq}}{A}$$

is a proper rational function, an explicit formulation using convolutions is obtained:

$$g_k = \sum_{q=1}^{n} h_{kq} * f_q \qquad \text{for } k = 1, \ldots, n$$

This is essentially the definition of matrix convolution: $\{g_k\} = \{h_{kq}\} * \{f_q\}$; and it is the generalization of the convolution formula of previous sections.

Problems

37. In the sketch, find i_1 and i_2 if the system starts dead.

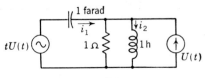

FIGURE P 37

38 In the sketch, let $i_1(0+) = 2$ and $i_2(0+) = 0$.   Find $i_2(t)$.

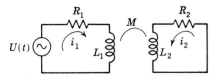

FIGURE P 38

Additional Problems for Chapter 2

39. Let the bar denote the complex conjugate. Show that if $F(p) = L(f)_p$, then $\overline{F(\bar{p})} = L(\bar{f})_p$; and that if f is real-valued, $F(\bar{p}) = \overline{F(p)}$.

40. Let f have exponential bounds such that the corresponding strip of convergence contains $p = 0$.   Find the relationship between

$$\int_{-\infty}^{\infty} t^n f(t)\, dt$$

and $F^n(0)$, where $F^n(p)$ denotes the nth derivative of F.   Use the relationship to compute

$$\int_{-\infty}^{\infty} t^n \exp\left(-\frac{t^2}{2}\right) dt$$

given that $L[\exp(-t^2/2)] = \sqrt{2\pi}\, \exp(p^2/2)$.

41. Let $f(t) = 0$ for $t < 0$, let $f(t) = f_0(t)$ for $0 < t < T$, let $f_0(t) = 0$ for $t > T$, and let $f(t + T) = f(t)$ for $t > 0$.   Find $L(f)_p$ in terms of $L(f_0)_p$.   Recall that if $|a| < 1$,

$$\sum_{k=0}^{\infty} a^k = \frac{1}{1-a}$$

and observe that

$$f(t) = \sum_{k=0}^{\infty} f_0(t + kT)$$

42. Given that $L[J_0(t)]_p = 1/\sqrt{p^2 + 1}$ for Re $p > 0$, find

$$\lim_{t \to 0+} J_0(t)$$

43. (a) If $f(t) = e^{j\omega_0 t}$ for all real t, for what values of p does $L(f)_p$ exist?
(b) If $f(t) = e^{j\omega_0 t} U(-t)$, for what values of p does $L(f)_p$ exist?

44. Find $L[U(t) \sinh t]$, $L[U(t) \cosh t]$, and $L[U(-t) \cos t]$.

45. Show that

$$L[f(at)]_p = \frac{1}{|a|} F\left(\frac{p}{a}\right)$$

where a is real and $F = L(f)$.

46. Find three functions of t for which $1/(p^2 + p)$ is the analytic continuation of their transforms.

47. (Use Theorem 36.)   Show that if

$$L(f)_{j\omega} = 0 \qquad \text{for } |\omega| > B$$
$$L(h)_{j\omega} = 0 \qquad \text{for } |\omega| > B$$

and

$$g(t) = \int_{-\infty}^{\infty} f(t - \tau) h(\tau) \, d\tau$$

then

$$g\left(\frac{n\pi}{B}\right) = \frac{\pi}{B} \sum_{k=-\infty}^{\infty} f\left(\frac{n\pi}{B} - \frac{k\pi}{B}\right) h\left(\frac{k\pi}{B}\right)$$

In particular, show that

$$\int_{-\infty}^{\infty} f(t) h(t) \, dt = \frac{\pi}{B} \sum_{k=-\infty}^{\infty} f\left(\frac{k\pi}{B}\right) h\left(\frac{k\pi}{B}\right)$$

48. Let

$$f(t) = \begin{cases} e^t & \text{for } t < 0 \\ 1 & \text{for } t > 0 \end{cases}$$

Use two-sided Laplace transforms to find a continuous solution to $g'' + m^2 g = f$.

49. Find a kernel $k(t, \Delta\tau)$ such that

$$\lim_{\Delta\tau \to 0} \int_{-\infty}^{\infty} f(t - \tau) k(\tau, \Delta\tau) \, d\tau = f'(t)$$

The shorthand used to depict this situation is the derivative of the δ function:

$$\int_{-\infty}^{\infty} f(t - \tau) \delta'(\tau) \, d\tau = f'(t)$$

An advantage of such notation is that it permits one to pretend that

$$g = h * f + \sum_{k=0}^{n} a_k f^k(t)$$

can be written as $g = \tilde{h} * f$, where

$$\tilde{h} = h + \sum_{k=0}^{n} a_k \delta^k(t)$$

50. When the strip of convergence of the transforms of $U(t)f(t)$ and $U(-t)f(t)$ do not have any values of p in common, $L(f)$ does not exist; however, the transforms of $U(t)f$ and $U(-t)f$ can be used to represent f. Specifically, find the following f (for which the two-sided transform does not exist):

$$f(t) = \frac{1}{2\pi j} \int_{1-j\infty}^{1+j\infty} e^{pt} \frac{[1 - \exp(-Tp/2)]^2}{p[1 - \exp(-Tp)]} \, dp - \frac{1}{2\pi j} \int_{-1-j\infty}^{-1-j\infty} e^{pt} \frac{[1 - \exp(Tp/2)]^2}{p(1 - \exp Tp)} \, dp$$

3

FOUNDATIONS OF
OPERATIONAL ANALYSIS

The preceding chapter presented the customary theories of operational analysis. Even though many useful results were obtained, the insight into the subject available to this point is not entirely satisfactory. The following are typical unanswered questions:

1. Recall that $H = L(h)_p$ is the transfer function when $g = h * f$ both for sinusoidal inputs (Chap. 1, Theorem 6) and for Laplace-transformable inputs (Chap. 2, Theorem 20). Is this an accident, or is there a basic concept which makes the relationship between these two theories obvious? Also, does this basic idea motivate other similar theories, and, for that matter, does it render the invention of the Laplace transform obvious? In Chap. 2, $L(f)$ was pulled out of a hat and then found to be useful.

2. Is there a simple, explicit description of the relationship between input and output for all systems to which the theory is applicable?

3. Is there more than one basic approach to operational analysis?   This chapter provides insight which makes these questions and similar questions transparent.   Also, this chapter serves as a review in that nearly all the results in Chaps. 1 and 2 are rederived here.   The results are obtained here as simple consequences of the definitions of the circuits to be analyzed.

3-1 LINEAR TIME-INVARIANT SYSTEMS

From an analytical viewpoint a circuit performs a transformation of input functions of time into corresponding output functions of time.   Let D denote a set of acceptable inputs of interest and let V be a set of functions which contains all outputs produced by elements of D.   Of course, D and V are sets of complex-valued† functions of time.   The transformation from D into V performed by the circuit will be denoted by Φ, that is, $\Phi: D \to V$, and if $f \in D$ is a specific input, the output produced by f is $\Phi(f)$, as shown.

We assume that Φ is well defined; i.e., for any $f \in D$, $\Phi(f)$ exists and is unique.

The system is *linear* for the set D iff D is a linear space and whenever $f_1 \in D$, $f_2 \in D$, and a_1 and a_2 are scalars; then

$$\Phi(a_1 f_1 + a_2 f_2) = a_1 \Phi(f) + a_2 \Phi(f)$$

Recall that if g is related to f by a linear differential equation, then there are homogeneous solutions.   We shall not concern ourselves with the homogeneous solutions in this chapter; hence the solution of such a differential equation will be a linear transformation of the driving function, and the corresponding Φ will be well defined.

Let f_τ denote the function obtained by translating the function f by an amount τ in time so that $f_\tau(t) = f(t + \tau)$ for all t, and f_τ will be called the τ translate of f.   A system is time-invariant iff translation of the input in time always produces the same translation in time of the output.   If $g = \Phi(f)$, let $\Phi(f)_\tau$ denote g_τ; that is, $\Phi(f)_\tau$ denotes the τ translate of the output of the system produced by the input f.   Put precisely, the system is *time-invariant* for D iff for any $f \in D$, $f_\tau \in D$ for every real τ (that is, D is closed with respect to time translation) and for all $f \in D$ and all real τ,

$$\Phi(f_\tau) = \Phi(f)_\tau$$

As a simple example, let p be a fixed complex number and let D_p be the set of all functions‡ of the form $f(t) = Ae^{pt}$, where A is an arbitrary complex

---

† The physical meaning of complex-valued inputs is covered in Chap. 4.
‡ This set D_p is not the same as the set in Chap. 1; however, there is a close t'e to be displayed later.

number. Clearly, D_p is a linear space over the field of real or complex numbers; i.e., if $f_1 \in D_p$, $f_2 \in D_p$, and a_1 and a_2 are constants, then $a_1 f_1 + a_2 f_2 = a_1 A_1 e^{pt} + a_2 A_2 e^{pt} = (a_1 A_1 + a_2 A_2) e^{pt}$ is an element of D_p. Also, D_p is closed with respect to time translation; for if $f(t) = A e^{pt}$, then $f_\tau(t) = A e^{p(t+\tau)} = (A e^{p\tau}) e^{pt}$, which is clearly an element of D_p. Suppose we consider simply a differentiator so that $\Phi(f) = f'$. This is a linear time-invariant circuit. Also, $\Phi(f) = h * f$ is a linear time-invariant circuit. If $\Phi(f) = f + 2(f')^2$, then Φ is not linear for D_p unless $p = 0$; but Φ is time-invariant. If $g = \Phi(f)$ so that $g(t) = tf(t)$ for each $f \in D_p$ and all t, then Φ is linear but not time-invariant. All these observations are nearly obvious; the proof will be given for $h * f$ and for $tf(t)$. If

$$g(t) = \int_{-\infty}^{\infty} f(t - u)h(u) \, du$$

then $\displaystyle\int_{-\infty}^{\infty} f_\tau(t - u)h(u) \, du = \int_{-\infty}^{\infty} f(t + \tau - u)h(u) \, du = g(t + \tau) = g_\tau(t)$

That is, $h * f$ is time-invariant. Of course $h * f$ is linear since integration is linear. Now, suppose $g_1 = tf_1$, $g_2 = tf_2$. Then

$$\Phi(a_1 f_1 + a_2 f_2) = (a_1 f_1 + a_2 f_2)t = a_1 t f_1 + a_2 t f_2 = a_1 g_1 + a_2 g_2$$

Thus, $\Phi(f) = tf$ is linear. Let $g = \Phi(f) = tA e^{pt}$. Then $\Phi(f_\tau) = t e^{p(t+\tau)}$, but $g_\tau(t) = (t + \tau)A e^{p(t+\tau)} \neq \Phi(f_\tau)$, so that $\Phi(f) = tf$ is not time-invariant.

CHARACTERIZATION IN THE TIME DOMAIN

We consider the question of finding a simple, explicit mathematical description of linear time-invariant circuits. The most general such system normally analyzed is a convolution plus a linear combination of derivatives (with constant coefficients). Various delays (or anticipations) could be included with each derivative, and the equation describing the system would be the following:

$$g(t) = \int_{-\infty}^{\infty} f(t - \tau)h(\tau) \, d\tau + \sum_{k=0}^{K} \sum_{n=0}^{N} a_{kn} f^n(t - \tau_k)$$

where f^n denotes the nth derivation of f.

More generality is possible; e.g., the sums can be infinite rather than finite, and for that matter the definition of convolution can be generalized somewhat by resorting to a theory of integration more general than Riemann integration and/or by using an elaborate limiting operation in place of

$$\lim_{a \to \infty} \lim_{b \to \infty} \int_{-a}^{b} f(t - \tau)h(\tau) \, d\tau$$

(for example, limit in the mean, as discussed in Chap. 10). Actually, all three of these methods for generalizing the description of a linear time-invariant system involve limiting operations (limit of partial sums defines the infinite sum, limit of approximating sums defines the integral, and limit of the integral on a finite interval defines the integral over the infinite interval). There is no unique way to proceed with such generalizations, and one is led to guess that any linear time-invariant system can be described mathematically as either

$$g = h * f + \sum_{k=0}^{K} \sum_{n=0}^{N} a_{kn} f^n(t - \tau_k)$$

or a limit of such transformations.

By taking a close look at this transformation, it can be seen that the general nature of linear time-invariant transformations can be described even more simply.

Note that

$$\int_{-\infty}^{\infty} f(t - \tau)h(\tau) \, d\tau$$

is the limit of linear combinations of the following form:

$$\sum_{k=1}^{K} f(t - \tau_k)h(\tau_k) \, \Delta\tau_k$$

Note also that $f'(t - \tau_k)$ is the limit (as $\Delta\tau \to 0$) of the linear combination

$$\frac{1}{\Delta\tau} f(t + \Delta\tau - \tau_k) - \frac{1}{\Delta\tau} f(t - \tau_k)$$

Also $$f''(t) = \lim_{\Delta\tau \to 0} \frac{f(t + 2\Delta\tau) - 2f(t + \Delta\tau) + f(t)}{(\Delta\tau)^2}$$

Also $$\int_{-\infty}^{\infty} f(t - \tau)h(\tau) \, d\tau + \sum_{k=0}^{K} \sum_{n=0}^{N} a_{kn} f^n(t - \tau_k)$$

is itself the limit of a finite linear combination of the form

$$\sum_{m=0}^{M} b_m f(t - \tau_m)$$

which is simple indeed. In turn, the limit of limits of such finite sums will be the limit of such finite sums.

Pseudo Theorem 1. If $\Phi: D \to V$ is a (reasonable) linear time-invariant system and if f is an arbitrary element of D and $g = \Phi(f)$, then either there is a set of fixed (not dependent on which input f is considered) numbers $(b_1, \ldots, b_m; \tau_1, \ldots, \tau_m)$ such that

$$g(t) = \sum_{m=1}^{M} b_m f(t - \tau_m)$$

or g is the limit of functions which can be obtained by such linear combinations. In the cases where a limit is involved, there will be a fixed sequence of sets of numbers $(b_{1n}, \ldots, b_{M_n n}; \tau_{1n}, \ldots, \tau_{M_n n})$ such that

$$\lim_{n \to \infty} g_n(t) = g(t)$$

where $$g_n(t) = \sum_{m=1}^{M_n} b_{mn} f(t - \tau_{mn})$$

The fact that the b_m's and the τ_m's are not functions of time (t) accounts for the time-invariant property of the system, and the fact that a linear combination of the $f(t - \tau_k)$'s is used accounts for the linearity. In turn, the general mathematical description of systems which are only linear or only time-invariant can be obtained by removing the corresponding restriction on the relation

$$\sum_{m=1}^{M} b_m f(t - \tau_m)$$

For example, any linear (possibly time-varying) system can be described by

$$\sum_{m=1}^{M} b_m(t) f[t - \tau_m(t)]$$

or by the limit of such sums; as a case in point,

$$\int_{-\infty}^{\infty} h(t, u) f(u) \, du$$

is the limit of the following sum:

$$\sum_{m=1}^{M} h(t, u_m) f[t - \tau_m(t)] \, \Delta u_m \qquad \text{if } \tau_m(t) = t - u_m$$

Of course, in this example $b_m(t) = h(t, u_m) \Delta u_m$.

The prospects for a detailed proof of the above theorem are not attractive, but there is no difficulty with convolution and derivatives. The theorem can be viewed as the definition of what a general linear time-invariant transformation of a complex-valued function of a real variable should be. However, one must be specific about the limiting operations which are admissible before trying to show that all operations satisfying the abstract definition (given at the beginning of this section) admit to an explicit description of the type displayed above. To carry out such a proof, appropriate continuity conditions would be required.

3-2 EXISTENCE AND UNIQUENESS OF THE NOTION OF A TRANSFER FUNCTION

In considering exponentially amplitude-modulated sinusoids or in considering Laplace transforms, it was found that corresponding to linear time-invariant operations there are transfer functions. For example, if $g = h * f$, then $G = HF$, where H is the transfer function and in fact

$$H(p) = \int_{-\infty}^{\infty} e^{-pt} h(t) \, dt$$

when considering either Laplace transforms or response to functions of the form $Ae^{\sigma t} \cos(\omega t + \alpha)$. The questions to be considered are the following: Is the existence of a transfer function a consequence of the general (abstract) definition of linear time-invariant systems given in Sec. 3-1, and is the notion of transfer function unique? The following two theorems form the basis for all operational analysis of linear time-invariant systems. A simple unified picture of operational analysis will follow from these theorems.

As in the examples of Sec. 3-1, let D_p be the set of complex-valued exponential functions of complex frequency p; that is, p is a fixed complex number and $f \in D_p$ iff there exists a complex number A such that $f(t) = Ae^{pt}$ for all real t.

Theorem 2. Let D_p as defined above be a set of acceptable inputs for a linear time-invariant system for which the transformation of inputs into outputs is denoted by Φ; then for fixed p there exists a constant H such that $\Phi(f) = Hf$ for any f in D_p.

The important conclusion of the theorem is that exponential inputs of complex frequency p produce exponential outputs of the same complex frequency. If p is changed, the "constant" H may change; we define the transfer function of the system as H as a function of p, namely, $H(p)$. The theorem establishes the existence of the transfer function without resorting to details such as differential equations which may provide a mathematical characterization of the transformation Φ.

PROOF: Let u be the unit exponential, that is, $u(t) = e^{pt}$; and let $\tilde{g} = \Phi(u)$. Then $u_\tau(t) = e^{p(t+\tau)}$ or $u_\tau = e^{p\tau}u$. Hence, $\Phi(u_\tau) = \Phi(e^{p\tau}u) = e^{p\tau}\Phi(u) = e^{p\tau}\tilde{g}$ by linearity. Of course, we also have $\Phi(u_\tau) = \tilde{g}_\tau$ by time invariance. Thus

$$\tilde{g}_\tau(t) = \tilde{g}(t + \tau) = e^{p\tau}\tilde{g}(t)$$

for all t for any τ. In particular, $g(0 + \tau) = e^{p\tau}\tilde{g}(0)$ for all τ; that is, $\tilde{g}(\tau)$ is a constant, namely, $\tilde{g}(0)$, times $e^{p\tau}$ for all real τ. We define $H = \tilde{g}(0)$. Then $\Phi(u) = \tilde{g}$, where $\tilde{g}(t) = He^{pt}$ for all real t. In turn, if $f = Ae^{pt}$ is an arbitrary element of D_p, $\Phi(f) = \Phi(Au) = A\Phi(u) = AHe^{pt} = HAe^{pt} = Hf$, as was to be shown.

As a simple example, consider a convoluting system; i.e., for any input f the corresponding output g is

$$g(t) = \int_{-\infty}^{\infty} h(\tau)f(t - \tau) \, d\tau$$

To determine the value of the transfer function at p, we let $f(t) = e^{pt}$. Then

$$g(t) = \int_{-\infty}^{\infty} h(\tau)e^{p(t-\tau)} \, d\tau = e^{pt} \int_{-\infty}^{\infty} h(\tau)e^{-p\tau} \, d\tau$$

Hence, in this special case,

$$H(p) = \int_{-\infty}^{\infty} h(\tau)e^{-p\tau}\, d\tau$$

as expected; i.e., the general definition of transfer function provided by the above theorem agrees with previously used formulas for the transfer function.

Functions which have the special property depicted in Theorem 2 are termed eigenfunctions (or proper functions). Specifically, if $\Phi: D \to V$ and f is such that $\Phi(f)$ is a constant times f, then f is called an *eigenfunction* of Φ. The constant is called the eigenvalue. Thus the theorem states that exponentials are eigenfunctions of all linear time-invariant operations (systems). We have defined the transfer function as the eigenvalue as a function of the frequency of the exponential.

Theorem 2 provides a very simple formula for computing the output of a system when the input is simply an exponential function; specifically, mere multiplication is involved. What good is such a theorem when we wish to consider nonexponential inputs? The general plan of operational analysis is to express any input of interest as a linear combination of exponentials (sum and/or integral over the frequencies of the input) and then to find the output to the linear combination as the linear combination of outputs produced by individual exponential inputs. Suppose there is a class of functions other than exponentials which are eigenfunctions for all linear time-invariant systems. Then this class of functions could be used as the basis for operational analysis just as well as exponential functions are used. In turn, one could develop an operational discipline corresponding to each such class of functions. The following theorem eliminates this threat by showing that exponential functions are unique in the role of eigenfunctions for all linear time-invariant operators.

Theorem 3. Let D be a linear space† of complex-valued functions of time (over the field of complex scalars), let D be closed with respect to time translation (that is, $f \in D$ implies $f_\tau \in D$), for each linear time-invariant system let there exist a constant such that $\Phi(f)$ is this constant times f for any $f \in D$, and let some $f \in D$ be continuous and not zero for at least one time. Then there exists a complex number p such that D is D_p; that is, D is the set of exponential functions of frequency p.

PROOF: The theorem can be proved by considering a rather small class of linear time-invariant systems, namely, systems which merely translate the input in time to produce the output. Let $H(\tau)$ be the multiplicative con-

---

† In Theorems 2 and 3 the domain for Φ is not of much importance in that the important considerations in the proofs deal with specific inputs [$u(t) = e^{pt}$ in Theorem 2 and an input which is continuous and not zero at some time in Theorem 3]. In Theorem 2 it is natural to use D_p; however, here if we start with a specific f for which $\Phi(f) = Hf$, the natural set of inputs D to be used is not quite obvious. Problem 11 constructs such a "natural" linear space D.

stant when $\Phi(f) = f_\tau$. The important step in the proof is to show now that there exists a p such that $H(\tau) = e^{p\tau}$. After this is done, we have for any $f \in D$

$$f_\tau(t) = f(t + \tau) = e^{p\tau}f(t) \qquad \text{for all } t \text{ and all } \tau$$

In turn, $f(\tau) = e^{p(\tau)}f(0)$, which proves that D is D_p. Also, by Theorem 2, D_p does satisfy all the hypotheses of Theorem 3; hence Theorem 3 is not vacuous. In the light of Theorem 1, it is not surprising that properties of time-shifting systems should provide the key to properties of all linear time-invariant systems. To carry out the important step in the proof, note that

$$f(t + \tau_1 + \tau_2) = H(\tau_1 + \tau_2)f(t)$$

and $$f(t + \tau_1 + \tau_2) = H(\tau_2)f(t + \tau_1) = H(\tau_1)H(\tau_2)f(t)$$

For some $f(t) \neq 0$ we can divide and obtain $H(\tau_1 + \tau_2) = H(\tau_1)H(\tau_2)$. The other property of H which we need is continuity. We first establish that H is continuous at zero. Note that $f(t + 0) = H(0)f(t)$ and hence $H(0) = 1$. Also $f(t + \delta) = H(\delta)f(t)$; hence if f is an element of D for which $f(t) \neq 0$ and if f is continuous at t,

$$H(\delta) = \frac{f(t + \delta)}{f(t)}$$

$$\lim_{\delta \to 0} H(\delta) = \lim_{\delta \to 0} \frac{f(t + \delta)}{f(t)} = \frac{f(t)}{f(t)} = 1$$

That is, H is continuous at zero. Finally, since $H(\tau + \delta) = H(\delta)H(\tau)$,

$$\lim_{\delta \to 0} H(t + \delta) = \lim_{\delta \to 0} H(\delta)H(\tau) = H(\tau)$$

That is, the continuity of H at zero implies continuity everywhere. It is rather well known that if $H(0) = 1$, $H(\tau_1 + \tau_2) = H(\tau_1)H(\tau_2)$, and H is continuous, then there exists a p such that $H(\tau) = e^{p\tau}$. For completeness, the details of this last aspect of the proof will now be given.

By induction,

$$H(\tau_1 + \tau_2 + \cdots + \tau_n) = H(\tau_1)H(\tau_2) \cdots H(\tau_n)$$

As a special case, let n and m be integers. Then

$$\left[H\left(\frac{n}{m}\right)\right]^m = H(n) = [H(1)]^n$$

Therefore, $H(n/m)$ is an mth root of $[H(1)]^n$. Since

$$H(0) = 1 = H(-1)H(1)$$

$H(1) \neq 0$. Let $H(1) = e^\sigma e^{j\theta}$, where σ and θ are real. Let n/m be written in the lowest terms.† Then

$$H\left(\frac{n}{m}\right) = \exp\left(\frac{n}{m}\sigma\right) \exp\left[j(\theta + 2\pi k)\frac{n}{m}\right]$$

for some specific integer k where we can (and will) take $0 \le k \le m - 1$. For each n/m, k takes on a specific value; hence k can be considered a function defined on the rationals, and it will be denoted by $k(n/m)$. Since H is continuous, $H(n/m)$ is continuous on the rationals. In turn, the angle $(n/m)\theta + (n/m)k(n/m)2\pi$ is a continuous function of n/m. For this to be the case, $k(n/m)$ must be continuous (save at $n/m = 0$, where k can be defined arbitrarily—we shall define it by continuity at $n/m = 0$). Since k is integer-valued and continuous on the rationals, k must in fact be constant. Let $\theta + 2\pi k = \omega$. Then, on the rationals, $H(n/m) = e^{(n/m)p}$ if we set $p = \sigma + j(\theta + 2\pi k)$. Finally, since $H(\tau)$ is continuous and the continuation of a function from the rationals to the reals is unique when continuity is preserved, $H(\tau) = e^{p\tau}$.

From a logical viewpoint it is interesting to consider possible implications between the following three properties:

1. Φ is linear.
2. Φ is time-invariant.
3. If f is an exponential of arbitrary complex frequency p, then $\Phi(f)$ is an exponential of the same complex frequency. In this case $\Phi(Ae^{pt}) = F(p, A)e^{pt}$, where F is a complex-valued function of amplitude and frequency.

The important content of Theorem 2 is that properties 1 and 2 imply property 3. The following examples establish that no one of the above properties implies any other where f denotes an arbitrary input and g denotes the corresponding output:

1. $g(t) = tf(t)$: property 1, but not property 2 or 3
2. $g(t) = [f(t)]^2$: property 2, but not property 1 or 3
3. $\Phi: D_p \to D_p$ with $\Phi(Ae^{pt}) = A^2e^{pt}$: property 3, but not property 1 or 2

It can be shown that any two of the above properties imply the third (e.g., see Prob. 6); actually, to show that properties 3 and 2 imply property 1, one must assume that F is a very well-behaved function.

Recall that, given a transformation Φ, a function f of the domain of Φ is called an eigenfunction of Φ iff $\Phi(f)$ is a constant times f. The constant is

† Usually one would write $[H(n/m)]^m = e^{n\sigma}e^{jn\theta}$, and hence

$$H\left(\frac{n}{m}\right) = e^{(n/m)\sigma} \exp\left(j\frac{n\theta + i2\pi}{m}\right)$$

where i is an integer; however, $\exp[j(\theta + 2\pi k)(n/m)]$ gives all the possible values of $H(n/m)$. To see this, consider $k_1 \ne k_2$ with k_1 and k_2 between 0 and $m - 1$. Clearly, these provide different roots, for if $2\pi k_1(n/m) = 2\pi k_2(n/m) + 2\pi s$, where s is an integer, then $n/m = s/(k_1 - k_2)$, but n/m was assumed to be in lowest terms and $|k_1 - k_2| < m$. And of course there are only m distinct mth roots, so the form used for $H(n/m)$ in the proof is acceptable.

called the eigenvalue corresponding to f. The significant content of Theorems 2 and 3 can be summarized by the following remark: Exponential functions and only exponential functions are eigenfunctions of all linear time-invariant systems. The eigenvalue as a function of the frequency of the exponential is (by definition) the transfer function of the system. The mathematical characterization of a linear time-invariant system may be very complicated; however, in the face of an exponential input the complication withers, and all the system can do is multiply by a constant.

The utility of Theorem 2 is extended beyond exponential inputs by the use of superposition; i.e., we express inputs of interest as linear combinations of exponentials. For example, let $H(p)$ be the transfer function corresponding to Φ. If the input is

$$f(t) = \sum_{k=1}^{n} C_k \exp p_k t$$

then the output is

$$G(f) = \sum_{k=1}^{n} C_k H(p_k) \exp p_k t$$

This can be extended further by generalizing the sum to infinite series and/or to integrals.

The Laplace transform is simply a generalization obtained by considering those inputs which can be expressed thus:

$$f(t) = \frac{1}{2\pi j} \int_{\sigma-j\infty}^{\sigma+j\infty} e^{pt} F(p) \, dp$$

For such an input, it is seen that (under reasonable conditions) the corresponding output is

$$\Phi(f) = g(t) = \frac{1}{2\pi j} \int_{\sigma-j\infty}^{\sigma+j\infty} e^{pt} H(p) F(p) \, dp$$

To see this, consider a finite-sum approximation to f:

$$f(t) \cong \frac{1}{2\pi j} \sum_{k=-N}^{N} \exp (p_k t) F(p_k) \, \Delta p_k$$

The output produced by this approximating input is clearly

$$\frac{1}{2\pi j} \sum_{k=-N}^{N} \exp (p_k t) F(p_k) H(p_k) \, \Delta p_k$$

In the limit as

$$\max_{k} |\Delta p_k|$$

goes to zero, the approximating inputs approach f; and the outputs produced by the approximating inputs approach

$$\frac{1}{2\pi j} \int_{\sigma-j\infty}^{\sigma+j\infty} e^{pt} H(p) F(p) \, dp$$

which is the desired result. Note that if $G(p)$ is the Laplace transform of the output, then $G = HF$.

The above, with the example given after Theorem 2, provides a conceptually attractive proof of the convolution theorem.

It can also be seen that the operator L_0 discussed in Chap. 1 is the simple extension of the eigen property of exponentials obtained by considering linear combinations of the following form:

$$f(t) = \tfrac{1}{2} A e^{pt} + \tfrac{1}{2} \bar{A} e^{\bar{p}t} = |A| e^{\sigma t} \cos (\omega^t + \alpha)$$

where $p = \sigma + j\omega$ and $A = |A| e^{j\alpha}$. Of course in this case $L_0(f) = A$. If $g = \Phi(f)$, then

$$g(t) = \tfrac{1}{2} A H(p) e^{pt} + \tfrac{1}{2} \bar{A} H(\bar{p}) e^{\bar{p}t}$$

If $H(\bar{p}) = \overline{H(p)}$, then g is real-valued, $L_0(g)$ exists, and $L_0(g) = H(p) L_0(f)$, which contains all the results of Sec. 1-2. The condition $H(\bar{p}) = \overline{H(p)}$ is related to real systems as opposed to complex systems; this is discussed later.

The above observations indicate that *sinusoidal steady state*, Fourier series, and two-sided Laplace (and hence Fourier) transforms are all obtained by considering linear combinations (and various generalizations of linear combinations) of exponential functions. It would seem, then, one can invent forms of operational analysis by inventing methods for generalizing the notion of *linear combinations of exponentials*. That such is the case will now be illustrated by the invention of an operational calculus (to be called area transforms) which is general enough to include all the above forms as special cases.

3-3 AREA TRANSFORMS

In terms of the complex p (frequency) plane, a series of the form

$$f(t) = \sum_k C_k \exp p_k t$$

corresponds to a linear combination of discrete frequencies, and

$$\frac{1}{2\pi j} \int_{\sigma-j\infty}^{\sigma+j\infty} e^{pt} F(p) \, dp$$

corresponds to the superposition of frequencies along the line Re $p = \sigma$ with a density (continuous weighting) $F(p)$. However, integration (of the ordinary Riemann or Lebesgue type) is not strictly a generalization of summation in that a sum is not a special case of an integral; e.g., there is no $F(p)$ such that

$$\frac{1}{2\pi j} \int_{\sigma-j\infty}^{\sigma+j\infty} e^{pt} F(p) \, dp = \sum_k C_k \exp p_k t$$

Of course, δ functions can be used for F to obtain a sum from an integral, which means that a sum can be written as the limit of an integral; e.g., if $p_k = \sigma + j\omega_k$,

$$\sum_k C_k \exp p_k t = \lim_{\epsilon \to 0} \frac{1}{2\pi j} \int_{\sigma-j\infty}^{\sigma+j\infty} e^{pt} \sum_k \delta_\epsilon(\omega - \omega_k) \, dp$$

where
$$\delta_\epsilon(\omega) = \begin{cases} \dfrac{2\pi}{\epsilon} & \text{if } 0 < \omega < \epsilon \\ 0 & \text{for other } \omega \end{cases}$$

By introducing a more general form of integral (namely, a Stieltjes integral), we can treat infinite sums and ordinary integrals simultaneously. To state the definitions and theorems for area transforms in their general form, it is necessary to use Stieltjes integrals; however, in nearly all the applications and examples ordinary Riemann integrals can be used. There will be no attempt (and there is no need) to review the theory of Stieltjes integration here; however, its use in operational analysis is discussed further in Chap. 10. For this chapter, merely let dF_s indicate that discrete as well as continuous weighting in the frequency plane is permitted. The subscript s denotes *Stieltjes weighting*. In addition to the need to include both continuous and discrete weighting of frequencies to obtain generality, the possibility of using complex frequencies over the entire complex p plane should be included. Note that two-sided Laplace transforms use only frequencies along a line in the p plane.

The key idea† for the invention of area transforms was that of using superposition of exponentials of all possible complex frequencies. In a theory which includes frequencies over the entire plane, a continuous distribution of frequencies takes the following form:

$$f(t) = \frac{1}{4\pi^2} \int_{-\infty}^{\infty} \int_{-\infty}^{\infty} e^{pt} F(\omega, \sigma) \, d\omega \, d\sigma$$

Functions of the form

$$\frac{1}{2\pi} \int_{-\infty}^{\infty} e^{\sigma t} e^{j\omega t} F(\sigma + j\omega) \, d\omega \qquad \text{and} \qquad \sum_k C_k e^{p_k t}$$

can be included as special cases by the use of appropriate δ functions. It is somewhat better in a very general theory to use two-dimensional Stieltjes weighting thus:

$$f(t) = \frac{1}{4\pi^2} \int_{-\infty}^{\infty} \int_{-\infty}^{\infty} e^{pt} \, dF_s(\omega, \sigma)$$

† First presented in Ref. 8.

This includes integrals along lines (such as the line Re $p = \sigma$) as well as discrete frequency contributions.

Hence we define area transforms thus: f is *area-transformable* iff there exists a function $F_s(\omega, \sigma)$ such that

$$f(t) = \frac{1}{4\pi^2} \int_{-\infty}^{\infty} \int_{-\infty}^{\infty} e^{pt} \, dF_s(\omega, \sigma)$$

Also f is area-transformable with continuous weighting iff there exists a function $F(\omega, \sigma)$ such that

$$f(t) = \frac{1}{4\pi^2} \int_{-\infty}^{\infty} \int_{-\infty}^{\infty} e^{pt} F(\omega, \sigma) \, d\omega \, d\sigma$$

If f is the input to a system having a transfer function $H(p)$, one would expect the output to be

$$g(t) = \frac{1}{4\pi^2} \int_{-\infty}^{\infty} \int_{-\infty}^{\infty} e^{pt} H(p) \, dF_s$$

This can easily be proved to be the case (see Chap. 10 for the proofs). For example, for a differentiator suppose we can differentiate under the integral sign:

$$f(t) = \frac{1}{4\pi^2} \int_{-\infty}^{\infty} \int_{-\infty}^{\infty} e^{\sigma t} e^{j\omega t} F(\omega, \sigma) \, d\omega \, d\sigma$$

$$f'(t) = \frac{1}{4\pi^2} \int_{-\infty}^{\infty} \int_{-\infty}^{\infty} [e^{\sigma t}(j\omega)e^{j\omega t} + e^{j\omega t}\sigma e^{\sigma t}] F(\omega, \sigma) \, d\omega \, d\sigma$$

$$= \frac{1}{4\pi^2} \int_{-\infty}^{\infty} \int_{-\infty}^{\infty} (\sigma + j\omega) e^{\sigma + j\omega t} F(\omega, \sigma) \, d\omega \, d\sigma$$

$$= \frac{1}{4\pi^2} \int_{-\infty}^{\infty} \int_{-\infty}^{\infty} e^{pt} p F(\omega, \sigma) \, d\omega \, d\sigma$$

and p is the transfer function of a differentiator.

The detailed development of the theory of area transforms will be left for Chap. 10; in particular, the problem of transforming f to find its area transform F_s is solved in Chap. 10. The key to finding an F_s, given a transformable function f, is provided by two-dimensional Fourier transforms. The important point of this brief discussion of area transforms is that the concepts provided by the theorems of Sec. 3-2 gave us the ability to invent versions of operational analysis; in fact, the most general form of operational analysis which is possible was invented. One can hardly question the claim that the desired unified picture of operational analysis has been obtained; namely, operational analysis has its basis in the representation of functions of time as the superposition of those (unique) functions which are eigenfunctions for all linear time-invariant operators (namely, exponential functions).

As an appetizer for the discussion of area transforms in Chap. 10, an example will be mentioned here.   Recall the classical example of a function which was not Laplace-transformable, $\exp \frac{1}{2}t^2$, or even $U(t) \exp \frac{1}{2}t^2$.   Such a function is area-transformable.   One can represent $\exp \frac{1}{2}t^2$ by using frequencies along the line $\text{Im } p = 0$, that is, by using frequencies only along the σ axis.   The weighting of the frequencies is of the form $\exp (-\frac{1}{2}\sigma^2)$; in detail, it is not difficult to verify (see Prob. 8) that

$$\exp \frac{1}{2} t^2 = \frac{1}{\sqrt{2\pi}} \int_{-\infty}^{\infty} e^{\sigma t} \exp \left(-\frac{1}{2} \sigma^2 \right) d\sigma$$

This *area transform pair* follows naturally from the transformation theorem given in Chap. 10.

3-4 OTHER CIRCUIT PROPERTIES

The crucial assumptions to be made about circuits in order that they can be easily analyzed are linearity and time invariance.   These and these alone are needed to formulate the grand theory which was given in Chaps. 1 and 2 and which was crystallized in Sec. 3-2.   However, there are other major restrictions on circuits which are often of interest.   These restrictions are seldom helpful in simplifying the analysis, but they are sometimes of practical importance.   The other restrictions or properties which will be defined and discussed briefly in the remainder of this chapter are the following: realness, realizability, and stability.   Each of the properties will be defined *in the time domain*, and the discussions will include a characterization of the properties in terms of the transfer function (frequency-response function).

REAL PARAMETER SYSTEMS

The system is *real* iff real-valued inputs always produce real-valued outputs.   Nearly all applications of circuit analysis in the past have been concerned with real (also called real parameter) circuits; however, the analysis of real systems is most easily developed as a special case of the analysis of complex systems.   More important is the fact that applications of complex parameter systems have been overlooked because of misconceptions† about the physical meaning of complex-valued functions.

In the past, complex-valued inputs were considered only because it was noted that for the many systems of interest the output produced by the real part of a complex-valued input was equal to the real part of the output produced by the complex-valued input.   This is attractive when the system is more easily analyzed for the complex-valued input.   This technique can be applied only for real systems; precisely, we have the following theorem.

---

† Some people have the misconception that complex-valued functions do not occur physically.

Theorem 4. Let $\Phi: D \to V$ be linear for D with the field of complex scalars, and let $f \in D$ imply that Re f is an element of D; then $\Phi(\text{Re } f) = \text{Re } \Phi(f)$ iff Φ is real (for D).

PROOF: Let $\text{Re } f = x$ and $f = x + jy$. For the *if* part, observe that $y \in D$ since $x = \text{Re } f \in D$ and $y = (-j)(f - x)$. Hence by linearity $\Phi(x + jy) = \Phi(x) + j\Phi(y)$. $\Phi(x)$ and $\Phi(y)$ are real, since Φ is real iff real inputs produce real outputs. In turn, $\text{Re } \Phi(f) = \Phi(x) = \Phi(\text{Re } f)$, as was to be shown. For the *only if*, we wish to show that $f \in D$ and f real imply that $\Phi(f)$ is real, and we are given $\Phi(\text{Re } f) = \text{Re } \Phi(f)$. This is even more obvious than the *if* part of the theorem in that, since f is real, $\Phi(f) = \Phi(\text{Re } f) = \text{Re } \Phi(f)$, which is certainly real.

An often-used application of the above theorem is the following: Let Φ be a real linear time-invariant system for which $H(p)$ is the transfer function. Suppose $f(t) = Ae^{\sigma t} \cos (\omega t + \alpha)$ is the input where everything is real. If $p = \sigma + j\omega$, then $f = \text{Re } (Ae^{j\alpha}e^{pt})$. The output produced by $Ae^{j\alpha}e^{pt}$ is $H(p)Ae^{j\alpha}e^{pt}$. Hence if $Be^{j\beta} = H(p)Ae^{j\alpha}$, where B and β are real, Theorem 4 above gives

$$\Phi[Ae^{\sigma t} \cos (\omega t + \alpha)] = Be^{\sigma t} \cos (\omega t + \beta) = \text{Re } [H(p)Ae^{j\alpha}e^{pt}]$$

This example contains all the results of Sec. 1-2.

Recall that $Ae^{\sigma t} \cos (\omega t + \alpha) = \frac{1}{2}(Ae^{j\alpha}e^{pt} + Ae^{-j\alpha}e^{\bar{p}t})$ and hence directly from linearity we get

$$\Phi[Ae^{\sigma t} \cos (\omega t + \alpha)] = \tfrac{1}{2}Ae^{j\alpha}H(p)e^{pt} + \tfrac{1}{2}Ae^{-j\alpha}H(\bar{p})e^{\bar{p}t}$$

whether or not Φ is real. However, if the system is real, the indicated output must be real, which yields the following characterization of real systems in terms of their transfer functions. Let $\tilde{D}_p$ be exponentials of complex frequency p along with the real parts of such functions.

Theorem 5. Let Φ be linear and time-invariant with transfer function H. Then Φ is real for $\tilde{D}_p$ iff $H(\bar{p}) = \overline{H(p)}$.

PROOF: First the case for p real will be considered; in this case

$$\Phi(Ae^{\sigma t}) = AH(\sigma)e^{\sigma t}$$

Then for the *only if*, $H(\sigma)$ must be real so that the output will be real, and then $H(\bar{\sigma}) = \overline{H(\sigma)}$. For the *if*, we are given that $\overline{H(\sigma)} = H(\bar{\sigma}) = H(\sigma)$, and hence $H(p)$ is real when p is real; in turn, $AH(\sigma)e^{\sigma t}$ is real, as was to be shown. If p is not real, consider the output $\Phi[Ae^{\sigma t} \cos (\omega t + \alpha)] = \frac{1}{2}Ae^{j\alpha}H(p)e^{pt} + Ae^{-j\alpha}H(\bar{p})e^{\bar{p}t}$. For the *if*, $H(\bar{p}) = \overline{H(p)}$, which implies that $\Phi[Ae^{\sigma t} \cos (\omega t + \alpha)]$ is real. For the *only if*, we have that $\frac{1}{2}Ae^{j\alpha}H(p)e^{pt} + \frac{1}{2}Ae^{-j\alpha}H(\bar{p})e^{\bar{p}t}$ is real and hence is equal to its own conjugate

$$\tfrac{1}{2}Ae^{-j\alpha} \overline{H(p)}e^{\bar{p}t} + \tfrac{1}{2}Ae^{j\alpha} \overline{H(\bar{p})}e^{pt}$$

If we take $A \neq 0$, the equality can hold only if

$$\overline{H(p)} = H(\bar{p})$$

as was to be shown.

As an example, suppose

$$H(p) = \int_{-\infty}^{\infty} h(t)e^{-pt}\,dt$$

Then it is clear that $H(\bar{p}) = \overline{H(p)}$ iff h is real-valued.

The above discussion defines and characterizes real systems. Also, it is obvious that the theory we have developed in the book can be applied quite well without the assumption that the systems are real. Systems which are not necessarily real will often be referred to as complex (or complex parameter) systems. The physical interpretation and possible utility of complex systems beg investigation at this point; however, this will be left for Chap. 4.

REALIZABILITY

Let $\Phi: D \to V$. Then Φ is *realizable* for D iff whenever f_1 and f_2 are elements of D with $f_1(t) = f_2(t)$ for $t \leq T$, then $\Phi(f_1) = \Phi(f_2)$ when these outputs are evaluated at times less than or equal to T. In simple terms, a system is realizable iff the present value of the output never depends on future values of the input.

Suppose $f_1 \in D$ and $f_2 \in D$ with $f_1(t) = f_2(t)$ for $t \leq T$; then if we consider a *convoluting system* having impulse response h,

$$\int_{-\infty}^{\infty} f_1(t - \tau)h(\tau)\,d\tau = \int_{-\infty}^{\infty} f_2(t - \tau)h(\tau)\,d\tau \qquad \text{for } t \leq T$$

or $\qquad \displaystyle\int_{-\infty}^{t-T} [f_1(t - \tau) - f_2(t - \tau)]h(\tau)\,d\tau = 0 \qquad \text{for all } t \leq T$

The integral from $t - T$ to ∞ is automatically zero by the assumption made on (f_1, f_2). If D contains enough appropriate (f_1, f_2), then the above equation can hold only if $h(\tau) = 0$ for $\tau < 0$.

This conclusion can be obtained more directly. We think of $h(t)$ as the response of the system when a *sharp pulse* is applied at $t = 0$. Clearly, the output should be zero for $t < 0$ since the system does not anticipate the arrival of the applied impulse. One will often see convolution written as

$$\int_0^{\infty} f(t - \tau)h(\tau)\,d\tau$$

and if $f(t) = 0$ for $t \leq 0$, this reduces to

$$\int_0^t f(t - \tau)h(\tau)\,d\tau$$

Of course, if $h(\tau) = 0$ for $\tau \leq 0$, $H(p) = L(h)_p$ converges for all Re p sufficiently large. This characterizes realizable systems in terms of their frequency-response functions. This characterization is not useful as a test if $H(p)$ is given as, say, a rational function; however, if it is known that the system is realizable we at least know that $h = L^{-1}(H)$ should be taken along a line to the right of all the poles of H.

STABILITY

Let $\Phi: D \to V$. Then Φ is *stable*† iff whenever the input is bounded, then the output is bounded.

The basic theorem on stability for convoluting systems is the following.

Theorem 6. Let $g = h * f$. Then the system is stable iff

$$\int_{-\infty}^{\infty} |h|\, dt < \infty$$

PROOF: For the *if* part, suppose f is bounded by M. Then

$$|g(t)| \leq \int_{-\infty}^{\infty} |h(\tau)|\, |f(t - \tau)|\, d\tau \leq M \int_{-\infty}^{\infty} |h(\tau)|\, d\tau \qquad \text{for all } t$$

For the *only if*, suppose

$$\int_{-\infty}^{\infty} |h| = \infty$$

We can take the following as a bounded f which produces an unbounded output: $f(-\tau) = e^{-j\theta(\tau)}$, where‡ $\theta(\tau)$ is the angle of $h(\tau)$; that is, $h = |h|e^{j\theta}$. Then

$$g(0) = \int_{-\infty}^{\infty} e^{-j\theta(\tau)} h(\tau)\, d\tau = \int_{-\infty}^{\infty} |h|\, d\tau = \infty$$

As described by the following familiar theorem, stability can easily be tested by the location of the poles of the transfer function.

Theorem 7. Let $H(p)$ be a proper rational function and let $h(\tau) = 0$ for $\tau < 0$; then the system is stable iff the poles of H have negative real parts (are strictly in the left half plane).

For the *if* part, suppose the poles of H have negative real parts. Then by direct computation of h we find h to be a sum of terms of the form

$$Ct^n e^{pt}\, U(t)$$

with Re $p < 0$; in turn,

$$\int_{-\infty}^{\infty} |h| < \infty$$

which ensures stability.

For the *only if*, suppose H has poles in the right half plane. With $h(\tau) = 0$ for $\tau \leq 0$, $H(p)$ converges for Re p large. In turn, the inversion formula

† There is some room for doubt as to the best way to define stability. The definition used here is satisfactory for most of the purposes of the book.

‡ If h is real-valued, we simply have

$$f(-\tau) = \begin{cases} 1 & \text{if } h(\tau) > 0 \\ 0 & \text{if } h(\tau) = 0 \\ -1 & \text{if } h(\tau) < 0 \end{cases}$$

is taken to the right of all the poles, and it includes terms of the form

$$Ct^n e^{pt} U(t)$$

with Re $p > 0$.   It is obvious that such terms render

$$\int_{-\infty}^{\infty} |h| = \infty$$

However, the rigorous proof of this seems to be a bit involved and will be omitted (the difficulty is the possibility that these "big terms" may tend to cancel each other).

It is very interesting to note that the transfer function for stable non-realizable systems may have poles in the right half plane.   For example,

$$h(t) = e^{-|t|}   \text{all real } t$$

corresponds to a stable system, but its transfer function

$$H(p) = \frac{-2}{p^2 - 1} |\text{Re } p| < 1$$

has a pole at $p = 1$.

Problems

The following examples of circuits (or transformations) are referred to in Probs. 1 through 4.   Let f denote an arbitrary input and let g denote the corresponding output. On the assumption that the set of inputs D under consideration is rich with elements, it is of no importance what D actually is; however, to be specific, let D be the set of all complex-valued functions of a real variable (t) which have a derivative everywhere. Also, let the elements of D be absolutely integrable.

1. $g = -2f^3$.
2. $g(t) = jf'(5)$ for all t (prime denotes derivative).
3. $g(t) = (\sin t)f(t)$ for all t.
4. $g(t) = f(2t)$ for all t (like playing a record at twice the intended speed).
5. $g(t) = e^{j\omega t}[f(t)]^2$ for all t.
6. $g = \text{Re } f$.
7. $g(t) = \int_{t-1}^{t} f(\tau)\, d\tau.$
8. $g(t) = \int_{-\infty}^{\infty} h(t, \tau)f(\tau)\, d\tau,$ where

$$\int_{-\infty}^{\infty} |h(t, \tau)|\, d\tau < \infty$$

and h is complex rather than real-valued.
9. $g = \bar{f}$ (where bar denotes conjugate).
10. $g(t) = \int_{-\infty}^{\infty} h(t - \tau)[f(\tau)]^2\, d\tau,$ where h is real-valued and

$$\int_{-\infty}^{\infty} |h| < \infty$$

11. $g(t) = f(t + 1)$ for all t.

1. Which of the above circuits are linear?
2. Which of the above circuits are time-invariant?
3. Which of the above are real?
4. Which of the above are realizable?
5. Very mild conditions were imposed upon D in Theorem 3. However, if we assume that the elements of D have a derivative, then the conclusion that the elements of D must be exponentials can be obtained quickly by considering a differentiator rather than a circuit which translates in time; show this.
6. In connection with the discussion of properties 1 to 3 given after Theorem 3, prove that properties 1 and 3 imply property 2. Consider the domain for Φ to be D_p.
7. Find

$$f(t) = \frac{1}{4\pi^2} \int_{-\infty}^{\infty} \int_{-\infty}^{\infty} e^{pt} F(\omega, \sigma) \, d\omega \, d\sigma$$

if

$$F(\omega, \sigma) = \begin{cases} 1 & \text{for } |\omega| < 1 \text{ and } |\sigma| < 1 \\ 0 & \text{for other } p \end{cases}$$

Does this f have an ordinary two-sided Laplace transform?

8. Establish the area transform pair

$$\frac{1}{\alpha} \exp \frac{t^2}{2\alpha^2} = \frac{1}{\sqrt{2\pi}} \int_{-\infty}^{\infty} e^{\sigma t} \exp\left(-\tfrac{1}{2}\alpha^2\sigma^2\right) d\sigma$$

This is easily proved by completing the square on the exponent $(\sigma t - \tfrac{1}{2}\alpha^2\sigma^2)$ and using the fact that

$$\int_{-\infty}^{\infty} e^{-\frac{1}{2}\theta^2} \, d\theta = \sqrt{2\pi}$$

9. The special area transform pair

$$\frac{1}{\alpha} \exp \frac{t^2}{2\alpha^2} = \frac{1}{\sqrt{2\pi}} \int_{-\infty}^{\infty} e^{\sigma t} \exp\left(-\tfrac{1}{2}\alpha^2\sigma^2\right) d\sigma$$

provides a method for area-transforming any function which "grows slower than" $\exp(t^2/2\alpha^2)$ for some α sufficiently small. To see this, let $f(t)$ be given and let there exist an α such that

$$\int_{-\infty}^{\infty} \exp \frac{-t^2}{2\alpha^2} |f(t)| \, dt$$

is finite. Then if $g(t) = \exp(-t^2/2\alpha^2)f(t)$, let its Fourier transform be

$$G(\omega) = \int_{-\infty}^{\infty} e^{-i\omega t} g(t) \, dt$$

Now assuming that the area transform pair for $(1/\alpha)\exp(t^2/2\alpha^2)$ given above is correct, show that

$$f(t) = \frac{1}{\sqrt{2\pi}\,2\pi} \int_{-\infty}^{\infty} \int_{-\infty}^{\infty} e^{pt} G(\omega) e^{-\frac{1}{2}\alpha^2\sigma^2} \, d\omega \, d\sigma$$

10. (a) If $H(p) = \exp p^2$ is the transfer function of a circuit, is the circuit a real parameter circuit?
    (b) If the input for this circuit is $2j \exp(2t + j3t)$ for all t, what is the output?
    (c) If the input is $2e^{2t}[\cos(3t + \pi/2)]$, what is the output?
    (d) If $H(p) = 1/(jp + 1)$, is the circuit a real parameter circuit? Find the outputs for this circuit when subjected to the inputs of (b) and (c).

11. Let $\Phi(f) = Hf$ (that is, let f be an eigenfunction for Φ with eigenvalue H), let Φ be linear and time-invariant, and let D be all functions obtained as finite linear combinations of translates of f. That is, $q \in D$ iff there exist complex numbers $a_1, \ldots, a_n$ and real numbers $\tau_1, \ldots, \tau_n$ such that

$$q(t) = \sum_{k=1}^{n} a_k f(t + \tau_k)$$

Observe that D is a linear space and is closed with respect to translation on the t axis. Show that each $q \in D$ is an eigenfunction of Φ with eigenvalue H; that is, for any $q \in D$, $\Phi(q) = Hq$.

12. *Generalization of Theorem 7.*   Let

$$H(p) = \int_{-\infty}^{\infty} e^{-pt} h(t) \, dt$$

and let H be a proper rational function.   Show that H is the transfer function of a stable convoluting circuit iff Re $p = 0$ is in the strip of convergence of $L(h)$.

APPLICATIONS
AND EXTENSIONS

Considerable analytical capability was developed in the preceding chapters; however, most of the example problems and applications were straightforward. Here in the second part of the book more advanced applications are developed and the associated results are deeper (not readily anticipated). Some new analytical tools are developed here in Part II, but the emphasis is on clever (or even exciting) applications. Of course, as one might expect, a certain amount of hard work accompanies the coups.

Throughout Part II the work borders on systems analysis, and in Chap. 9 a rather solid introduction to some aspects of the analysis of electronic systems is given. With the exception that Chap. 9 rests on the results in Chaps. 4 and 8, the various chapters are nearly self-contained. Hence any subset of chapters can be covered in any order without much difficulty.

4

COMPLEX
PARAMETER SYSTEMS

In this chapter the fundamental concepts of complex parameter systems are presented. The physical role of such systems is described, and a procedure for the synthesis of complex parameter systems with real parameter systems is given. We then observe that our concepts can be generalized further to what is termed general complex filters. As final considerations, complex systems are used in a proof of the *positive real* property of passive networks, and a general *optical synthesis* of complex parameter systems is described briefly. Actually the concept of complex systems is only introduced in this chapter and then exploited in later chapters. In particular, a synthesis procedure involving real bandpass networks is given in Chap. 6, and interesting applications are covered in Chap. 9.

4-1 INTERPRETATION AND SYNTHESIS WITH REAL SYSTEMS

The basic physical interpretation follows directly from the definition of a complex number as an ordered pair of real numbers. Of course, a complex-valued function is an ordered pair of real-valued functions. Thus if the input (or output) to a system is a pair of real-valued functions rather than a single real-valued function, the input can be viewed as a single complex-valued input. Thus, suppose the two real inputs are f_r and f_i. Then we define the complex-valued input as (f_r, f_i) or $f = f_r + jf_i$. Similarly, the

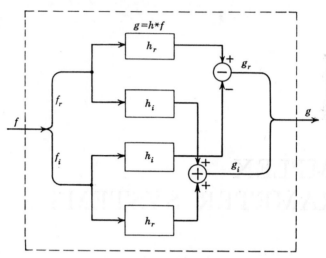

FIGURE 4-1.   Synthesis of complex-valued impulse response h with real parameter systems.

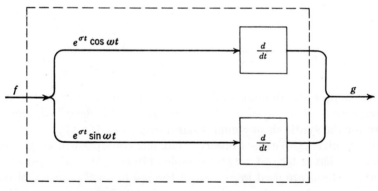

FIGURE 4-2. $g = f'$, with f complex.

two outputs are $(g_r, g_i) = g$. A typical complex parameter system takes the following form: $g = h * f$, where all quantities are complex-valued. Such a complex system can readily be synthesized with real systems if we simply make the expansion

$$g_r + jg_i = (h_r + jh_i) * (f_r + jf_i) = (h_r * f_r - h_i * f_i) + (h_r * f_i + h_i * f_r)$$

which results in the block diagram of Figure 4-1.

For example, suppose $g = f'$ and $f(t) = e^{pt}$. This situation can be synthesized as shown in Figure 4-2.

As another example, suppose instantaneous voltage and current are related, $E = jI$. This amounts to a j-ohm *resistor* (not reactive). Such a situation is depicted in Figure 4-3: $I(t) = Ae^{j\alpha}e^{j\omega t}$.

The interesting question is that of the existence of practical applications of complex inputs and outputs of complex parameter systems. Important applications in radar and communication systems are described in Chap. 9. The application to communications will be described briefly here for illustrative purposes.

Suppose $A(t) \cos [\omega_0 t - \alpha(t)]$ is received and at the receiver the functions $\cos \omega_0 t$ and $\sin \omega_0 t$ are available. If the received signal is mixed with $\cos \omega_0 t$

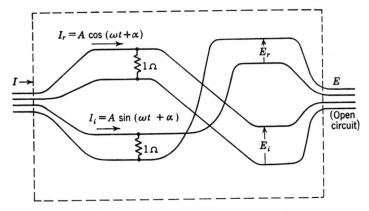

FIGURE 4-3. Pure imaging resistor of j ohms.

and only the difference frequency is retained, we get $A(t) \cos \alpha(t)$. If the received signal is mixed with $\sin \omega_0 t$ and only the difference frequency is retained, we get

$$A(t) \sin \alpha(t)$$

From the received real signal we have now obtained an ordered pair of signals:

$$f_r(t) = A(t) \cos \alpha(t)$$
$$f_i(t) = A(t) \sin \alpha(t)$$
and
$$f(t) = A(t) \exp j\alpha(t)$$

In a communication system, $A(t)$ (amplitude modulation) and/or $\alpha(t)$ (phase or frequency modulation) normally carry the information of interest. If the local oscillator ($\cos \omega_0 t$ and $\sin \omega_0 t$ generators) is synchronized in frequency and locked in phase to the incoming signal, f_r and/or f_i could just as well carry the information of interest. In this case we would have real and/or imaginary part modulation. The block diagram of the system takes the form shown in Figure 4-4.   The role of the complex parameter filter (the receiver—save for mixers and detectors) is to reject noise outside the spectrum occupied by f and to amplify f to a convenient level.   The system of Figure 4-4 might be described as a coherent video receiver with four video strips used to synthesize the desired complex-valued impulse response.   As will be shown in Chap. 6, the same performance can be obtained with a single i-f strip; however, for analytical purposes and most conceptual purposes, the system of Figure 4-4 is preferable.

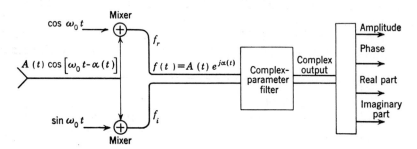

FIGURE 4-4.   Complex parameter receiver.

4-2   GENERAL COMPLEX FILTERS

In view of the above physical interpretations of complex signals and complex parameter filters, the idea that complex-valued quantities are never themselves physical quantities is absurd.   The flaw in the above generalization of our concepts is that it did not go quite far enough.   Specifically, a complex parameter filter is not an adequately general transformation of a complex-valued function in that more general transformations can be considered within the attractive mathematical framework available.   What has been overlooked is the possibility of including conjugate linear transformations.   Let $\Phi: D \rightarrow V$, where D is a linear space over the field of complex numbers.   Then Φ is *conjugate linear* iff whenever f_1 and f_2 are elements of D,

$$\Phi(f_1 + f_2) = \Phi(f) + \Phi(f_2)$$

and whenever $f \in D$ and c is a complex number,

$$\Phi(cf) = \bar{c}\Phi(f)$$

where the bar denotes the complex conjugate.

At first glance one may fear that an entire theory analogous to that developed for linear time-invariant systems must be developed for conjugate linear time-invariant systems.   Theorem 1 removes this threat by linking linear and conjugate linear operators.

If $\Phi: D \rightarrow V$, let $\bar{\Phi}$ denote the following:

$$\bar{\Phi}(f) = \overline{\Phi(f)}$$

That is, the output produced by $\bar{\Phi}$ is the complex conjugate of the output produced by Φ. The following theorem ties the theory of conjugate linear transformations to the theory of linear transformations.

Theorem 1. The transformation Φ is conjugate linear iff $\bar{\Phi}$ is linear.

PROOF: If Φ is conjugate linear,

$$\Phi(af) = \bar{a}\Phi(f) \qquad \text{and} \qquad \bar{\Phi}(af) = a\bar{\Phi}(f)$$

Of course,

$$\Phi(f_1 + f_2) = \Phi(f_1) + \Phi(f_2) \qquad \text{iff} \qquad \bar{\Phi}(f_1 + f_2) = \bar{\Phi}(f_1) + \bar{\Phi}(f_2)$$

Thus Φ is linear. If $\bar{\Phi}$ is linear,

$$\bar{\Phi}(af) = a\bar{\Phi}(f)$$

which implies

$$\Phi(af) = \bar{a}\Phi(f)$$

and hence Φ is conjugate linear.

It is clear from this theorem that everything developed for the theory of linear systems carries over to conjugate linear systems. For example,

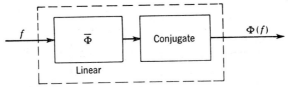

FIGURE 4-5. Synthesis of conjugate linear system with linear system.

to synthesize a conjugate linear Φ, we can synthesize the linear transformation $\bar{\Phi}$ and follow this with a complex conjugator as shown in Figure 4-5.

There is yet another consideration. Suppose we consider both linear and conjugate linear transformations. These could be cascaded and/or paralleled. It is easy to see that a system of cascaded linear and conjugate linear subsystems is itself either linear or conjugate linear, being linear iff there are an even number of conjugate linear subsystems. Hence only parallel combinations need be considered; however, a system of parallel linear (conjugate linear) subsystems is linear (conjugate linear). Hence any system which can be constructed with linear and conjugate linear subsystems can always be represented by an ordinary linear system Φ_o in parallel with a conjugate linear system Φ_c, as shown in Figure 4-6.

Finally, it should be noted that the above is simply a slightly disguised version of the general theory of linear transformations of spaces of ordered pairs of real-valued functions. With the usual matrix algebra,† let

$$f = \begin{pmatrix} f_r \\ f_i \end{pmatrix}$$

† A knowledge of matrix algebra is hardly required for the few simple remarks which follow.

be an element of D and let $\Phi : D \to V$, where V is also a set of ordered pairs of real-valued functions. Then Φ is linear iff there is a matrix of four linear transformations defined on the appropriate components of the elements of D for which

$$g = \Phi(f) = \begin{pmatrix} \Phi_1 & \Phi_2 \\ \Phi_3 & \Phi_4 \end{pmatrix} \begin{pmatrix} f_r \\ f_i \end{pmatrix}$$

$$\begin{pmatrix} g_r \\ g_i \end{pmatrix} \equiv \begin{pmatrix} \Phi_1(f_r) + \Phi_2(f_i) \\ \Phi_3(f_r) + \Phi_4(f_i) \end{pmatrix}$$

Of course this matrix equation is equivalent to the pair of ordinary equations $g_r = \Phi_1(f_r) + \Phi_2(f_i)$ and $g_i = \Phi_3(f_r) + \Phi_4(f_i)$. In terms of networks, the Φ_i's are real parameter systems used to synthesize a system having two real inputs and two real outputs.

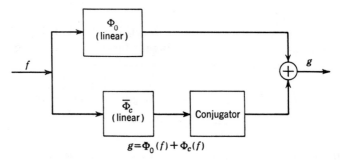

$$g = \Phi_0(f) + \Phi_c(f)$$

FIGURE 4-6.   General complex parameter system.

Let $\Phi_{or}(f) = \text{Re } \Phi_o(f)$, $\Phi_{oi}(f) = \text{Im } \Phi_o(f)$, etc. Then we have a natural one-to-one correspondence between general complex transformations

$$\begin{aligned}
g = \Phi_o(f) + \Phi_c(f) &= \Phi_o(f_r) + j\Phi_o(f_i) + \Phi_c(f_r) - j\Phi_c(f_i) \\
&= [\Phi_{or}(f_r) - \Phi_{oi}(f_i) + \Phi_{cr}(f_r) + \Phi_{ci}(f_i)] \\
&\quad + j[\Phi_{oi}(f_r) + \Phi_{or}(f_i) + \Phi_{ci}(f_r) - \Phi_{cr}(f_i)]
\end{aligned}$$

and matrix transformations

$$\begin{pmatrix} g_r \\ g_i \end{pmatrix} = \begin{pmatrix} \Phi_1 & \Phi_2 \\ \Phi_3 & \Phi_4 \end{pmatrix} \begin{pmatrix} f_r \\ f_i \end{pmatrix}$$

as follows. The general complex filter (Φ_o, Φ_c) is equivalent to the matrix operator

$$\begin{pmatrix} \Phi_1 & \Phi_2 \\ \Phi_3 & \Phi_4 \end{pmatrix}$$

iff

$$\Phi_{or} + \Phi_{cr} = \Phi_1$$
$$\Phi_{ci} - \Phi_{oi} = \Phi_2$$
$$\Phi_{oi} + \Phi_{ci} = \Phi_3$$
$$\Phi_{or} - \Phi_{cr} = \Phi_4$$

This is the case iff

$$\Phi_{or} = \tfrac{1}{2}(\Phi_1 + \Phi_4)$$
$$\Phi_{cr} = \tfrac{1}{2}(\Phi_1 - \Phi_4)$$
$$\Phi_{ci} = \tfrac{1}{2}(\Phi_3 + \Phi_2)$$
$$\Phi_{oi} = \tfrac{1}{2}(\Phi_3 - \Phi_2)$$

It is generally simpler to employ general (linear plus conjugate linear) complex filters in the analysis of such systems than to resort to matrix notation.   More important, there is a practical difference between ordinary complex parameter receivers Φ_o and general complex parameter receivers (Φ_c along with Φ_o).   Though it is not obvious, it turns out that to gain advantages from the use of general complex filters, a phase lock on the receiver is required; but only close carrier-frequency tracking is required in most ordinary complex parameter receivers.   This need for phase lock is described to some extent in Chap. 9.

The practical distinction between complex parameter filters and general complex parameter filters is most easily described after some results on the optimization of filters (or receivers) have been obtained.   As it stands now, we have no basis for determining what is a good receiver and we have no theory of performance which leads to a rational choice of Φ_o and Φ_c.   However, with the tools of Chap. 8 it is possible to show that for the majority of important systems the optimum Φ_c is $\Phi_c = 0$.   Specifically (with a signal-to-noise ratio or a least-squares error criterion), $\Phi_c = 0$ is optimum in the following cases:

1. Radar systems.

2. In all receivers which do not have the local oscillator locked in phase to the received carrier.

3. In a communications system which uses real and imaginary part modulation, but for which the signals of these two channels have identical but independent statistics.   In this case there is phase lock, but still the optimum Φ_c is zero.

The point to be stressed here is that our mathematical partition of general complex parameter filters into ordinary ($\Phi_c = 0$) and nonordinary ($\Phi_c \neq 0$) complex parameter filters is miraculously the same as the partition of receivers into those appropriate to most applications and those useful in but a few special applications.   Note that if one looks only at the matrix formulation there is no reasonable way to discover this important partition of all possible receivers.   Except for Sec. 9-4, we shall restrict our attention to ordinary complex parameter filters in the remainder of the book.

4-3   THE POSITIVE REAL PROPERTY OF PASSIVE NETWORKS

The work on complex-valued inputs of the form Ae^{pt} and on real and complex parameter networks provides tools for a very simple derivation of a famous property of passive networks.   Consider a two-terminal passive network. To be specific, let the input (generally denoted by f, but denoted by i in this case) be driving current and the output be the terminal voltage, thus:

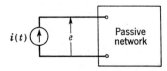

In addition to being passive, let the network be real, linear, and time-invariant; and let the driving current be the usual complex-valued function

$$i(t) = Ie^{pt}$$

where I is a complex constant. Subscripts 1 and 2 will be used to denote real and imaginary parts; for example, $i = i_1 + ji_2$. If Φ denotes the transformation performed by the circuit, we have

$$e = e_1 + je_2 = \Phi(i_1 + ji_2) = \Phi(i_1) + j\Phi(i_2)$$

and since Φ is a real parameter system, $\Phi(i_1)$ and $\Phi(i_2)$ are real. In turn, $e_1 = \Phi(i_1)$ and $e_2 = \Phi(i_2)$. Thus, as illustrated in Sec. 4-1, the actual circuit configuration for $e = \Phi(i)$ with $i = Ie^{pt}$ is the ordered pair of circuits shown, having real inputs (where α is the argument of the complex number I).

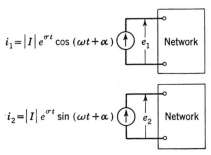

Note that $e_1 i_1 + e_2 i_2$ is the actual instantaneous power delivered to the (ordered pair of circuits) circuit by the complex driving current i. Let $Z(p)$ be the impedance of the circuit; of course the transfer function is the impedance when we have a two-terminal network for which the input is the current and the output is the voltage. Then $e = iZ$. Observe that (bar denotes conjugate)

$$e\bar{\imath} = (e_1 i_1 + e_2 i_2) + j(e_2 i_1 - e_1 i_2)$$

and hence $P = \mathrm{Re}\ (ie)$ is the actual instantaneous power delivered to the ordered pair of networks. Let $\mathrm{Re}\ Z(p) = R(p)$, and we have

$$P = \mathrm{Re}\ (\bar{\imath}e) = \mathrm{Re}\ (\bar{\imath}iZ) = \mathrm{Re}\ (|i|^2 Z) = |i|^2\ \mathrm{Re}\ Z = |i|^2 R(p)$$

With $i = Ie^{\sigma t}e^{j\omega t}$, $|i|^2 = |I|^2 e^{2\sigma t}$. Thus $P = |I|^2 e^{2\sigma t}R(p)$ is the instantaneous power delivered to the circuit. Suppose $R(p)$ (which is real by the definition, that is, R is the real part of Z) is negative. This means that the circuit, rather than receiving power from the source, is actually supplying power to the source. What is more, if $\sigma \geq 0$,[†] the network delivers arbitrarily large amounts of energy (one integrates the power over a large time interval). Such a delivery of energy is in violation of the assumption that the circuit is *passive*. Hence we have the following.

Theorem 2. If $Z(p)$ is the driving-point impedance (or admittance) of a real, linear, time-invariant, passive network, then Re $Z(p) \geq 0$ when Re $p \geq 0$.[†] Also, recall (Sec. 3-4) that without the use of the passive assumption (only realness along with linear time invariance was used), $Z(\bar{p}) = \overline{Z(p)}$; and hence, if p is real (say $p = \sigma$), then $Z(\bar{\sigma}) = Z(\sigma) = \overline{Z(\sigma)}$, which means that Z is real when evaluated on the real axis in the p plane.

The proof for admittance goes in the same way, except that voltage is taken as the input and then $Y(p)$ becomes the transfer function.

Let F be a complex-valued function of the complex frequency. Then F is called a positive real function[‡] iff $F(p)$ is real when p is real and Re $F(p) \geq 0$ whenever Re $p \geq 0$. Of course, Theorem 2 states that if a two-terminal network is linear, time-invariant, real, and passive, then its driving-point impedance and admittance are positive real functions. We could proceed to show that the implication also goes the other way. Specifically, if $F(p)$ is a positive real rational function, then there exists a linear, time-invariant, real, passive, lumped, finite RLC network such that $F(p)$ is its driving-point impedance (admittance). The demonstration of this is better left to a course on network synthesis.

When passive networks having many terminals are considered, a condition on the impedance matrix is obtained which is a generalization of the positive real property discussed above. The art of finding networks corresponding to given positive real functions (or matrices) is the major concern of classical network synthesis.

4-4 OPTICAL SYNTHESIS OF COMPLEX PARAMETER FILTERS

In Figure 4-1 a general method for synthesizing a complex parameter filter with four real parameter filters was given. It has been pointed out that coherent video receivers with *quadrature mixers* lead naturally to a complex-valued input for such filters. The role of such receivers in radar and communications is analyzed in Chap. 9. Also, the use of a single real parameter bandpass amplifier to provide the equivalent of a video complex parameter filter is described in Chap. 6.

[†] For lossless networks $Z(p)$ may have some poles on the line Re $p = 0$; such points are excluded from consideration.

[‡] A rather poor choice of terminology since F is neither real nor positive. Also, poles of F are not considered in the definition.

In this section a method for synthesizing an arbitrary complex parameter filter is described. To some extent the method is described in order to fight the prejudice that transfer functions must be rational functions. It will be seen that in optical synthesis one can simply "paint" any desired frequency response. Optical synthesis can be done in the time domain (i.e., impulse response is used directly); or optical synthesis can be done in the frequency domain. Only a simple version of the latter will be described here. No attempt will be made to survey the many techniques available in optical synthesis.

The digital and analog data-processing techniques developed over the past score of years have been very successful and hence have led to a change of emphasis from how to implement to what to implement. The major analytical problem is the calculation of optimum processing and associated

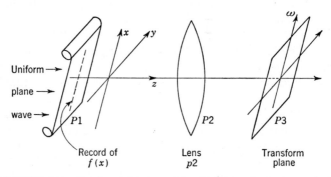

FIGURE 4-7.   Configuration for taking Fourier transforms optically.

performance obtainable. The synthesis problem remains essential to the overall engineering problem; however, it no longer dominates the scene. The simple synthesis procedure described below provides some evidence that filter synthesis is no longer a frightfully difficult problem.

In optical synthesis the function of time to be filtered must first be converted into a function of position. For the moment, suppose the input to the filter is real-valued and, to keep matters simple, it is converted into a function of position by recording the signal on film. The function recorded on film will be called $f(x)$, and it is "displayed" in plane $P1$ of Figure 4-7. A uniform plane wave of light is transmitted through the film; the light which emerges is amplitude-modulated by f. If the light on the left side of plane $P1$ is monochromatic with uniform amplitude and phase† (i.e., a plane wave of light), then on the right side of plane $P1$ the phase will be

---

† By starting with a point source of light a lens can be used to produce the uniform phase (and amplitude). The light should be very nearly sinusoidal over time intervals having a length determined by differences in the various light paths in the optical system. This calls for a light source with a narrow electromagnetic spectral width.

constant and the amplitude will be $f(x)$. That is, the film spatially ampli-
tude-modulates the light with $f(x)$. If a complex-valued input for the
filter is of interest, some additional system complexity is needed. The usual
practical procedure is to introduce (or retain) a carrier on the original signal.
Suppose f is complex-valued and α is the argument (angle) of f. Then,
rather than f, we record $|f(x)| \cos [\omega x + \alpha(x)] = \frac{1}{2}f(x)e^{j\omega x} + \frac{1}{2}\bar{f}(x)e^{-j\omega x}$.
It will be clear shortly that the term $\frac{1}{2}\bar{f}(x)e^{-j\omega x}$ can be removed in the frequency plane; also, the complex carrier $e^{j\omega x}$ on f does not present any
problem in the filter design (see Prob. 7).

Practical matters are not of interest in this discussion; so we shall assume
that $\alpha(x)$ is introduced as spatial phase modulation of the light. This can
be done by cutting glass with a thickness variation determined by $\alpha(x)$.
At the position x the light is sinusoidal in time (monochromatic) and the
amplitude and phase on the right side of plane $P1$ are determined by $f(x)$.
If the light is described in terms of, say, its electric field, the instantaneous
field at x is $|f(x)| \cos [\omega_0 t + \alpha(x)]$, where ω_0 is the frequency of the light
(for example, $\omega_0 \cong 3 \times 10^{15}$ radians/sec). Thus $f(x)$ appears as the phasor
(L_0 transform) of the light at x.

Enough for the problem of preparing f for optical filtering. The key to
the scheme of interest here is the fact that we can use optics to obtain the
Fourier transform of f. Once this transform $F(\omega) = L(f)_{j\omega}$ is obtained, it
is easy to multiply F by the desired filter frequency response $H(\omega)$. Finally,
the inverse Fourier transform is taken optically to obtain

$$g(x) = L^{-1}(HF)_x = \int h(x - u)f(u) \, du$$

where h is the impulse response of the system.

By the way, it is obvious that only one dimension was needed to record
$f(x)$; yet there are two dimensions available in the optics (x and y). In
some systems two-dimensional filtering of a function of two variables is
called for. In others, the y dimension is used for additional filters (channels). For example, it is easy to obtain a thousand one-dimensional systems. The mathematical descriptions of two-dimensional and one-dimensional filtering systems are essentially the same. The main difference is
that in one-dimensional filtering systems *cylindrical* lenses are used, but in
two-dimensional systems *spherical* lenses are used. An ideal spherical lens
introduces a phase shift of the light proportional to the square of the distance
from the center of the lens. That is, a phase shift of $k(x^2 + y^2)$ is introduced
by a spherical lens. A cylindrical lens introduces a phase shift of kx^2. As
will be seen shortly, the constant k is simply related to the focal length
of the lens.

To keep the notation simple, consider the one-dimensional system of
Figure 4-8. Observe that $s = \sqrt{a^2 + (x - u)^2}$ and we restrict $(x - u)^2/a^2$
to being small; then $s \cong a + (x - u)^2/2a$. In turn, the phasor of the light

at u is (the constant phase of $2\pi a/\lambda$ is dropped)

$$\int_{-X}^{X} f(u) \exp\left[-j\frac{\pi}{\lambda a}(x-u)^2\right] du$$

The lens† introduces a multiplicative phase of kx^2, and we take $k = \pi/\lambda a$, and a is the focal length of the lens. Further propagation to plane $P3$

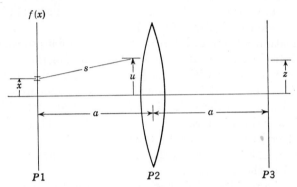

$f(x)$

$P1$ $P2$ $P3$

FIGURE 4-8.   Derivation of transform relation.

introduces another integral with a quadratic kernel, and finally the phasor of the light at z is

$$F_0(z) = \iint f(u) \exp\left(j\frac{\pi}{\lambda a}x^2\right) \exp\left[-j\frac{\pi}{\lambda a}(x-u)^2 - j\frac{\pi}{\lambda a}(z-x)^2\right] dx\, du$$

If we introduce $\pi(2uz - 2uz)/\lambda a$ in the exponent, F_0 can be written thus:

$$\int_{-X}^{X} f(u) \exp\left(j\frac{2\pi}{\lambda a}uz\right) \left\{\int_{-X}^{X} \exp\left[-j\frac{\pi}{\lambda a}(x-u-x)^2\right] dx\right\} du$$

However, if X is large, the term in the brackets is approximately

$$\int_{-\infty}^{\infty} \exp\left(-j\frac{\pi}{\lambda a}\theta^2\right) d\theta$$

which is a constant.   Hence

$$F(\omega) = F_0\left(-\frac{\lambda a}{2\pi}\omega\right)$$

is essentially the Fourier transform of f.

To filter f with the transfer function $|H(\omega)|e^{j\phi(\omega)}$, we insert a transparency of $|H(\omega)|$ in plane $P3$ along with a phase shift (say cut glass) of $\phi(\omega)$.   Then

† The sign of the phase shift depends on whether the lens is concave or convex, we want a convex lens.   Also the nonzero thickness of the lens complicates the analysis; however, such complications will not be discussed here.

on the right side of *P3* we have *FH*, and it remains only to go through another lens to obtain the inverse transform.

Again, as a practical matter, it is possible to accommodate ϕ without the use of glass in plane *P3*. Of course if *f* is real and no phase shift is desired, filter synthesis is indeed a simple matter. We paint the desired $H(\omega)$ on film and put it between a pair of lenses. For example, to block a band of frequencies we simply place the appropriate stop in plane *P3*.

The above synthesis procedure works equally well for either real or complex parameter systems. It is obvious that $H(\omega)$ can be arbitrary; there simply is no reason for the restriction $H(-\omega) = \overline{H(\omega)}$ found in real parameter systems. In Chap. 6 the complex parameter system $H(\omega) = 0$ for $\omega < 0$ and $H(\omega) = 1$ for $\omega > 0$ is of interest. It is obvious that such a filter is easily synthesized by the above procedure.

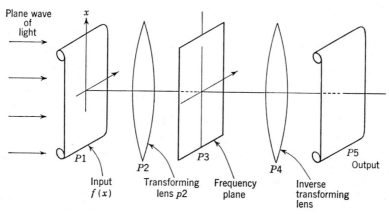

FIGURE 4-9. Complete filtering system.

The overall system takes the form shown in Figure 4-9. At the right of plane *P1* the complex input *f* appears as the phasor of the light, and at plane *P5* the complex output *g* appears as the phasor of the light. An interferometer† can be used in recording the output if the actual complex *g* rather than $|g|^2$ is of interest. Also, with an interferometer, general complex filters, rather than ordinary complex filters, can be synthesized; however, this is best left for a more detailed discussion of optical synthesis.

Problems

1. *A Result Similar to Theorem 1.* Let *D* be closed with respect to taking complex conjugates; i.e., when $f \in D$, $\bar{f} \in D$. Let $\Phi: D \to V$ and let $\tilde{\Phi}(f) \equiv \Phi(\bar{f})$. Prove that Φ is conjugate linear iff $\tilde{\Phi}$ is linear. This means that any conjugate linear system can be synthesized as a linear system preceded by a conjugator (rather than followed by a conjugator as in Theorem 1).

† Film alone tends to read out proportional to $|g|^2$.

2. Let D be a linear space (of complex-valued functions) over the field of complex scalars; prove that D is closed with respect to taking real parts iff D is closed with respect to taking complex conjugates.

3. If y and f are real, the analog computer shown is to solve the equation $y'' + y' + y = f$. One sometimes wishes to solve differential equations having complex coefficients.

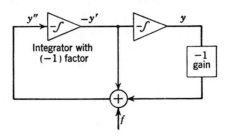

FIGURE P 3

Suppose the equation is $y'' + jy' + y = f$, where $f = e^{j\omega t}$. Find the computer diagram which solves (synthesizes) this equation. Of course, $y = y_r + jy_i$ is now a complex-valued function.

4. If $H(\omega) = 1$ for $\omega > 0$ and $H(\omega) = 0$ for $\omega < 0$ is the transfer function of a network and $f(t) = \sin t$ (all t) is the input, what is the output?

5. Which of the following functions are positive real?

$$\frac{1}{p} \qquad \frac{1}{p^2} \qquad \frac{1}{p^2 + p}$$

6. If F and G are positive real functions, is $F[G(p)]$ necessarily a positive real function? Is $FG/(F + G)$?

7. (*a*) Let F be the Fourier transform of f. If the energy of f is centered at $\omega = 0$ in the sense that $F(\omega) \cong 0$ for $|\omega| > B$, show that the energy of $e^{-j\omega_0 t}f(t)$ is centered at $-\omega_0$ in the sense that its Fourier transform is approximately zero for $|\omega + \omega_0| > B$.

(*b*) The signal $|f(t)| \cos [\omega_0 t + \alpha(t)]$ can be complex-filtered to obtain $f(t)e^{j\omega_0 t}$ by rejecting the energy in the negative half of the frequency plane. If we use a filter having an impulse response $h(t)e^{j\omega_0 t}$ and if h has its energy concentrated in frequencies $|\omega| \ll \omega_0$, the negative frequencies will be rejected. If a transparency is available for plane $P3$ of Figure 4-9 which will synthesize the impulse response h, how does one adjust this transparency to synthesize $h(t)e^{j\omega_0 t}$?

(*c*) Show that $[f(t)e^{j\omega_0 t}] * [h(t)e^{j\omega_0 t}] = [f(t) * h(t)]e^{j\omega_0 t}$.

8. Show that with a spherical lens, two-dimensional Fourier transforms can be taken and hence filters for functions of two variables can be synthesized. In this case $g(x, y) = \int\int h(x - u, y - v)f(u, v)\, du\, dv$.

9. An important step in the derivation of Sec. 4-4 involved approximating

$$a \sqrt{1 + \frac{(x - u)^2}{a^2}}$$

with the first two terms of the binomial series $\sqrt{1 + z} \cong 1 + \frac{1}{2}z$. We require an approximation which is accurate to a fraction of a wavelength. Suppose $\lambda = 0.5 \times 10^{-4}$ cm and $a = \frac{1}{2}$ m. Use the next term as an estimate of error and find the limit on $|u - x|$, which keeps the error less than $\frac{1}{4}\lambda$.

5

SYSTEM RESPONSE TIME

In this chapter the length of time required for a system to respond to stimulus (input) will be studied quantitatively. The study has three major aspects: (1) formulation of definitions of response time, (2) derivation of simple expressions for response time, (3) derivation of relationships between response time and properties of the frequency response of the system. This is a major problem area which has application to pulse circuits, servomechanisms, antennas, communication systems, and sensors such as radar and infrared scanners. In the various areas of application of the notion of response time, special terms have evolved. In servomechanisms and pulse circuits the term used for response time is rise time. In antennas, beam width corresponds to response time. In communications, sample rate is approximately the inverse of response time. Finally, in sensors, resolution corresponds to response time. Some of these applications will be discussed briefly in this chapter and some are discussed in Chaps. 8 and 9;

however, the principal objective of this chapter is to develop the mathematical theory for response time.

Consider a convoluting system having an impulse response h:

$$g(t) = \int_{-\infty}^{\infty} f(t - \tau)h(\tau)\, d\tau$$

If h differs significantly from zero over a certain time interval of length Δt, $g(t)$ involves a weighting of values of f over a time interval of said length. The length of this time interval is what is meant by response time. The system may present time delay as well as a positive response time, as indicated in Figure 5-1 for a real parameter system.

Quantitative definitions of response time will be selected more or less on the basis of what will lead to an attractive mathematical theory. If h is real, the sign of h has no bearing on the length of the time interval over which h differs significantly from zero. Hence the definition of response

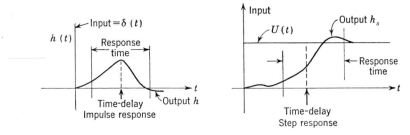

FIGURE 5-1. Response time and delay.

time should involve $|h|$ rather than h. More generally, if h is complex-valued, $|h|$ should be used in the definition. Some aspects of the theory are simpler when h is real and nonnegative, which is a condition very nearly satisfied in some applications (such as pulse circuit design). This special case will be covered in Sec. 5-1, and the general case (arbitrary complex-valued h) will be covered in Sec. 5-2.

5-1 RESPONSE TIME FOR MONOTONE SYSTEMS

A system will be called *monotone* iff it is real and its response to the unit step function $U(t)$ is a monotone function of time (either nondecreasing or nonincreasing). To be specific, it will be assumed that the step response is nondecreasing; the slight modifications of the theory necessary for the nonincreasing case are obvious. Recall that the impulse response h is the derivative of the step response (if the derivative exists). That is,

$$h(t) = \lim_{\theta \to 0} \frac{h_s(t + \theta) - h_s(t)}{\theta}$$

and if $\theta > 0$, clearly the numerator of the difference quotient is nonnegative and, in turn, h is nonnegative. That is, the derivative of an increasing function is positive. Thus it is seen that a convoluting system is monotone iff its impulse response is real and nonnegative (nonpositive if a system having a nonincreasing step response is considered). In pulse circuit design and control systems a monotone circuit is said to have no overshoot, as shown in Figure 5-2.

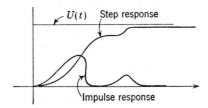

FIGURE 5-2. Step response for monotone system.

In experimental work, delay is usually defined as the time after the application of $U(t)$ at which the output attains 0.5 of its final value. If the impulse response is nonnegative and

$$\frac{h(t)}{\int_{-\infty}^{\infty} h(t)\, dt}$$

is viewed as a probability density function, this experimental definition corresponds to the median of this probability density. If $h(t)$ is viewed as

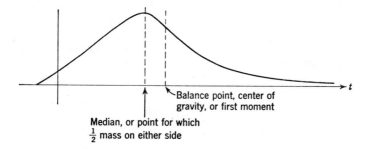

FIGURE 5-3. Measures of delay.

mass distributed along the t axis, the experimental definition corresponds to that point on the t axis such that half the mass is situated on either side. A somewhat comparable measure of delay is (the t coordinate of) the center of gravity of h:

$$\bar{t} \equiv \frac{\int_{-\infty}^{\infty} t h(t)\, dt}{\int_{-\infty}^{\infty} h(t)\, dt}$$

This is a much more attractive definition of delay for analytical purposes, and it will be used when we restrict our attention to nonnegative h. As the *center of a probability density function*, $\bar{t}$ is called the first moment.

Our chief concern is with response time, and here also, common experimental definitions have no appeal from an analytical viewpoint. In pulse circuits the response time (rise time) is usually defined as the time required for the output to rise from 0.1 to 0.9 of its final value† when the system is subjected to the unit step input $U(t)$. If h is viewed as a distributed mass, radius of gyration is a well-known measure of the width of h (this corresponds to the standard deviation of a probability density function). This is the measure of response time which will be used here, and it will be denoted by σ:

$$\sigma^2 \equiv \frac{\int_{-\infty}^{\infty} (t - \bar{t})^2 h(t)\, dt}{\int_{-\infty}^{\infty} h(t)\, dt}$$

Of course,

$$\sigma^2 \int_{-\infty}^{\infty} h(t)\, dt$$

is the moment of inertia of the mass h about the axis in the plane of the mass which is perpendicular to the t axis and located at the center of gravity.

Clearly, σ is a measure of the spread of h on the time axis. However, σ is not total duration (but more nearly a half duration). In comparison with the experimental definition, 2.5σ is usually close to the experimental definition. Specifically, in Chap. 2, Prob. 25, experimental rise times of $2.3T$ and $1.6T$ were found for an RC circuit and a shunt-compensated RC circuit. These circuits had σ's of T and $0.65T$, respectively, as will be computed later in this section.

Enough struggling with subjective matters. The basic theory for response time consists in applying Theorem 13, Chap. 2. For delay calculations we have

$$\bar{t} \equiv \frac{\int_{-\infty}^{\infty} th(t)\, dt}{\int_{-\infty}^{\infty} h(t)\, dt}$$

but

$$H(p) = \int_{-\infty}^{\infty} e^{-pt} h(t)\, dt \qquad \text{and} \qquad H'(p) = -\int_{-\infty}^{\infty} te^{-pt} h(t)\, dt$$

If these two formulas are evaluated at $p = 0$, we get the numerator and denominator for $\bar{t}$ thus:

$$\bar{t} = \frac{-H'(0)}{H(0)}$$

† If a system does not pass direct current [that is, $H(0) = 0$], final value refers to the value of the output well after high-frequency effects have passed but at a time small compared with the time constants of a-c coupling networks.

For the numerator in the definition of σ^2, observe that

$$\int_{-\infty}^{\infty} (t - \bar{t})^2 h(t)\, dt = \int_{-\infty}^{\infty} t^2 h(t)\, dt - 2\bar{t} \int_{-\infty}^{\infty} th(t)\, dt + (\bar{t})^2 \left[\int_{-\infty}^{\infty} h(t)\, dt \right]$$

When this is divided by

$$\int_{-\infty}^{\infty} h(t)\, dt$$

we have
$$\sigma^2 = \frac{\displaystyle\int_{-\infty}^{\infty} t^2 h(t)\, dt}{\displaystyle\int_{-\infty}^{\infty} h(t)\, dt} - 2(\bar{t})^2 + (\bar{t})^2$$

Let the first term be denoted by $\overline{t^2}$. Then

$$\sigma^2 = \overline{t^2} - (\bar{t})^2$$

It only remains to find a simple formula for $\overline{t^2}$. If the formula for $H(p)$ is differentiated twice under the integral sign, we get

$$H''(p) = \int_{-\infty}^{\infty} t^2 e^{-pt} h(t)\, dt$$

and hence
$$\overline{t^2} = H''(0)$$

In summary, we have the following theorem.

Theorem 1. If h satisfies the conditions of Theorem 13, Chap. 2, then system delay and response time are given in terms of the transfer function thus:

$$\bar{t} = \frac{-H(0)}{H(0)} \qquad \sigma = \left\{ \frac{H''(0)}{H(0)} - \left[\frac{H'(0)}{H(0)} \right]^2 \right\}^{\frac{1}{2}}$$

Also, if
$$\overline{t^2} = \frac{\displaystyle\int_{-\infty}^{\infty} t^2 h(t)\, dt}{\displaystyle\int_{-\infty}^{\infty} h(t)\, dt}$$

$$\sigma^2 = \overline{t^2} - (\bar{t})^2 \qquad \text{and} \qquad \overline{t^2} = \frac{H''(0)}{H(0)}$$

The value of the theorem rests in the fact that it is usually easier to work with transfer functions than with impulse-response functions; also it is easier to differentiate than to integrate.

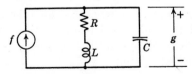

Example 1 (*Shunt Peaking in Collector or Plate Circuit of an Amplifier*). Consider the circuit shown in the above sketch. The transfer function is

$$H(p) = \frac{(1/pC)(R + pL)}{(1/pC) + R + pL}$$

It is easy to see that $h \geq 0$ iff the circuit is not underdamped, and hence we shall make this restriction: $(RC)^2 \geq 4LC$ (this keeps the poles of H on the real axis). Let $LC = \theta(RC)^2$, and we restrict θ to a factor between 0 and $\frac{1}{4}$. Observe that $L/R = LC/RC = \theta(RC)$; so if $RC = T$, we have

$$H(p) = R \frac{1 + \theta T p}{1 + Tp + \theta T^2 p^2}$$

We now wish to find $H'(0)$ and $H''(0)$. It is easy enough to differentiate and evaluate at $p = 0$; however, it is even easier to find the Taylor series for H (about $p = 0$) by long division and then identify the first three coefficients as $H(0)$, $H'(0)$, and $\frac{1}{2}H''(0)$. The long division follows:

$$
\begin{array}{r}
1 + (\theta - 1)Tp + (1 - 2\theta)T^2 p^2 + \cdots \\
1 + Tp + \theta T^2 p^2 \overline{\smash{\big)}\, 1 + \theta T p} \\
\underline{1 + Tp + \theta T^2 p^2} \\
(\theta - 1)Tp - \theta T^2 p^2 \\
\underline{(\theta - 1)Tp + (\theta - 1)T^2 p^2 + (\theta - 1)\theta T^3 p^3} \\
(1 - 2\theta)T^2 p^2 - (\theta - 1)\theta T^3 p^3
\end{array}
$$

Thus
$$H(0) = R$$
$$H'(0) = R(\theta - 1)T$$
$$H''(0) = 2(1 - 2\theta)T^2 R$$

In turn, $\bar{t} = (1 - \theta)T$ and

$$\sigma^2 = T^2[(2 - 4\theta) - (1 - \theta)^2] = T^2(1 - 2\theta - \theta^2)$$

Of course it is clear that σ^2 is a decreasing function of θ; therefore, for minimum response time θ should be made as large as permitted,[†] $\theta = \frac{1}{4}$. In this case

$$\bar{t} = \tfrac{3}{4}T \qquad \text{and} \qquad \sigma = \sqrt{\tfrac{7}{16}T^2} \cong 0.65T$$

Note that $\theta = 0$ corresponds to no compensation, and then $\sigma = T$. Problem 1 extends this example to cover some other compensation schemes.

Theorem 1 accounts for one reason that the definitions used for delay and response time are attractive. The other reason is the simple result of Theorem 2 for overall delay and response time of a cascade of systems in terms of individual delays and rise times.

Theorem 2. Let monotone systems be cascaded; let the individual delays be $\bar{t}_1, \bar{t}_2, \ldots, \bar{t}_n$ and the individual response times be $\sigma_1, \sigma_2, \ldots, \sigma_n$. Then the delay for the overall system is $\bar{t} = \bar{t}_1 + \bar{t}_2 + \cdots + \bar{t}_n$, and the response time for the overall system is

$$\sigma = \sqrt{\sigma_1{}^2 + \sigma_2{}^2 + \cdots + \sigma_n{}^2}$$

The proof can easily be carried out by using the definitions directly; how-

---

† When $\theta > \frac{1}{4}$, h is not nonnegative and the definitions of $\bar{t}$, σ, etc., used here in Sec. 5-1 no longer provide a reasonable measure of spread on the t axis (see Sec. 5-2).

ever, the formulas provided by Theorem 1 will be used here. The proof will be by induction. Clearly, the theorem is true for $n = 1$. Let the transfer functions be $H_1, H_2, \ldots, H_n$; let $H = H_1 H_2 \cdots H_n$; and let $G = H_1 H_2 \cdots H_{n-1}$. Assume that the theorem is true for $n - 1$. Then

$$\bar{t}_1 + \bar{t}_2 + \cdots + \bar{t}_{n-1} = -\frac{G'(0)}{G(0)}$$

Of course, $\bar{t} = -H'(0)/H(0)$. Since $H = GH_n$, $H' = G'H_n + GH'_n$ and hence

$$\bar{t} = -\frac{G'(0)H_n(0) + G(0)H'_n(0)}{G(0)H_n(0)}$$

$$= -\left[\frac{G'(0)}{G(0)} + \frac{H'_n(0)}{H(0)}\right] = \bar{t}_1 + \bar{t}_2 + \cdots + \bar{t}_{n-1} + \bar{t}_n$$

which was to be shown for delay.

For response time, observe that $H'' = G''H_n + 2G'H'_n + GH''_n$, and hence $\overline{t^2}$ for the overall system is

$$\frac{G''(0)}{G(0)} + 2\frac{G'(0)H'_n(0)}{G(0)H_n(0)} + \frac{H''_n(0)}{H(0)}$$

That is, $\qquad \overline{t^2} = \overline{\theta^2} + 2(\bar{t}_1 + \bar{t}_2 + \cdots + \bar{t}_{n-1})\bar{t}_n + \overline{t_n^2}$

where $\overline{\theta^2}$ is the second moment for the cascade of systems 1 through $n - 1$. However, $\overline{t^2} = \sigma^2 + (\bar{t})^2$, and by the first part of the proof,

$$(\bar{t})^2 = [(\bar{t}_1 + \bar{t}_2 + \cdots + \bar{t}_{n-1}) + \bar{t}_n]^2 = 2\bar{t}_n(\bar{t}_1 + \cdots + \bar{t}_{n-1})$$
$$+ (\bar{t}_n)^2 + (\bar{t}_1 + \cdots + \bar{t}_{n-1})^2$$

The two equations for $\overline{t^2}$ give $\sigma^2 = \overline{\theta^2} - (\bar{t}_1 + \cdots + \bar{t}_{n-1})^2 + \overline{t_n^2} - (\bar{t}_n)^2$. However, $\overline{t_n^2} - (\bar{t}_n)^2 = \sigma_n^2$ and $\overline{\theta^2} - (\bar{t}_1 + \cdots + \bar{t}_{n-1})^2$ is the square of the response time of the cascade of the first $n - 1$ systems. Since it is assumed that the theorem holds for $n - 1$, this response time squared is $\sigma_1^2 + \cdots + \sigma_{n-1}^2$. Thus we get $\sigma^2 = \sigma_1^2 + \cdots + \sigma_{n-1}^2 + \sigma_n^2$, as was to be shown.

Before leaving the special case of monotone systems, a test in terms of the transfer function will be mentioned. The test provided by the following theorem is rather deep mathematically but of modest practical value. A useful necessary condition is that $|H(j\omega)| \le H(0)$; that is, if the system is monotone, then the amplitude gain at any frequency is no greater than[†] the d-c gain. To see this, recall that

$$H(j\omega) = \int_{-\infty}^{\infty} h(t)e^{-j\omega t}\, dt$$

and hence $\qquad |H(j\omega)| \le \int_{-\infty}^{\infty} |he^{-j\omega t}|\, dt = \int_{-\infty}^{\infty} |h|\, dt$

[†] When considering a-c-coupled amplifiers which have fairly good low-frequency response, the coupling networks which make $H(0) = 0$ can be neglected as far as many transient considerations are concerned.

but if $h \geq 0$, we have

$$|H(j\omega)| \leq \int_{-\infty}^{\infty} h(t) \, dt = H(0)$$

In what follows we consider only pure imaginary p, and we shall write $H(\omega)$ in place of $H(j\omega)$. Also, to state the general case, systems for which only the step response need exist are considered, and hence we should replace

$$H(\omega) = \int_{-\infty}^{\infty} e^{-j\omega t} h(t) \, dt$$

with

$$H(\omega) = \int_{-\infty}^{\infty} e^{-j\omega t} \, dh_s(t)$$

We consider only monotone systems for which h_s is bounded. Since

$$h_s(t) = \int_{-\infty}^{t} h(\tau) \, d\tau$$

and $h \geq 0$, this corresponds to the system's being stable, that is,

$$\int_{-\infty}^{\infty} |h(\tau)| \, d\tau < \infty$$

Theorem 3. $H(\omega)$ is the frequency response of a monotone stable system iff H is continuous at $\omega = 0$ and for arbitrary complex numbers $(a_1, \ldots, a_n)$ and arbitrary real numbers $(\omega_1, \ldots, \omega_n)$

$$\sum_{k=1}^{n} \sum_{m=1}^{n} a_k \bar{a}_m H(\omega_k - \omega_m) \geq 0$$

Only the *only if* part of the theorem will be proved; the *if* part is quite difficult. This theorem, and in fact all of Sec. 5-1, is mathematically equivalent to results well known and much used in probability theory. The fact that these results occur in another area only increases our interest in them. For the *only if*, let

$$Z = \sum_{k=1}^{n} a_k e^{-j\omega_k t}$$

Then

$$\bar{Z} = \sum_{m=1}^{n} \bar{a}_m e^{j\omega_m t}$$

and

$$|Z|^2 = \sum_{k=1}^{n} \sum_{m=1}^{n} a_k \bar{a}_m e^{-j(\omega_k - \omega_m)t}$$

Since $h(t) \geq 0$ (we should say, since h_s is nondecreasing; then we could use a Stieltjes integral),

$$\int_{-\infty}^{\infty} |Z|^2 h(t) \, dt \geq 0$$

However, this gives

$$\int_{-\infty}^{\infty} \sum_{k}^{n} \sum_{m}^{n} a_k \bar{a}_m e^{-j(\omega_k - \omega_m)t} h(t) \, dt \geq 0$$

or

$$\sum_{k}^{n} \sum_{m}^{n} a_k a_m H(\omega_k - \omega_m) \geq 0$$

as was to be shown.

5-2 RESPONSE TIME FOR ARBITRARY SYSTEMS

Suppose for the moment that h is real.   Then

$$\sigma^2 = \frac{\int_{-\infty}^{\infty} (t - \bar{t})^2 h(t) \, dt}{\int_{-\infty}^{\infty} h(t) \, dt}$$

might be zero (or very small), not because h is not spread out on the t axis, but because the contributions to the numerator where $h > 0$ might be canceled by the contributions where $h < 0$.   Thus it is seen that only $|h|$ is involved in our intuitive notion of the spread of h on the t axis; also, $|h|$ serves for complex h as well as for real h.   Not much progress can be made with the theory if we simply try to work with $|h|$ in the way we worked with h in Sec. 5-1; however, if we work with $|h|^2$ the theory develops quite nicely.   As far as *spread on the t axis* is concerned, $|h|^2$ is as satisfactory as $|h|$—the concepts remain the same though there are obviously quantitative differences.

One natural notion of response time is then

$$\alpha^2 \equiv \frac{\int_{-\infty}^{\infty} (t - \bar{t})^2 \, |h(t)|^2 \, dt}{\int_{-\infty}^{\infty} |h(t)|^2 \, dt}$$

where

$$\bar{t} = \frac{\int_{-\infty}^{\infty} t |h(t)|^2}{\int_{-\infty}^{\infty} |h(t)|^2 \, dt}$$

It develops that in some cases it is quite worthwhile to consider another measure for spread on the t axis.   This alternative definition will be referred to as *equivalent rectangle;* specifically, let ρ be the width of a rectangle having the same area as $|h(t)|^2$ and having the same peak value as $|h(t)|^2$.   If $|h(t_0)|^2$ is the peak value of h, then

$$\rho = \frac{\int_{-\infty}^{\infty} |h(t)|^2 \, dt}{|h(t_0)|^2}$$

For reasonable impulse responses, both ρ and α provide useful measures of response; however, for peculiar impulse responses such as that shown in Figure 5-4, ρ is a very dubious measure.

With the new definitions on hand we can proceed with the theory. It develops that our achievement of generality is accompanied by a loss of one attractive type of result; that is, the author is not aware of any general result (Prob. 5 gives special results) comparable to Theorem 2 for cascaded systems when ρ or α is used to measure response time. On the other hand, the topic of optimization of system frequency response for minimum response time blossoms in this section. We start by deriving expressions for α and ρ in terms of the frequency-response function. In this section, $\bar{t}$ and t_0 are not given any attention, and hence they are assumed to equal zero. This

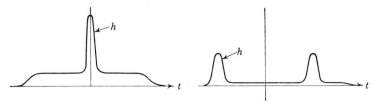

FIGURE 5-4.   Impulse responses for which ρ is not suitable.

involves replacing $h(t)$ with $h(t - \bar{t})$ or $h(t - t_0)$ as the case may be; in turn, the transfer function is modified by a linear phase term $e^{-j\omega\bar{t}}$ or $e^{-j\omega t_0}$. These modifications simplify the equations, and it is easy to see the effects of dropping these assumptions.

Theorem 4.   With the above conventions,

$$\rho = \frac{2\pi \int_{-\infty}^{\infty} |H(\omega)|^2 \, d\omega}{\left| \int_{-\infty}^{\infty} H(\omega) \, d\omega \right|^2}$$

and

$$\alpha^2 = \frac{\int_{-\infty}^{\infty} |H'(\omega)|^2 \, d\omega}{\int_{-\infty}^{\infty} |H(\omega)|^2 \, d\omega}$$

where $H'(\omega) = dH/d\omega$.

For the proof, recall Parseval's theorem (Chap. 2, Theorem 23):

$$\int_{-\infty}^{\infty} |h(t)|^2 \, dt = \frac{1}{2\pi} \int_{-\infty}^{\infty} |H(\omega)|^2 \, d\omega$$

For ρ we also use the fact that

$$h(0) = \frac{1}{2\pi} \int_{-\infty}^{\infty} e^{j0\omega} H(\omega) \, d\omega$$

which, joined with Parseval's theorem, gives

$$\rho = \frac{(1/2\pi) \int_{-\infty}^{\infty} |H(\omega)|^2 \, d\omega}{\left| (1/2\pi) \int_{-\infty}^{\infty} H(\omega) \, d\omega \right|^2}$$

as was to be shown. The formula for α^2 involves two applications of

Parseval's theorem, one for h and the other for $th(t)$.   Recall that

$$H(\omega) = \int_{-\infty}^{\infty} e^{-j\omega t}h(t)\, dt$$

and hence
$$H'(\omega) = -j\int_{-\infty}^{\infty} e^{-j\omega t}th(t)\, dt$$

(Chap. 2, Theorem 13); thus $jH'(\omega)$ is the Fourier transform of $th(t)$.   In turn,

$$\int_{-\infty}^{\infty} |th(t)|^2\, dt = \frac{1}{2\pi}\int_{-\infty}^{\infty} |jH'(\omega)|^2\, d\omega = \frac{1}{2\pi}\int_{-\infty}^{\infty} |H'(\omega)|^2\, d\omega$$

Finally,
$$\alpha^2 = \frac{\int_{-\infty}^{\infty} t^2|h(t)|^2\, dt}{\int_{-\infty}^{\infty} |h|^2\, dt} = \frac{(1/2\pi)\int_{-\infty}^{\infty} |H'(\omega)|^2\, d\omega}{(1/2\pi)\int_{-\infty}^{\infty} |H(\omega)|^2\, d\omega}$$

as was to be shown.

   With the above formulas on hand we can study the dependence of system response time on features of the frequency-response function.   If the system is to pass certain frequencies and reject others, the amplitude response $|H|$ may not be at the "designer's" disposal (at least to any large extent); in this case one may wish to know what phase response provides shortest response time for a fixed $|H|$.   Also, if noise is present at the input, the phase response can be varied without changing the noise level at the output (see Chap. 8), and hence the amplitude response might be determined by noise considerations and the phase response adjusted to provide nearly minimum response time.   The next theorem shows that for any fixed amplitude response, a constant (or linear) phase response minimizes the response time—a rather nice result.

   Theorem 5.   (a) Let $H(\omega) = A(\omega)e^{j\phi(\omega)}$, where A is fixed, real, and nonnegative.   Then the response time ρ is minimized if ϕ is a constant (or linear).

   (b) Also let H' exist except possibly at isolated points where $H(\omega) = 0$. At such points let H be at least continuous; then any $\phi(\omega)$ which is constant between adjacent zeros of H minimizes α.   As usual, any linear phase $j\omega l$ can be subtracted from a minimizing $\phi(\omega)$ without changing α since this only translates h along the t axis.

   PROOF: Since

$$\rho = \frac{2\pi\int_{-\infty}^{\infty} |H|^2\, d\omega}{\left|\int_{-\infty}^{\infty} H\, d\omega\right|^2}$$

and $|H|^2$ is fixed, we wish to choose the phase of H to maximize

$$\left|\int_{-\infty}^{\infty} H(\omega)\, d\omega\right|$$

However,
$$\left|\int_{-\infty}^{\infty} H(\omega)\, d\omega\right| \le \int_{-\infty}^{\infty} |H(\omega)|\, d\omega$$

and we get equality only if the phase of H is a constant.

Turning to α, observe that $H'(\omega) = A'(\omega)e^{j\phi} + A(\omega)j\phi'(\omega)e^{j\phi}$; hence

$$\alpha^2 = \frac{\int_{-\infty}^{\infty} |A'(\omega) + jA(\omega)\phi'(\omega)|^2 \, d\omega}{\int_{-\infty}^{\infty} |H|^2 \, d\omega}$$

since the factor $e^{j\phi}$ has no effect on $|H'|$. Of course A' is real and $A\phi'$ is real, and hence the way to minimize $|A' + j\phi'A|^2 = (A')^2 + (\phi'A)^2$ is to make $\phi' = 0$, which means ϕ is a constant. However, we need only make $A\phi' = 0$; hence at points where $A(\omega) = 0$, ϕ' need not be zero. In fact, if $A(\omega)$ goes through zero smoothly, ϕ can have a jump discontinuity at the zero of A without the factor $A\phi'$ contributing to α.

The fact that the two frequency responses shown in Figure 5-5 provide the same radius of gyration response times but the second has a better

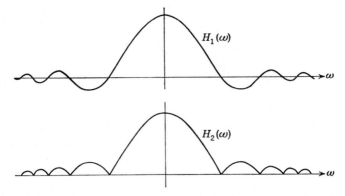

FIGURE 5-5.   Responses having equal resolution in terms of radius of gyration.

equivalent rectangle response time is quite interesting. From the standpoint of having $H(\omega)$ correspond to a low-distortion system, clearly H_2 is better than H_1; for with H_1 both amplitude and phase distortion are present at frequencies where $H_1(\omega) < 0$, while with H_2 only amplitude distortion is present.

Suppose we have a real, realizable system. Then $H(-\omega) = \bar{H}(\omega)$, which implies $\phi(-\omega) = -\phi(\omega)$. If ϕ is constant we get $\phi = 0$ and $H(-\omega) = H(\omega)$. That is, H is an even function. In turn, $h(t)$ is even, which contradicts the condition that $h(t) = 0$ for $t < 0$. However, if a large time delay can be tolerated h can be made nearly even about $\bar{t}$, as shown in Figure 5-6. Such an h can be made to have very nearly a minimum response time.

We now turn to the effects of amplitude-frequency response on response time. It develops that the response time can be made arbitrarily small if the bandwidth is made large; hence the appropriate problem is to minimize response time when the bandwidth is limited in some sense. Obviously, we need a measure of the spread of $H(\omega)$ on the ω axis to provide a quantitative notion of bandwidth. One such measure is the radius of gyration of $|H(\omega)|^2$.

An additional analytical tool is needed to handle the optimization of amplitude frequency response. Specifically, these problems will be handled with the Schwarz inequality, a very important inequality also used in Chap. 8. Its derivation will be given as a preliminary.

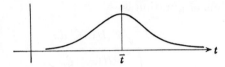

FIGURE 5-6.   Nearly linear phase response.

Theorem 6 (Schwarz Inequality). Let $p(t)$ be real and nonnegative and let $x(t)$ and $y(t)$ be complex-valued functions for which

$$\int_{-\infty}^{\infty} |x(t)|^2 p(t)\, dt \qquad \text{and} \qquad \int_{-\infty}^{\infty} |y(t)|^2 p(t)\, dt$$

exist (are finite); then

$$\left| \int_{-\infty}^{\infty} x(t)\bar{y}(t)p(t)\, dt \right|^2 \le \left(\int_{-\infty}^{\infty} |x|^2 p\, dt \right)\left(\int_{-\infty}^{\infty} |y|^2 p\, dt \right)$$

with equality iff one of the functions (x or y) is a constant times the other [save at points where $p(t) = 0$].

PROOF: The theorem is obvious if $y(t) = 0$ [zero where $p(t) \ne 0$]. Assume $y(t) \ne 0$ in the sense that

$$\int_{-\infty}^{\infty} |y|^2 p\, dt > 0$$

Let
$$y_0(t) = \frac{y(t)}{\left(\int_{-\infty}^{\infty} |y|^2 p\, dt \right)^{\frac{1}{2}}}$$

and let
$$\gamma = \int_{-\infty}^{\infty} x(t)\bar{y}_0(t)p(t)\, dt$$

Then since $(x - \gamma y_0)(\bar{x} - \bar{\gamma}\bar{y}_0) = |x - \gamma y_0|^2 \ge 0$,

$$\int_{-\infty}^{\infty} (x - \gamma y_0)(\bar{x} - \bar{\gamma}\bar{y}_0)p\, dt \ge 0$$

with equality iff $x = \gamma y_0$. However, expansion gives

$$\int_{-\infty}^{\infty} |x|^2 p\, dt + |\gamma|^2 \int_{-\infty}^{\infty} |y_0|^2 p\, dt - \gamma \int_{-\infty}^{\infty} y_0\bar{x}p\, dt - \bar{\gamma} \int_{-\infty}^{\infty} x\bar{y}_0 p\, dt \ge 0$$

Also
$$\int_{-\infty}^{\infty} |y_0|^2 p\, dt = 1$$

and we get
$$\int |x|^2 p\, dt + |\gamma|^2 - \gamma\bar{\gamma} - \bar{\gamma}\gamma \ge 0$$

That is,
$$\int |x|^2 p\, dt - |\gamma|^2 \ge 0$$

or substituting for $|\gamma|^2$ gives

$$\int_{-\infty}^{\infty} |x|^2 p \, dt \geq \frac{\left| \int_{-\infty}^{\infty} x(t)\bar{y}(t)p(t) \, dt \right|^2}{\int_{-\infty}^{\infty} |y|^2 p \, dt}$$

which is the desired result.

Returning to response time in the presence of bandwidth restrictions, we consider two notions of bandwidth: radius of gyration and *maximum frequency*. The radius of gyration is

$$\beta^2 = \frac{\int_{-\infty}^{\infty} \omega^2 |H(\omega)|^2 \, d\omega}{\int_{-\infty}^{\infty} |H(\omega)|^2 \, d\omega}$$

It is assumed that

$$\bar{\omega} = \int_{-\infty}^{\infty} \omega |H|^2 \, d\omega = 0$$

This is no restriction in that a translation of H by an amount ω corresponds to multiplying h by $e^{j\omega t}$, which has no effect on α (or ρ). The use of maximum frequency assumes that $H(\omega) = 0$ outside some interval on the frequency axis, and we define r as half the length of the (smallest such) interval. The next two theorems establish broad bandwidth as a necessary condition for fast response time.

Theorem 7.   For arbitrary H (or h), $\alpha\beta \geq \frac{1}{2}$.   Equality is obtained iff

$$h(t) = Ce^{j\bar{\omega}t} \exp\left[-\frac{(t - \bar{t})^2}{4\alpha^2} \right]$$

Note that $h \geq 0$ if $\bar{\omega} = 0$ and $C > 0$; that is, this sense of minimum response time can be obtained with a monotone system.

PROOF: Recall from Theorem 4 and the definition of β that

$$\alpha^2\beta^2 = \frac{\int_{-\infty}^{\infty} |H'|^2 \, d\omega \int_{-\infty}^{\infty} \omega^2 |H|^2 \, d\omega}{\int_{-\infty}^{\infty} |H|^2 \, d\omega \quad \int_{-\infty}^{\infty} |H|^2 \, d\omega}$$

By the Schwarz inequality,

$$\alpha^2\beta^2 \geq \frac{\left| \int_{-\infty}^{\infty} \omega \bar{H} H' \, d\omega \right|^2}{\left(\int |H|^2 \, d\omega \right)^2}$$

By Theorem 5, H can be assumed real; observe that

$$HH' = \frac{1}{2} \frac{d}{d\omega} H^2$$

Hence the numerator can be written thus:

$$\frac{1}{4} \left| \int_{-\infty}^{\infty} \omega \frac{d}{d\omega} H^2 \, d\omega \right|^2$$

We now integrate by parts and obtain the following for the integral:

$$\omega H^2 \Big]_{-\infty}^{\infty} - \int_{-\infty}^{\infty} H^2 \, d\omega$$

Simple reasoning gives $\omega H^2 \to 0$ as $|\omega|$ gets large. Then we have $\alpha^2 \beta^2 \geq \frac{1}{4}$.

It remains to be shown that this lower bound can actually be obtained. We get equality only if

$$H' = a\omega H$$

Solving this differential equation, we get

$$H(\omega) = C \exp \frac{a\omega^2}{2}$$

For β to be finite, a is negative (only a negative real part is required; however, to minimize $\alpha^2 \beta^2$ we know that H must have constant phase; therefore, the imaginary part of a is taken as zero). We can solve for a in terms of β to obtain

$$a = -\frac{1}{2\beta^2} \qquad \text{see Prob. 6}$$

Finally, with $H' = a\omega H$,

$$\alpha^2 \beta^2 = |a|^2 \left| \frac{\int \omega^2 |H|^2 \, d\omega}{\int |H|^2 \, d\omega} \right|^2 = \frac{1}{4\beta^4} (\beta^2)^2 = \frac{1}{4}$$

as was to be shown.

It is important to note that there is no upper bound on the product of time duration and frequency duration. For example, let

$$h(t) = \frac{\sqrt{a + jb}}{\sqrt{2\pi}} \exp\left[-\frac{t^2}{2} (a + jb) \right]$$

Then

$$H(\omega) = \exp\left[-\frac{\omega^2}{2(a + jb)} \right]$$

(This is obtained as a generalization of Example 2, Chap. 2). The time duration is proportional to $1/\sqrt{a}$, and the frequency duration is proportional to

$$\sqrt{\frac{a^2 + b^2}{a}}$$

[one over the real part of $1/(a + jb)$]. The product is proportional to

$$\sqrt{\frac{a^2 + b^2}{a^2}}$$

which can be made arbitrarily large by making b large.

The intuitive idea is that b corresponds to the rate of frequency modulation. If a is fixed, the time duration is fixed since a determines the pulse width. Then by taking large values of b, arbitrarily large bandwidths can be covered. The bandwidth is of the order of $b/\sqrt{a}$, since b is the FM rate (in radians per second squared) and $1/\sqrt{a}$ is the pulse duration; in turn, the highest frequency is $b/\sqrt{a}$. Finally, the product of bandwidth and time duration is about b/a, which agrees with the exact value of $\alpha\beta$ if $b \gg a$.

Using equivalent rectangle to measure time duration (response time) and maximum frequency to measure bandwidth, a result similar to that of Theorem 7 can easily be obtained.

Theorem 8. If $H(\omega) = 0$ for $|\omega| > r$, then $r\rho \geq \pi$ with equality iff $H(\omega)$ is constant for $|\omega| < r$, in which case

$$h(t) = C \frac{\sin rt}{t}$$

PROOF: From Theorem 4,

$$\rho = \frac{2\pi \int_{-r}^{r} |H|^2 \, d\omega}{\left| \int_{-r}^{r} H \, d\omega \right|^2}$$

Apply the Schwarz inequality to the denominator with the integrand viewed as $1H$. Then

$$\rho \geq \frac{2\pi \int_{-r}^{r} |H|^2 \, d\omega}{\left(\int_{-r}^{r} d\omega \right) \left(\int_{-r}^{r} |H|^2 \, d\omega \right)} = \frac{2\pi}{2r}$$

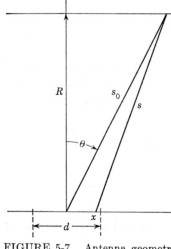

That is,

$$\rho r \geq \pi$$

FIGURE 5-7.   Antenna geometry.

In the light of Theorems 5, 7, and 8, some simple observations can be made: (1) to obtain "fast" time response, it is necessary but not sufficient to have a broad system bandwidth; (2) phase response other than constant or linear phase response (which produces delay) increases the response time obtainable, and there is no upper bound.

Before we proceed with some additional results (similar to those in Theorems 7 and 8, but of less importance), the application of the theory to antennas will be described. In this application, the restriction that $H(\omega) = 0$ for $|\omega| > r$ occurs quite naturally; to some extent this application is the reason for considering this restriction. Suppose that a linear antenna can be constructed in such a way that the radiated electric field across its face is sinusoidal in time with an amplitude and phase depending on position according to the complex-valued function of position $H_0(x)$. The antenna pattern is obtained by superposition of the contributions along the antenna. The distance traveled by the incremental wave from $(x, x + dx)$ varies with position, as shown in Figure 5-7.

$$s_0 = \sqrt{R^2 + (R \tan \theta)^2} = R \sqrt{1 + (\tan \theta)^2} \cong R \left[1 + \frac{(\tan \theta)^2}{2} \right]$$

$$s = \sqrt{R^2 + (R \tan \theta - x)^2} \cong R \left[1 + \frac{(R \tan \theta - x)^2}{2R^2} \right]$$

If $H_0(x) = A(x)e^{j\phi(x)}$, the sine wave received from $(x, x + dx)$ is $A \cos [\omega_0(t - s/c) + \phi] dx = A \cos [\omega_0 t + \phi - 2\pi s/\lambda] dx$, where c is the velocity of light and $2\pi c/\omega = \lambda$. If we use a reference phase of $2\pi s_0/\lambda$ when at a distance s_0, the received signal can be written as

$$A \cos \left[\omega t + \phi + \frac{2\pi}{\lambda} (s_0 - s) \right] dx$$

However, if θ is small and R is large,

$$s_0 - s \cong x \tan \theta - \frac{x^2}{2R}$$

By the far field we mean that R is very large and hence $x^2/2R$ can be neglected. The important thing is for

$$\frac{(d/2)^2}{2R} \ll \lambda$$

Let $\tan \theta \cong \theta$.

Using the usual method for adding sine waves of the same frequency (Chap. 1), we have the amplitude and phase of the signal received at an angle θ determined by

$$\int_{-d/2}^{d/2} A(x)e^{j\phi(x)} \exp \left(j \frac{2\pi}{\lambda} x\theta \right) dx$$

or, if $\qquad \omega = \frac{2\pi x}{\lambda} \qquad$ and $\qquad \lambda H_0 \left(\frac{\lambda \omega}{2\pi} \right) = H(\omega)$

$$h(\theta) = \frac{1}{2\pi} \int_{-\infty}^{\infty} e^{j\omega \theta} H(\omega) \, d\omega$$

Of course, $h(\theta)$ is the phasor of the signal received at an angle θ. Also, if $\pi d/\lambda = r$, $H(\omega) = 0$ for $|\omega| > r$.

Thus we see that the antenna pattern h is given as the inverse Fourier transform of the illumination function H. We think of H as a transfer function and of h as an impulse-response function. Fast response time corresponds to a narrow beam width, and the aperture of the antenna corresponds to the bandwidth restriction. In the light of Theorem 7 it is rather surprising that uniform illumination is sometimes not used. The next theorem leads to an illumination function often preferred. Beam width (or antenna resolution) is defined in terms of radius of gyration in this theorem, rather than in terms of equivalent rectangle as used in Theorem 8.

The analytical tool provided by Theorem 6 is adequate for most of our *optimization problems;* however, for the next two theorems it will be necessary to use the calculus of variations. Derivations of the methods provided by the calculus of variations are outside the scope of this book. For the remainder of this chapter the theorems rather than the proofs are of the most interest.

Theorem 9.   If $H(\omega) = 0$ for $|\omega| > r$, then α is a minimum iff

$$H(\omega) = C \cos\left(\frac{\pi}{2}\frac{\omega}{r}\right) \qquad \text{and} \qquad \alpha r \geq \frac{\pi}{2}$$

PROOF: To minimize α, H will have a constant phase; therefore, let H be real.   Also let $\int H^2$ be fixed for the moment.   Then we wish to minimize

$$\int_{-\infty}^{\infty} (H')^2 \, d\omega$$

subject to an integral constraint on H^2.   If $H(\omega)$ has a discontinuity, $\int(H')^2$ must be taken as infinite; intuitively we shall have the integral of the square of a δ function.   Then, since $H(\omega) = 0$ for $|\omega| > r$, we must take $H(\pm r) = 0$. The problem is to minimize

$$\int_{-r}^{r} (H')^2 \, d\omega$$

The differential equation (provided by the calculus of variations) for this problem is

$$H'' + \lambda H = 0$$

and since we want a minimum for $\int(H')^2$,

$$H(\omega) = C \cos\left(\frac{\pi}{2}\frac{\omega}{r}\right)$$

is the appropriate solution.   Also, the minimum value is seen to be

$$\alpha^2 = \frac{\pi^2}{4r^2} \frac{\int_{-\pi/2}^{\pi/2} \sin^2 \theta \, d\theta}{\int_{-\pi/2}^{\pi/2} \cos^2 \theta \, d\theta}$$

Thus we have

$$\alpha r \geq \frac{\pi}{2}$$

with equality iff *cosine weighting* is used.   Such an illumination function is common in antenna design.

For the sake of completeness, all other combinations will be considered.
Theorem 10.   For arbitrary H, $\rho\beta \geq 1$ with equality iff

$$h(t) = A \exp\left(-\frac{|t|}{T}\right)$$

PROOF

$$\rho\beta = 2\pi \frac{\int |H|^2 \, d\omega}{|\int H \, d\omega|^2} \sqrt{\frac{\int \omega^2 H^2 \, d\omega}{\int |H|^2 \, d\omega}} = 2\pi \sqrt{\frac{\int H^2 \int \omega^2 H^2}{(\int H \, d\omega)^4}}$$

where H should obviously have constant phase, and we take zero phase angle to be specific.   To use the calculus of variations, let $\int H^2$ and $\int H$ be fixed for the moment. Then we wish to minimize $\int \omega^2 H^2$ with two integral constraints. The differential equation to be solved is

$$\frac{\partial}{\partial H}(\omega^2 H^2) + \lambda_1 \frac{\partial H^2}{\partial H} + \lambda_2 \frac{\partial H}{\partial H} = 0$$

The solution is (new constants A and T are introduced in place of λ_1 and λ_2)

$$H(\omega) = \frac{2A}{T} \frac{1}{\omega^2 + (1/T)^2}$$

or, if we replace ω with p/j,

$$H(p) = \frac{2A}{T} \frac{-1}{p^2 - (1/T)^2} = \frac{-A}{p - 1/T} + \frac{A}{p + 1/T}$$

From this it is clear that

$$h(t) = A e^{-|t|/T}$$

In turn, by Parseval's theorem,

$$\int |H|^2 = 2\pi \int |h|^2 = 2\pi A^2 T$$

Also

$$\int \omega^2 |H|^2 = 2\pi \int |h'|^2 = \frac{2\pi A^2}{T}$$

and

$$\frac{1}{2\pi} \int H \, d\omega = h(0)$$

Hence

$$\int H \, d\omega = 2\pi A$$

To fix $\int H$ and $\int H^2$ is to fix A and T. However, substitution now shows that

$$(\rho\beta)_{\min} = 2\pi \sqrt{\frac{(2\pi A^2 T)(2\pi A^2)/T}{(2\pi A)^4}} = 1$$

Hence we see that the values of $\int H^2$ and $\int H$ are unimportant as far as the minimum value of $\rho\beta$ is concerned, which completes the proof.

At the outset, two notions of width on the time axis were introduced: radius of gyration and equivalent rectangle. However, in Theorem 7 the width on the frequency axis was taken as the highest frequency for which $H(\omega) \neq 0$; this amounts to an additional measure of the duration of a function which we shall call *overall duration*. With three quantitative measures now available for each of the two functions (h and H), there are a total of nine possible relations of the type given in Theorems 5 through 10. However, because of the symmetry of the transform-pair formulas, Theorems 7 through 10 actually account for seven possible formulations. The two remaining cases are not of much value in themselves, but their brief consideration provides some additional insight.

Suppose $h(t) = 0$ for $|t| > a$ and $H(\omega) = 0$ for $|\omega| > r$.   Then we have a contradiction; i.e., a function cannot be both time-limited and bandwidth-limited.†   Thus if overall duration is used in time and frequency, we have

$$ar \geq \infty$$

(that is, $ar = \infty$).   The only case not yet treated is that of measuring both time duration and frequency duration in terms of equivalent rectangles. The quantity to be minimized is then

$$\frac{\int |H|^2}{|\int H|^2} \frac{\int |H|^2}{|H(0)|^2}$$

However, if we permit H to have a very narrow spike around $\omega = 0$, $H(0)$ can be made arbitrarily large without making the numerator larger.   Hence the lower bound in this case is zero, but clearly equivalent rectangle is not an appropriate way to measure the width of an $H(\omega)$ such as that shown

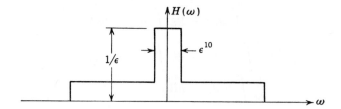

in the sketch.   The only thing interesting about this case is that it makes us wonder about the fact that no such complication occurred in Theorem 8. There was no such "spike" trouble in Theorem 8 because the bandwidth limit on $H(\omega)$ eliminated the possibility of $h(t)$ having a spike at $t = 0$.

The nine cases are summarized in Table 5-1, which shows the lower bounds on the product of time duration and bandwidth and shows the waveforms which achieve the lower bounds.   To facilitate comparison of the lower bounds, radius of gyration (α and β) will be multiplied by 2 (a somewhat larger factor should be used) to account for the fact that radius of gyration is more like a half width while equivalent rectangle is a total width.

† One easy way to see this is to assume that h is bandwidth-limited, then write h in terms of its samples by using the sampling theorem.   If h is also time-limited, there will be only a finite number of terms in the *sampled series version* of h; that is, h will be a sum of the form

$$h(t) = \sum_{k=1}^{n} C_k \frac{\sin K(t - a_k)}{t - a_k}$$

This is an analytic function of t; hence it cannot be zero on an interval without being identically zero (of course this follows from the principle of analytic continuation).

TABLE 5-1. MINIMUM RESPONSE TIME– BANDWIDTH PRODUCTS

Measure of Response Time (Time Duration)	Measure of Bandwidth (Frequency Duration)		
	Radius of Gyration	Equivalent Rectangle	Overall Duration
Radius of gyration	$(2\alpha)(2\beta) \geq 2$ Gaussian H or h Theorem 7	≥ 2 $H(\omega) = Ce^{-\lvert\omega\rvert/c}$	$(2\alpha)r \geq \pi$ Cosine $H(\omega)$ Theorem 9
Equivalent rectangle	$\rho(2\beta) \geq 2$ $h(t) = Ae^{-\lvert t\rvert/T}$ Theorem 10	≥ 0, but not significant	$\rho r \geq \pi$ $h(t) = \dfrac{\sin rt}{t}$ Theorem 8
Overall duration	$\geq \pi$ Cosine $h(t)$	$\geq \pi$ Rectangular $h(t)$	∞

α: radius of gyration of impulse response.
β: radius of gyration of frequency response.
ρ: equivalent rectangle of impulse response.
r: overall duration of frequency response.

Problems

1. The basic theory of response time for monotone circuits is given in Ref. 9.   One problem considered there is that of shunt peaking with an arbitrary (passive, linear time-invariant) reactance, as shown in Figure P 1*a*.

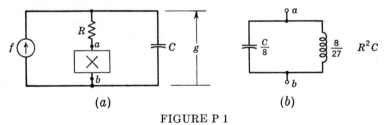

(a)   (b)

FIGURE P 1

(a) If X is as shown in Figure P 1*b*, find the response time (σ, as defined in Sec. 5-1).

(b) As more and more elements are permitted in the reactance circuit X, σ can be made smaller and smaller; the limiting behavior (when optimized for response time) is characterized by the following impulse-response function:

$$h(t) = R\frac{1}{T}\left(1 - \frac{t}{2T}\right) \qquad \text{for } 0 < t < 2T$$

and $h(t) = 0$ for other t, where $T = RC$.   Find $\bar{t}$ and σ corresponding to this impulse response.   Compare this σ with the σ of part a and with the σ for simple shunt peaking (critical damping).

2. Suppose a pulse amplifier is to be designed using tubes having $g_m = 3,000$ μmhos. The input and stray capacitance shunting each stage is $C = 15$ $\mu\mu$f. Each stage has a mid-band voltage amplification of $g_m R$, where R is the a-c load resistance. Compensation is used such that the response time for each stage is $\sigma = 0.5RC$. What is the minimum number of stages which can provide an overall voltage gain of at least 10^4 and an overall response time of no more than 0.1 μsec?

3. With the definitions of Sec. 5-2,

(a) Find the radius of gyration if $h(t) = e^{-|t|/T}$.

(b) Find the radius of gyration if $h(t) = (\sin rt)/t$.

4. If monotone systems are cascaded, the impulse response approaches a Gaussian response (central limit theorem in probability theory). To be specific, consider an RC circuit having

$$h(t) = \begin{cases} 0 & \text{for } t < 0 \\ \dfrac{1}{T}e^{-t/T} & \text{for } t > 0 \end{cases}$$

and, of course, for Re $p > -1/T$,

$$H(p) = \frac{1}{Tp + 1}$$

If n such circuits are cascaded, one would expect $\alpha\beta$ (as used in Theorem 7) to approach $\frac{1}{2}$ as n goes to infinity. Show that, for such a cascade of n systems,

$$\alpha\beta = \frac{1}{2}\sqrt{\frac{2n-1}{2n-3}}$$

for $n = 2$ or more.

5. Though there is no universal formula for response time of an overall system in terms of individual response times when the α or ρ of Sec. 5-2 is used as the definition of response time, in some special cases attractive formulas can be obtained.

(a) If systems having bandwidths $\beta_1, \ldots, \beta_n$ are cascaded and each system has minimum response time in the sense of Theorem 7, find the response time α in terms of the individual response times $\alpha_k = 1/2\beta_k$.

(b) If bandwidth-limited systems having $H_k(\omega) = 0$ for $|\omega| > r_k$ are cascaded and each system is optimum (minimum response time) in the sense of Theorem 8, find the overall equivalent-rectangle response time ρ in terms of the individual response times π/r_k.

6. If $H(\omega)$ of Theorem 7 is $H(\omega) = C \exp(a\omega^2/2)$, then by Example 2, Chap. 2,

$$h(t) = \frac{1}{2\pi}\int_{-\infty}^{\infty} e^{j\omega t}|C|^2 e^{-a\omega^2}\, d\omega = \frac{|C|^2}{\sqrt{4\pi a}}e^{-t^2/4a}$$

In the proof of Theorem 7 we used the fact that $a = 1/2\beta^2$. This is easily proved if we observe that

$$\frac{d^2h}{dt^2}\bigg|_{t=0} = \frac{-1}{2\pi}\int_{-\infty}^{\infty}\omega^2|C|^2 e^{-a\omega^2}\, d\omega$$

and hence

$$\beta^2 = -\frac{\dfrac{d^2h}{dt^2}\big|_0}{h(0)}$$

Compute β^2 from this formula.

7. Let ρ and α be the equivalent rectangle and radius of gyration of h as defined in Sec. 5-2. Find the $|h|^2$ which minimizes the ratio α/ρ. Find an $|h|^2$ which makes $\alpha/\rho = \infty$. Show that the minimum value of α/ρ is $1/(2\sqrt{3})$.

6

BANDPASS SYSTEMS, HILBERT TRANSFORMS, AND RELATIONS BETWEEN COMPONENTS OF TRANSFER FUNCTIONS

The theory given in previous chapters covers bandpass systems as well as low-pass systems; however, the material was covered in a way that provided intimacy only with low-pass systems (typically, audio or video circuits). The first objective of this chapter is to show that our intimate knowledge of low-pass systems can be carried over to bandpass systems by establishing an analogy (actually, an isomorphism) between low-pass and bandpass systems. The analogy obtained also has the following features:

1. It greatly simplifies the analysis of bandpass systems.

2. It provides another method for the synthesis of complex systems with real systems.

3. It leads to a simple procedure for the design of certain bandpass systems from known designs for low-pass systems.

4. It naturally leads to a transfer-function representation of Hilbert transforms, which is more attractive in most respects than the time-domain definition usually used for Hilbert transforms. Finally, after the Hilbert transform turns up, it is natural to study some of the relations between components of realizable transfer functions.

6-1 THE LOW-PASS REPRESENTATION FOR BANDPASS SIGNALS AND SYSTEMS

The theory of this section will be based on Fourier-transform analysis; however, the methods and many of the results apply to functions which are not Fourier-transformable. In particular, Wiener's generalized harmonic analysis can be used to extend the coverage to any function for which

$$\lim_{T \to \infty} \frac{1}{2T} \int_{-T}^{T} |f(t)|^2 \, dt$$

is finite. That is, the results generally apply to any function of finite average power. Most of the points of interest to us in Wiener's generalized harmonic analysis are given in Chap. 8. Of course, Fourier-transformable functions are functions of finite total energy,[†] that is,

$$\int_{-\infty}^{\infty} |f|^2 < \infty$$

It is undesirable to restrict the results to Fourier-transformable functions; however, it is a just price to pay for the resulting simplicity of the analysis. Once the methods are well understood, it is fairly easy to generalize through the use of the results of Chap. 8.

Let $F(\omega)$ be the Fourier transform of $f(t)$, that is,

$$F(\omega) = \int_{-\infty}^{\infty} \exp\,(-j\omega t) f(t) \, dt$$

Of course,

$$f(t) = \frac{1}{2\pi} \int_{-\infty}^{\infty} \exp\,(j\omega t) F(\omega) \, d\omega \quad \text{and} \quad \int_{-\infty}^{\infty} |f(t)|^2 \, dt = \frac{1}{2\pi} \int_{-\infty}^{\infty} |F(\omega)|^2 \, d\omega$$

[†] If we rely on Theorem 11, Chap. 2, we actually assume that

$$\int_{-\infty}^{\infty} |f(t)| \, dt < \infty$$

If f is bounded, this implies that

$$\int_{-\infty}^{\infty} |f|^2 < \infty$$

We shall call $|F(\omega)|^2$ the energy density of f. It is easy to see that $|F(\omega)|^2$ is indicative of the distribution of the energy of f over frequency. In particular, if f is sent through a network which has the frequency response

$$H(\omega) = \begin{cases} 1 & \text{for } \omega_1 < \omega < \omega_2 \\ 0 & \text{for other } \omega \end{cases}$$

it is easy to see that the total energy of the output is

$$\frac{1}{2\pi} \int_{\omega_1}^{\omega_2} |F(\omega)|^2 \, d\omega$$

Recall that $F(\omega)$ and $F(-\omega)$ are related by $F(\omega) = \overline{F(-\omega)}$ iff f is real-valued, while for complex-valued functions the behaviors of $F(\omega)$ and $F(-\omega)$ are quite independent. This difference in the freedom available for F in the real and complex cases results in a significant difference in the natural meaning of real bandpass function and complex bandpass function.

Of course f is a bandpass function centered at the frequency ω_0 iff f has negligible energy outside some frequency interval centered at ω_0. In the complex case it is natural to take this to mean† that $F(\omega) \cong 0$ for $|\omega - \omega_0| > W$, where W will be referred to as the bandwidth of f. It might be more nearly correct to call W the half bandwidth; however, if a quantitative measure is desired, some definition of *spread on the ω axis* analogous to those in Chap. 5 can be used. Though the condition $F(\omega) \cong 0$ for $|\omega - \omega_0| > W$ is reasonable for a complex-valued function, it will not do for a real-valued function. For if $F(\omega) \neq 0$ for ω close to ω_0 and $F(-\omega) = \overline{F(\omega)}$, then $F(\omega) \neq 0$ for ω close to $-\omega_0$. Thus, we call f a real bandpass function iff $F(\omega) \cong 0$ when $|\omega - \omega_0| > W$ and $|\omega + \omega_0| > W$ and of course $F(\omega) = \overline{F(-\omega)}$.

The first problem of interest is to obtain a correspondence between bandpass and low-pass functions. To each bandpass function, we shall associate a low-pass function which can be viewed as the modulation of $e^{j\omega_0 t}$ in the complex case and the modulation of $\cos \omega_0 t$ in the real case. Of course, such an association or correspondence is a transformation; the transformation involved is very simple, and we could get along well without introducing a symbol for it. However, as was done with phasors in Chap. 1, the transformation will be denoted by L_0. The same symbol was used for the *phasor transform*, and in fact the correspondence to be discussed here is a generalization of the phasor transform (in the real case) which reduces to L_0 of Chap. 1 if the modulations are constant (constant amplitude and phase). The first theorem establishes the existence of the desired correspondence.

Theorem 1 (*Complex Case*). If $f_b(t)$ is a bandpass function centered at ω_0 and having bandwidth W, then there exists a unique low-pass function

† Or, better yet,

$$\int_{\omega_0 - W}^{\omega_0 + W} |F(\omega)|^2 \, d\omega \cong \int_{-\infty}^{\infty} |F(\omega)|^2 \, d\omega$$

$f_v(t)$ for which $f_b(t) = f_v(t)e^{j\omega_0 t}$. We shall sometimes denote f_v by $L_0(f_b)$. The function f_v is low-pass in the sense that its Fourier transform is (essentially) zero for $|\omega| > W$.

PROOF: Define f_v thus: $f_v(t) = f_b(t)e^{-j\omega_0 t}$. Then, by the shift theorem, the Fourier transform of f_v is $F_v(\omega) = F_b(\omega + \omega_0)$, which is zero for $|\omega| > W$. Obviously f_v is unique; i.e., if $f_{v1}(t)e^{j\omega_0 t} = f_b(t) = f_{v2}(t)e^{j\omega_0 t}$, then $f_{v1} = f_{v2}$ since $e^{j\omega_0 t}$ is never zero. The real case is not quite so trivial.

Theorem 1 (Real Case). Let f_b be a real bandpass function for which $F_b(\omega) = 0$ when $|\omega - \omega_0| > W$ and $|\omega + \omega_0| > W$, and let $W < \omega_0$. Then there exists a unique complex-valued low-pass function $f_v = L_0(f_b)$ for which $F_v(\omega) = 0$ for $|\omega| > W$ and $f_b(t) = A(t) \cos [\omega_0 t + \alpha(t)]$, where A and α are real with $Ae^{j\alpha} = f_v$.

PROOF: For now and for future reference we introduce the following frequency-response function:

$$V(\omega) = \begin{cases} 2 & \text{if } \omega > 0 \\ 1 & \text{if } \omega = 0 \\ 0 & \text{if } \omega < 0 \end{cases}$$

We then define f_v for the real case as the low-pass function corresponding to the complex-valued bandpass function obtained by passing f_b through a "system" having frequency response $V(\omega)$. That is, $F_{b+}(\omega) = V(\omega)F_b(\omega)$; then $F_{b+}(\omega) = 0$ for $|\omega - \omega_0| > W$ and

$$f_{b+}(t) = \frac{1}{2\pi} \int_{-\infty}^{\infty} e^{j\omega t}F_{b+}(\omega)\,d\omega$$

is a complex bandpass function. We define f_v as the low-pass function corresponding to f_{b+}. Of course, $F_v(\omega) = 0$ for $|\omega| > W$ by Theorem 1 for the complex case. It remains to be shown that $f_b(t)$ and $f_v(t)$ are related as claimed in the theorem. By the inversion formula and the definition of F_{b+},

$$f_b(t) = \frac{1}{2}\frac{1}{2\pi} \int_0^{\infty} e^{j\omega t}F_{b+}(\omega)\,d\omega + \frac{1}{2\pi} \int_{-\infty}^0 e^{j\omega t}F_b(\omega)\,d\omega$$

For the second term let $\omega = -u$, and let $\overline{F_b(-u)} = F_b(u)$ as implied by the realness of f_b; then the second integral becomes

$$\int_0^{\infty} e^{-jut}\overline{F_b(u)}\,du$$

which is half the conjugate of

$$\int_0^{\infty} e^{j\omega t}F_{b+}(\omega)\,d\omega$$

Hence $f_b(t) = \frac{1}{2}[f_{b+}(t) + \bar{f}_{b+}(t)]$

Now if $f_{b+}(t) = f_v(t)e^{j\omega_0 t} = A(t)e^{j[\omega_0 t + \alpha(t)]}$

then $f_b(t) = \frac{1}{2}A(t)[e^{j\omega_0 t + j\alpha(t)} + e^{-j\omega_0 t - j\alpha(t)}]$

$$= A(t) \cos [\omega_0 t + \alpha(t)]$$

as was to be shown.

The final question is that of the uniqueness of A and α; that is, given $A_1(t) \cos [\omega_0 t + \alpha_1(t)] = A_2(t) \cos [\omega_0 t + \alpha_2(t)]$ and given that the Fourier transforms of $A_1 e^{j\alpha_1}$ and of $A_2 e^{j\alpha_2}$ are zero for $|\omega| > W$, where $W < \omega_0$, we wish to show that these low-pass functions are equal. Let $F_{v1}(\omega)$ be the Fourier transform of $A_1 e^{j\alpha_1} = f_{v1}$, and let $F_{v2}(\omega)$ be the transform of $A_2 e^{j\alpha_2}$. It is easy to show that $\bar{F}_{v1}(-\omega)$ is the Fourier transform of $A_1 e^{-j\alpha_1} = \bar{f}_{v1}$. In turn, the transform of $f_b(t)$ can be written as

$$\tfrac{1}{2}F_{v1}(\omega - \omega_0) + \tfrac{1}{2}\bar{F}_{v1}(-\omega - \omega_0)$$

which must equal

$$\tfrac{1}{2}F_{v2}(\omega - \omega_0) + \tfrac{1}{2}\bar{F}_{v2}(-\omega - \omega_0)$$

When $|\omega - \omega_0| < W$, $\bar{F}_{v1}(-\omega - \omega_0) \cong 0$ and $\bar{F}_{v2}(-\omega - \omega_0) \cong 0$ since for such ω, $-\omega - \omega_0 < -2\omega_0 + W$ but $\omega_0 > W$ and hence $-\omega - \omega_0 < -W$ and $F_{v2} \cong 0$ when evaluated outside a bandwidth W centered at zero. Thus for such ω we get

$$F_{v1}(\xi) = F_{v2}(\xi) \qquad \text{for } |\xi| < W$$

But

$$F_{v1}(\omega) = F_{v2}(\omega) = 0 \qquad \text{for } |\omega| > W$$

Therefore, $F_{v1} = F_{v2}$ and in turn $f_{v1} = f_{v2}$, as was to be shown.

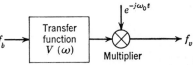

FIGURE 6-1. Generation of low-pass function in real case.

It may be worthwhile to summarize the above results. Any complex bandpass function is of the form of the product of a carrier $e^{j\omega_0 t}$ and a low-pass modulation function having the same bandwidth as the bandpass function. The low-pass function is given thus: $f_v = e^{-j\omega_0 t} f_b$. Any real bandpass function is of the form $A(t) \cos [\omega_0 t + \alpha(t)]$, where $f_v(t) = A(t)e^{j\alpha(t)}$ is a low-pass function. This low-pass function is obtained from the bandpass function, as shown in Figure 6-1. Since $V(-\omega) \neq \overline{V(\omega)}$, V corresponds to a complex parameter system. The operator L_0: $f_v = L_0(f_b)$ is obviously linear for both the complex and real case. Also, L_0 has a unique inverse if ω_0 is fixed; i.e., given f_v we can "reconstruct" f_b.

The correspondence between bandpass and low-pass functions obtained above is utilized in analysis by finding a similar correspondence between bandpass and low-pass systems. If we restrict our attention to convoluting systems, the impulse response of the low-pass system corresponding to a given bandpass system is taken as the L_0 transform of the impulse response of the given bandpass system.

Consider first the all-complex case. If

$$g_b(t) = \int_{-\infty}^{\infty} h_b(t - \tau)f_b(\tau) \, d\tau$$

where the energy of f_b is centered at ω_0, then $g_b = 0$ unless H_b (the Fourier transform of h_b) is also more or less centered at ω_0; this follows from the convolution theorem. Hence we shall assume that both f_b and h_b are centered at ω_0, which is usually the case in applications of the theory. We can write

$$f_b(t) = e^{j\omega_0 t}f_v(t) \qquad \text{and} \qquad h_b(t) = e^{j\omega_0 t}h_v(t)$$

Theorem 2 (Complex Case). If f_b and h_b are bandpass functions centered at ω_0, then $g_b = f_b * h_b$ is such a function; and if

$$g_v(t) = g_b(t)e^{-j\omega_0 t}$$

(and f_v and h_v are defined in a similar way), then

$$g_v = h_v * f_v$$

This theorem depicts an isomorphism (for convolution) between bandpass functions and corresponding low-pass functions. The proof is very simple:

$$g_b(t) = \int_{-\infty}^{\infty} f_b(t-\tau)h_b(\tau)\,d\tau = \int_{-\infty}^{\infty} \exp\left[j\omega_0(t-\tau)\right]f_v(t-\tau)\exp\left(j\omega_0\tau\right)h_v(\tau)\,d\tau$$

$$= \exp\left(j\omega_0 t\right)\int_{-\infty}^{\infty} f_v(t-\tau)h_v(\tau)\,d\tau$$

as was to be shown.

The case of real-valued bandpass functions is handled in a similar way. If f_b is a real bandpass function, we write $f_b(t)$ as

$$A(t)\cos\left[\omega_0 t + \alpha(t)\right]$$

where
$$A(t)e^{j\alpha(t)} \equiv f_v$$

is the associated low-pass function.

Theorem 2 (Real Case). If f_b and h_b are real bandpass functions having representations

$$A(t)\cos\left[\omega_0 t + \alpha(t)\right] \qquad \text{and} \qquad B(t)\cos\left[\omega_0 t + \beta(t)\right]$$

then
$$g_b = f_b * h_b$$

is a real bandpass function; and if the representation for g_b is

$$g_b(t) = \tfrac{1}{2}C(t)\cos\left[\omega_0 t + \gamma(t)\right]$$

then
$$C(t)e^{j\gamma(t)} = [A(t)e^{j\alpha(t)}] * [B(t)e^{j\beta(t)}]$$

or
$$g_v = \tfrac{1}{2}(h_v * f_v)$$

Here a real convolution is computed in terms of the convolution of two associated complex-valued functions. For the proof, consider

$$\tfrac{1}{4}(Ae^{j\alpha}e^{j\omega_0 t} + Ae^{-j\alpha}e^{-j\omega_0 t}) * (Be^{j\beta}e^{j\omega_0 t} + Be^{-j\beta}e^{-j\omega_0 t})$$

This can be written as the sum of four terms; if the first term of each set of parentheses is considered, we get

$$\int_{-\infty}^{\infty} A(t-\tau)e^{j\alpha(t-\tau)}e^{j\omega_0(t-\tau)}B(\tau)e^{j\beta(\tau)}e^{j\omega_0\tau}\,d\tau$$

$$= e^{j\omega_0 t}\int_{-\infty}^{\infty} A(t-\tau)e^{j\alpha(t-\tau)}B(\tau)e^{j\beta(\tau)}\,d\tau = e^{j\omega_0 t}(Ae^{j\alpha} * Be^{j\beta})$$

The last two terms give

$$e^{-j\omega_0 t}(Ae^{-j\alpha} * Be^{-j\beta})$$

A typical *cross term* is

$$e^{j\omega_0 t}\int_{-\infty}^{\infty} A(\tau)e^{-j2\omega_0\tau}e^{-j\alpha(\tau)}B(t-\tau)e^{j\beta(t-\tau)}\,d\tau$$

But note that $Be^{j\beta}$ is a low-pass function and $Ae^{-j\alpha}e^{-j2\omega_0\tau}$ is a complex band-pass function which is centered at $-2\omega_0$. If the highest frequency of $Be^{j\beta}$ minus the lowest frequency (this lowest frequency is a negative number) of $Ae^{-j\alpha}$ is less than $2\omega_0$, this *cross convolution* is zero since the spectra of the two functions involved do not overlap. In a similar fashion the other cross term is zero. Now let

$$Ce^{j\alpha} = Ae^{j\alpha} * Be^{j\beta}$$

We have

$$f_b * h_b = \tfrac{1}{4}e^{j\omega_0 t}(Ae^{j\alpha} * Be^{j\beta}) + \tfrac{1}{4}e^{-j\omega_0 t}(Ae^{-j\alpha} * Be^{-j\beta})$$

but the convolution of conjugates is equal to the conjugate of the convolution; hence

$$f_b * h_b = \tfrac{1}{4}e^{j\omega_0 t}Ce^{j\gamma} + \tfrac{1}{4}e^{-j\omega_0 t}Ce^{-j\gamma} = \tfrac{1}{2}C(t)\cos\left[\omega_0 t + \alpha(t)\right]$$

as was to be shown.

The following is an alternative proof (mentioned by Dr. R. O. Harger): Since $g_b = f_b * h_b$, the Fourier transform of g_b is $G_b = F_b H_b$; and if g_b is passed through the system having frequency response $V(\omega)$, we have $G_{b+} = VF_b H_b$, where G_{b+} is the Fourier transform of g_{b+} as defined in the proof of Theorem 1 (Real Case). In turn, since $V^2 = 2V$,

$$G_{b+} = \tfrac{1}{2}(VF_b)(VH_b) = \tfrac{1}{2}F_{b+}H_{b+}$$

or

$$g_{b+} = \tfrac{1}{2}(f_{b+} * h_{b+})$$

Then, by the complex case of Theorem 2, $g_v = \tfrac{1}{2}(f_v * h_v)$, as was to be shown.

One important interpretation of Theorem 2 for the real case is that it provides another method for synthesizing complex parameter systems with a real parameter system. In detail, we assume a complex-valued function $Ae^{j\alpha}$ is available, and we wish to filter it with a circuit having an impulse response $Be^{j\beta}$. We construct a real parameter circuit having an impulse response $B(t)\cos\left[\omega_0 t + \beta(t)\right]$, and then the signal $A\cos(\omega_0 t + \alpha)$ is used as the input to this circuit. Of course, $A\cos(\omega_0 t + \alpha)$ is readily obtained from $Ae^{j\alpha}$ through the use of amplitude and phase modulation. Also, if $Ae^{j\alpha}$ is available in the form of real and imaginary parts $A\cos\alpha$ and $A\sin\alpha$, we can obtain $A\cos(\omega_0 t + \alpha)$ by adding the outputs of two amplitude modulators which have *quadrature* carriers, that is,

$$A\cos(\omega_0 t + \alpha) = (A\cos\alpha)\cos\omega_0 t - (A\sin\alpha)\sin\omega_0 t$$

Finally, $\tfrac{1}{2}(Ae^{j\alpha} * Be^{j\beta})$, the desired output, can be obtained by demodulating the output of the real bandpass circuit.

EXAMPLE FOR THEOREM 2 (REAL CASE)

Suppose the transfer function of a circuit is

$$H(\omega) = \exp \frac{-(\omega - \omega_0)^2}{2W^2} + \exp \frac{-(\omega + \omega_0)^2}{2W^2}$$

where $\omega_0/W \gg 1$.   Suppose the input to the circuit is

$$\cos\left(\omega_0 t - \frac{m}{2} t^2\right)$$

which is a linear FM sweep.   To facilitate the analysis, we shall **consider** the input

$$f_b(t) = \exp \frac{-t^2 a^2}{2} \cos\left(\omega_0 t - \frac{m}{2} t^2\right)$$

and eventually we shall let a go to zero.   An *instantaneous frequency* of $\omega_0 - mt$ can be associated with f_b; and if a is small enough, $m/a \gg W$, the presence of the amplitude modulation

$$\exp \frac{-t^2 a^2}{2}$$

has very little effect on the response of the circuit.   However, the presence of

$$\exp \frac{-t^2 a^2}{2}$$

renders f_b a bandpass Fourier-transformable function.

As is well known (see Chap. 2, Example 2), the Fourier transform of a Gaussian function is a Gaussian function; hence, the impulse response corresponding to H is

$$h_b(t) = \sqrt{\frac{2}{\pi}} W \exp \frac{-t^2 W^2}{2} \cos \omega_0 t$$

Hence, by Theorem 2, the problem of finding $h_b * f_b$ can be solved by finding

$$2g_v(t) = \sqrt{\frac{2}{\pi}} W \exp \frac{-t^2 W^2}{2} * \exp\left[-\frac{t^2}{2}(a^2 + jm)\right]$$

Using the transform pairs of Gaussian functions, we get

$$2G_v(\omega) = \left(2 \exp \frac{-\omega^2}{2W^2}\right) \frac{\sqrt{2\pi}}{\sqrt{a^2 + jm}} \exp\left[-\frac{\omega^2}{2(a^2 + jm)}\right]$$

$$G_v(\omega) = \frac{\sqrt{2\pi}}{\sqrt{a^2 + jm}} \exp\left[\frac{-\omega^2}{2}\left(\frac{1}{W^2} + \frac{1}{a^2 + jm}\right)\right]$$

and

$$g_v(t) = \frac{1}{\sqrt{a^2 + jm}}\left(\frac{1}{W^2} + \frac{1}{a^2 + jm}\right)^{-\frac{1}{2}} \exp\left[-\frac{t^2}{2}\left(\frac{1}{W^2} + \frac{1}{a^2 + jm}\right)^{-1}\right]$$

Now if we let a go to zero,

$$g_v(t) = \sqrt{\frac{W^2}{W^2 + jm}} \exp\left(\frac{-t^2}{2} \frac{jmW^2}{W^2 + jm}\right)$$

The peak value of $|g|^2$ and its duration on the t axis are of the most interest. For the peak value we have

$$|g_v(0)|^2 = \frac{W^2}{\sqrt{W^4 + m^2}}$$

The spread on the t axis is determined by

$$\text{Re} \frac{jmW^2}{W^2 + jm} = \frac{m^2W^2}{W^4 + m^2}$$

Specifically, the radius of gyration of $|g_v(t)|^2$ is

$$\sigma = \frac{1}{\sqrt{2}} \sqrt{\frac{W^2}{m^2} + \frac{1}{W^2}}$$

Note that if m is fixed, one can minimize σ by taking $W^2 = m$. Such a minimization is useful in certain systems which are used to sense the passing of a linear FM sweep.

6-2 DESIGN OF BANDPASS CIRCUITS BY LOW-PASS ANALOGY

If one synthesizes a low-pass (possibly) complex impulse response

$$h_v(t) = |h_v(t)|e^{j\beta(t)}$$

it is easy to see that the impulse response

$$h_b(t) = |h_v(t)| \cos [\omega_0 t + \beta(t)]$$

can then be synthesized if AM and FM detectors and modulators are available. In the light of Theorem 2 (Real Case), the input

$$f_b(t) = |f_v(t)| \cos [\omega_0 t + \alpha(t)]$$

is detected (as described in Sec. 4-1) to obtain

$$f_v = |f_v|e^{j\alpha}$$

This is passed through the complex filter to obtain $f_v * h_v$, and finally the output of this complex filter is used to modulate $\cos \omega_0 t$ in amplitude and phase.

The point to be made in this section is that the bandpass impulse response

$$h_v(t) \cos \omega_0 t$$

where h_v is real, can be synthesized with ordinary tuned circuits (without the use of detectors and modulators) if one knows how to synthesize the low-pass impulse response $h_v(t)$.   Suppose a design for a low-pass network having the frequency response $H_v(\omega)$ is available, and by simple modifications we can obtain a bandpass frequency response

$$H_b(\omega) = H_v(\omega - \omega_0) + H_v(\omega + \omega_0)$$

Then, by the shift theorem of Fourier transforms, $h_b(t) = 2h_v(t) \cos \omega_0 t$. By the way, the factor 2 here absorbs the factor of $\frac{1}{2}$ present in Theorem 2 (Real Case).

   The problem of modifying the low-pass network to bring about the desired change in dependence on frequency is quite easy if an approximate solution is accepted.   Suppose the frequency-dependent elements are inductors and capacitors (this is the case in classical circuit design).   If an inductor L appears in the low-pass network as

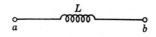

use

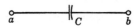

in the bandpass network.   If a capacitor C appears in the low-pass network as

use

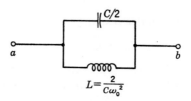

in the bandpass network.   Consider the case of the capacitor

$$Y_v(\omega) = j\omega C$$

and
$$Y_b(\omega) = \frac{j\omega C}{2} + \frac{C\omega_0^2}{2j\omega}$$

$$= j\omega C \left[\frac{1}{2}\left(1 - \frac{\omega_0^2}{\omega^2}\right)\right]$$

$$= j\omega C \frac{(1 + \omega_0/\omega^2)(1 - \omega_0/\omega)}{2}$$

For the inductor we get

$$Z_v(\omega) = j\omega L \qquad \text{and} \qquad Z_b(\omega) = \frac{j\omega L\,(1 + \omega_0/\omega)(1 - \omega_0/\omega)}{2}$$

All elements which are not frequency-dependent are left intact when the low-pass circuit is modified to obtain the desired bandpass network. The effect of replacing capacitors with appropriate parallel tuned circuits and inductors with series tuned circuits is seen to be the following: Whenever ω appears in the equations describing the low-pass circuit,

$$\omega \frac{(1 + \omega_0/\omega)(1 - \omega_0/\omega)}{2}$$

appears in the bandpass circuit. Hence if said modifications of a low-pass circuit are made, the transfer function of the circuit formed is

$$H_b(\omega) = H_v\left[\omega \frac{(1 + \omega_0/\omega)(1 - \omega_0/\omega)}{2}\right]$$

Let $H_v(\omega) \cong 0$ if $|\omega| > W$, where $W/\omega_0 \ll 1$. Then $H_b(\omega) \cong 0$ unless

$$\left|\omega \frac{(1 + \omega_0/\omega)(1 - \omega_0/\omega)}{2}\right| \leq W$$

which is pictured in Figure 6-2.

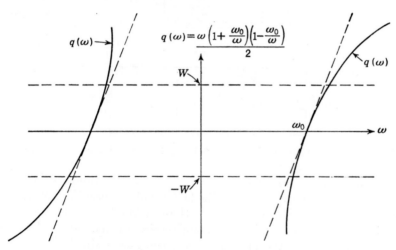

FIGURE 6-2. Approximations for $q(\omega)$.

In the range where $|q(\omega)| < W$, we have simple linear approximations; for $|\omega - \omega_0|$ small,

$$q(\omega) \cong (\omega - \omega_0) \frac{1 + \omega_0/\omega}{2} \cong \omega - \omega_0$$

since $\omega \cong \omega_0$. Similarly,

$$q(\omega) \cong \omega + \omega_0 \qquad \text{for } |\omega + \omega_0| \text{ small}$$

When neither $|\omega - \omega_0|$ nor $|\omega + \omega_0|$ is small, $H_b(\omega) \cong 0$ since then $q(\omega) > W$.

Hence

$$H_b(\omega) \cong \begin{cases} H_v(\omega - \omega_0) & \text{for } |\omega - \omega_0| < W \\ H_v(\omega + \omega_0) & \text{for } |\omega + \omega_0| < W \\ 0 & \text{for other } \omega \end{cases}$$

Finally, $$H_b(\omega) \cong H_v(\omega - \omega_0) + H_v(\omega + \omega_0)$$

since, for $|\omega - \omega_0|$ small,

$$H_v(\omega + \omega_0) \cong 0$$

and we get

$$H_b \cong H_v(\omega - \omega_0)$$

and so forth.   That is,

$$H_b(\omega) \cong H_v(\omega - \omega_0) + H_v(\omega + \omega_0)$$

since both sides are approximately zero when $|\omega \pm \omega_0|$ is large and the appropriate term approximates $H_v[q(\omega)]$ when $|\omega \pm \omega_0|$ is small (in which case the inappropriate term is nearly zero).

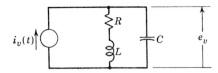

FIGURE 6-3.   A low-pass circuit.

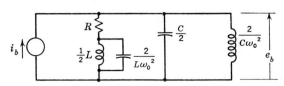

FIGURE 6-4.   Bandpass circuit analogous to the low-pass circuit shown in Figure 6-3.

Example 1.   Bandpass Pulse Amplifier.   As briefly discussed in Chap. 5, considerable design theory is available for pulsed circuits; however, the theory is developed for video circuits.   Here we briefly consider the problem of applying the results obtained for low-pass circuits to bandpass (i-f) circuit design.   To illustrate the ideas involved, consider a simple shunt-peaked video amplifier, as shown in Figure 6-3.   In radar applications, i_v is typically a pulse, and we shall consider a rectangular pulse to be specific.   This pulse is produced by amplitude detection of the modulation on a sine wave of high frequency; thus, prior to the problem of amplifying $i_v(t)$, we have a function of the form $i_b(t) = i_v(t) \cos \omega_0 t$ which we wish to amplify.   In view of the analogy between low-pass and bandpass systems we developed, the amplifier shown in Figure 6-4 would provide the same amplification of i_v as the above-mentioned video circuits.   If $i_b = i_v \cos \omega_0 t$, then

$$e_b = e_v \cos \omega_0 t$$

where e_v is the voltage which will be delivered by the video circuit if i_v is its input. For both networks the gain is determined by R, specifically, R times the transconductance for a tube amplifier.

An interesting problem presents itself: In practical designs the shunt capacitance represents stray capacitance and input capacitance of the next stage, and for a specific tube we are not free to replace C with $C/2$. In this case, if a bandpass amplifier is to be built we should think of C as fixed for this circuit and then introduce $2C$ in the low-pass amplifier used for the analysis by analogy, as illustrated in Figure 6-5.

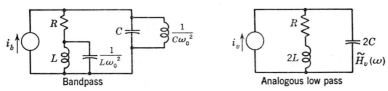

Bandpass   Analogous low pass

FIGURE 6-5. Appropriate low-pass circuit analogous to that shown in Figure 6-3.

With this analogy, the $\tilde{H}_v(\omega)$ relevant to finding the response of the amplifier is simply related to the frequency response which would be involved if the signal i_v were amplified directly in the presence of a stray capacitance C. Let this low-pass frequency response be $H_v(\omega)$, as depicted in Figure 6-6. Wherever $2j\omega C$ and $2j\omega L$ appear in the video circuit which depicts the behavior of the actual bandpass amplifier, $j\omega L$ and $j\omega C$ appear in the frequency response of a video amplifier of the same gain and the same stray capacitance. That is, $\tilde{H}_v(\omega) = H_v(2\omega)$.

The interesting problem is to compare the performance obtainable in the presence of the stray capacitance C when the amplification is done at video and the performance is obtained at intermediate frequency with the same tube or transistor. We are making the comparison on the basis of main-

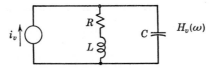

FIGURE 6-6. Video circuit possible with stray capacitance C.

taining the same gain at $\omega = 0$ (which corresponds to the gain at the carrier frequency in the bandpass case). Since $\tilde{H}_v(\omega) = H_v(2\omega)$, the effective bandwidth of the i-f amplifier is only one-half the bandwidth obtainable with a video amplifier. Of course, by effective bandwidth is meant the bandwidth of the frequency response operating on the video modulation of the i-f signal. This reduction by a factor of 2 applies to any reasonable method for measuring bandwidths. For example, if r is the highest frequency passed by $H_v(\omega)$, the highest frequency passed by $\tilde{H}_v(\omega)$ is determined by the equation $2\omega_{max} = r$ or $\omega_{max} = r/2$. Similarly, if r is the 3-db bandwidth, i.e., if

$$|H_v(r)| = 0.707$$

then

$$\left| \tilde{H}_v\left(\frac{r}{2}\right) \right| = |H_v(r)| = 0.707$$

Finally, the radius of gyration of $\tilde{H}_v(\omega)$ is half the radius of gyration of $H_v(\omega)$.

The loss of a factor of 2 can be viewed in terms of effective response time as well. If

$$h_v(t) = \frac{1}{2\pi} \int_{-\infty}^{\infty} e^{j\omega t} H_v(\omega) \, d\omega$$

and

$$\tilde{h}_v(t) = \frac{1}{2\pi} \int_{-\infty}^{\infty} e^{j\omega t} \tilde{H}_v(\omega) \, d\omega$$

then

$$\tilde{h}_v(t) = \frac{1}{2\pi} \int_{-\infty}^{\infty} e^{j\omega t} H_v(2\omega) \, d\omega$$

$$= \frac{1}{2} \frac{1}{2\pi} \int_{-\infty}^{\infty} \exp\left(ju\,\frac{t}{2} \right) H_v(u) \, du$$

$$= \frac{1}{2} h_v\left(\frac{t}{2}\right)$$

The $t/2$ in h_v indicates that the impulse response corresponding to $\tilde{h}_v$ is spread by a factor of 2 on the t axis in comparison with the impulse response $h(t)$. In particular, for any reasonable measure of response time, the

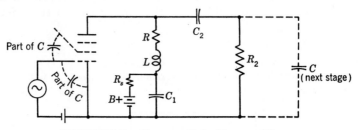

FIGURE 6-7.   Compensated video amplifier.

response time corresponding to $\tilde{h}_v$ is twice the response time corresponding to h_v. For example,

$$\bar{\rho} \equiv \frac{\int_{-\infty}^{\infty} |\tilde{h}_v(t)|^2 \, dt}{|\tilde{h}_v(0)|^2} = \frac{\frac{1}{4}\int_{-\infty}^{\infty} |h(t/2)|^2 \, dt}{\frac{1}{4}|h(0)|^2} = \frac{2\int_{-\infty}^{\infty} |h(u)|^2 \, du}{|h(0)|^2} = 2\rho$$

where ρ is the equivalent-rectangle response time of h.

The striking conclusion of the above considerations is as follows: The effective gain-bandwidth product obtainable for the purpose of video amplification in the presence of the limitation of a fixed stray (and input) capacitance is reduced by a factor of 2 when (double-sideband) real bandpass amplification is used in place of video amplification. In spite of this, the use of a few stages of i-f amplification can often be justified on the basis of the nonlinearity of the second detector for low-level inputs, noise rejection, ease of maintaining amplifier stability, and/or through the use of single-sideband operation; but these considerations are beyond the scope of the book.

One more remark about the low-pass–bandpass analogy is in order at this point. Suppose the circuit of Figure 6-7 is used as a video amplifier, the circuit is a-c-coupled and includes compensation for tilt (compensation for low-frequency response), as described in Sec. 2-5, and it also includes rise-time (response-time) compensation. The elements C_2 and R_2 are present to provide a-c coupling, which is desirable in that it eliminates otherwise serious problems in providing bias voltages for successive stages in cascaded amplifier design. The elements R_s and C_1 are present to provide better low-frequency response. If we blindly applied the design-by-analogy method to the above circuit to obtain an i-f amplifier design,

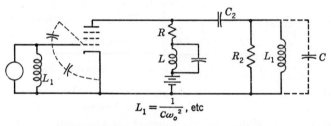

$$L_1 = \frac{1}{C\omega_o{}^2}, \text{ etc}$$

FIGURE 6-8. Appropriate i-f amplifier.

R_2, C_2, C_1, and R_s would remain in the circuit and C_1 and C_2 would be shunted by very small inductors. The i-f amplifier would contain 11 lumped passive elements plus stray capacitance (as well as the tube with a screen bias circuit). However, the a-c coupling problem is nil in a bandpass amplifier, and the elements R_s and C_1 are not needed. More important, the C_2 used for a-c coupling only blocks direct current and presents nearly a short circuit to alternating current. Hence it would certainly be fallacious to shunt C_2 with an inductor in the bandpass design. Hence, rather than an 11-element network at intermediate frequency, we have the seven-element network of Figure 6-8.

Example 2. Bandpass Circuits in Control Systems. In servomechanisms the overall frequency response nearly always corresponds to a low-pass system. Unlike video (or pulse) amplifiers, the low-pass amplifiers involved must be d-c-coupled. However, in view of bias problems and others associated with d-c amplifiers, bandpass amplifiers are often used along with a modulator at the input and a demodulator at the output. Synchronous electronic (or mechanical) modulators and demodulators are relatively easy to construct if it is assumed that a common reference sine wave is available at all places in the system. Of course an a-c coupling network can be used in the bandpass amplifier for bias purposes; such coupling has negligible effect on the gain at the carrier frequency, which corresponds to the d-c gain to the modulation of the carrier.   In this application, the *LC* elements are generally unrestricted (effects such as stray capacitance being negligible). Typically, if the equivalent lag network of Figure 6-9 is desired in the low-pass system, the circuit of Figure 6-10 is used in the actual bandpass system.

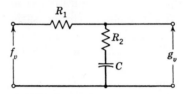

FIGURE 6-9.   A lag network.

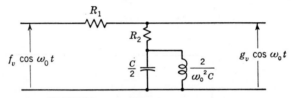

FIGURE 6-10.   Bandpass lag network.

Example 3.   Accuracy of the Approximation.   The high-pass–low-pass analogy developed in this section simplifies bandpass analysis and design considerably.   One shortcoming, however, is the approximate nature of the analogy.   One rather attractive method for obtaining an indication of the accuracy of the approximation is to solve some bandpass problems with and without the aid of the analogy and then compare results.   This is particularly attractive if we can find some problems which are not too difficult when done without the analogy.

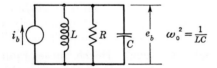
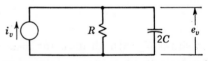

FIGURE 6-11.   Simple bandpass amplifier.

FIGURE 6-12.   Low-pass circuit analogous to the bandpass circuit shown in
Figure 6-11.

Consider the simple bandpass amplifier shown in Figure 6-11.   Our first problem is to select an i_b for which the circuit can be readily analyzed; the following three inputs can easily be handled:

1. $i_b(t) = e^{\sigma t} \cos \omega_0 t$

2. $i_b(t) = \begin{cases} \cos \omega_0 t & \text{for } t > 0 \\ 0 & \text{for } t < 0 \end{cases}$

3. $i_b(t) = (\cos \omega t) \cos \omega_0 t \qquad \omega \ll \omega_0$

The corresponding low-pass circuit is shown in Figure 6-12. The corresponding inputs are, respectively,

1. $i_v(t) = e^{\sigma t}$
2. $i_v(t) = \begin{cases} 1 & \text{for } t > 0 \\ 0 & \text{for } t < 0 \end{cases}$
3. $i_v(t) = \cos \omega t$

Since $Z(p) = R/(1 + 2Tp)$, where $T = RC$, the low-pass outputs are as follows:

1. $e_v(t) = \dfrac{R}{1 + 2\sigma T} e^{\sigma t}$
2. $e_v(t) = R(1 - e^{-t/2T})$
3. $e_v(t) = \dfrac{R}{\sqrt{1 + (2\omega T)^2}} \cos (\omega t - \theta)$

where $\tan \theta = j2T\omega$.

We can now proceed to compare an exact bandpass solution with the corresponding approximate low-pass solution. The first input will be discussed here, and the last two will be left as exercises. The approximate solution is

$$e_b(t) = \frac{R}{1 + 2\sigma T} e^{\sigma t} \cos \omega_0 t$$

The exact solution is readily found by the usual impedance concepts (Chap. 1). The impedance of the tuned circuit is

$$Z(p) = \left(\frac{1}{R} + pC + \frac{1}{pL}\right)^{-1} = \frac{(1/C)p}{p^2 + p/T + 1/LC}$$

The complex frequency of the input is $p = \sigma + j\omega_0$. Hence

$$Z = \frac{(1/C)(\sigma + j\omega_0)}{(\sigma + j\omega_0)^2 + (\sigma + j\omega_0)/T + \omega_0^2} = \frac{R}{1 + \sigma T(\sigma + j2\omega_0)/(\sigma + j\omega_0)}$$

We should expect the approximation to be good if the modulation $e^{\sigma t}$ is "slowly varying" in comparison with $\cos \omega_0 t$. This is the case if $\sigma \ll \omega_0$, which in turn gives

$$Z \cong \frac{R}{1 + 2\sigma T}$$

as predicted. A higher-order approximation is easily found if we consider the following:

$$\frac{\sigma + j2\omega_0}{\sigma + j\omega_0} = 1 + \frac{j\omega_0}{\sigma + j\omega_0} = 1 + \frac{1}{1 - j(\sigma/\omega_0)} \cong 1 + 1 + j\frac{\sigma}{\omega_0}$$

Thus

$$Z \cong \frac{R}{1 + 2\sigma T + j(\sigma T)(\sigma/\omega_0)}$$

It is seen that the actual phase of the carrier of e_b is about

$$-\frac{\sigma}{\omega_0}\frac{\sigma T}{1+2\sigma T} \qquad \text{radians}$$

rather than zero. There is also an error in the amplitude found by the low-pass analogy; specifically, the actual amplitude of the denominator is approximately

$$(1+2\sigma T)+\frac{1}{2}\frac{(\sigma T)^2}{1+2\sigma T}\left(\frac{\sigma}{\omega_0}\right)^2$$

and the value obtained by analogy was $1+2\sigma T$. For example, suppose $\sigma = 1/T$ (values of σ much larger than this result in considerable attenuation in the circuit). Then we should compare the denominators 3 and $3+\frac{1}{6}(\sigma/\omega_0)^2$. Even if ω_0 is only three times σ, the error in amplitude is less than 1 per cent. The corresponding phase shift is $\frac{1}{9}$ radian (about 7°) rather than zero, as given by bandpass analogy.

6-3   HILBERT TRANSFORMS

We now return to the relation between f_b and f_v for the real case, as shown in the sketch. A more detailed study of the transformation of f_b which

produces $\hat{f}$ leads to the important properties of Hilbert transforms. We change our emphasis now by concentrating on $\hat{f}$ rather than on f_v; properties (and problems) involving f_v are generally easily viewed in terms of corresponding properties of $\hat{f}$. In particular, recall that if

$$f_b(t) = A(t)\cos[\omega_0 t + \alpha(t)]$$

where A and α are low-pass functions, then $f_v = Ae^{j\alpha}$. Hence if f_b is the input to an amplitude detector, $A = |f_v| = |\hat{f}|$ is the output of the detector; and if f_b is the input to a phase (frequency) detector, $\alpha\, d\alpha/dt$ is the output. Correspondingly, the phase of $\hat{f}$ less $\omega_0 t$ is the output of such a phase detector and the time derivative of the phase of $\hat{f}$ less ω_0 is the output of such a frequency detector. Thus, as one would expect, $\hat{f}$ (or f_v) is utilized in the study of systems involving detector circuits; in fact, Sec. 6-2 is essentially a study of systems which involve amplitude detectors.

Since low-pass functions f_v are not discussed in this section, we shall change our notation somewhat; f_b will be replaced by f and, as indicated above, $\hat{f}$ is twice the part of f which occupies positive frequencies.

Recall that at the end of the proof of Theorem 1 (Real Case), we had $f_b = \frac{1}{2}(f_{b+} + \tilde{f}_{b+})$, which now reads $f = \frac{1}{2}(\hat{f} + \tilde{f})$, or $f = \text{Re}\,\hat{f}$. Let $f_i \equiv \text{Im}\,\hat{f}$;

the relation between this function and f is of chief interest in this section. Note that $f_i = (1/j)(\hat{f} - f)$ and since $\hat{f}$ can be viewed as the output of a filter for which f is the input, f_i can also be viewed as the output of a filter

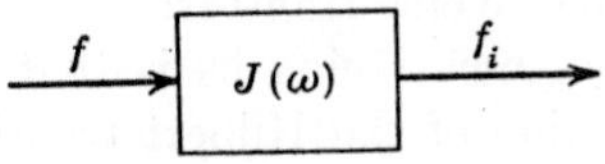

for which f is the input, as shown in the sketch.   Since $V(\omega)$ is the frequency response used to construct $\hat{f}$, the frequency response which will produce f_i is

$$J(\omega) = \frac{1}{j}[V(\omega) - 1]$$

This follows directly from

$$f_i = \frac{1}{j}(\hat{f} - f)$$

Therefore, $$J(\omega) = \begin{cases} -j & \text{for } \omega > 0 \\ 0 & \text{for } \omega = 0 \\ j & \text{for } \omega < 0 \end{cases}$$

Note that $J(\omega)$ corresponds to a real parameter system in that $J(-\omega) = \overline{J(\omega)}$. This is expected in that the output f_i is a real-valued function produced in response to the real-valued input f. Note also that f can generally

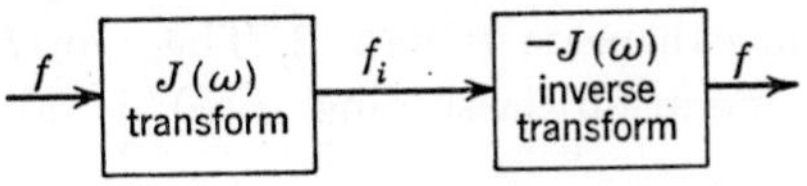

FIGURE 6-13.   Hilbert transform and its inverse.

be obtained from f_i by simple filtering (save for the direct current in f).   The filter required for this is

$$[J(\omega)]^{-1} = \begin{cases} j & \text{for } \omega > 0 \\ 0 & \text{by definition for } \omega = 0 \\ -j & \text{for } \omega < 0 \end{cases}$$

It is rather strange, but we see that the inverse filter is $-J(\omega)$; that is, $(J)^{-1} = -J$. We define the Hilbert transform of f as f_i. If f has no energy at $\omega = 0$, clearly the Hilbert transform has a unique inverse. These observations deserve formal recording.

Theorem 3.   Define the Hilbert transform of f (which now may be complex) as the output of the filter having frequency response $J(\omega)$ when f is the input. If f_i is the Hilbert transform of f, then the frequency response $-J(\omega)$ provides the inverse transform save for the d-c component of f. That is, if f has zero† direct current, then the Hilbert transform and inverse Hilbert transforms have frequency responses as depicted in Figure 6-13.

† $\lim\limits_{T \to \infty} \dfrac{1}{2T} \int_{-T}^{T} f(t)\, dt = 0.$

Many properties of Hilbert transforms are obvious in the light of the above definition; e.g., the Hilbert transform is linear. Of course, the main attraction of the *frequency-domain* definition of the Hilbert transforms is that it renders obvious the inverse transform.

The only basic problem now facing us is that of obtaining an explicit (time domain) representation of the Hilbert transform. For this, observe that if

$$J(\omega; \epsilon, A) = \frac{1}{\pi} \left(\int_{-A}^{-\epsilon} \frac{e^{-j\omega t}}{t} \, dt + \int_{\epsilon}^{A} \frac{e^{-j\omega t}}{t} \, dt \right)$$

$$= \frac{-j}{\pi} \left(\int_{-A}^{-\epsilon} \frac{\sin \omega t}{t} \, dt + \int_{\epsilon}^{A} \frac{\sin \omega t}{t} \, dt \right)$$

then

$$\lim_{\substack{\epsilon \to 0^+ \\ A \to \infty}} J(\omega; \epsilon, A) = \begin{cases} -j & \text{if } \omega > 0 \\ j & \text{if } \omega < 0 \\ 0 & \text{if } \omega = 0 \end{cases}$$

since

$$\int_{-\infty}^{\infty} \frac{\sin \omega t}{t} \, dt$$

has said values. In turn,

$$f_i(t) = \frac{1}{2\pi} \int_{-\infty}^{\infty} \lim_{\substack{\epsilon \to 0^+ \\ A \to \infty}} J(\omega; \epsilon, A) F(\omega) e^{j\omega t} \, d\omega$$

if $F(\omega)$ is the Fourier transform of $f(t)$. Since J is bounded, we can use the dominated convergence theorem (Chap. 2, Theorem 7) to interchange the integral and limit operation [assuming $F(\omega)$ is absolutely integrable]. This gives

$$f_i(t) = \lim_{\substack{\epsilon \to 0^+ \\ A \to \infty}} \frac{1}{2\pi} \int_{-\infty}^{\infty} J(\omega; \epsilon, A) F(\omega) e^{j\omega t} \, d\omega$$

Recall that J is the Fourier transform of $(1/\pi t) I(t; \epsilon, A)$, where

$$I(t; \epsilon, A) \equiv \begin{cases} 1 & \text{if } -A < t < -\epsilon \\ 1 & \text{if } \epsilon < t < A \\ 0 & \text{for other } t \end{cases}$$

Hence, by the convolution theorem,

$$f_i(t) = \lim_{\substack{\epsilon \to 0^+ \\ A \to \infty}} f * \left[\frac{1}{\pi t} I(t; \epsilon, A) \right]$$

or

$$f_i(t) = \lim_{\substack{\epsilon \to 0^+ \\ A \to \infty}} \left[\frac{1}{\pi} \int_{-A+t}^{-\epsilon+t} \frac{f(\tau)}{t - \tau} \, d\tau + \frac{1}{\pi} \int_{\epsilon+t}^{A+t} \frac{f(\tau)}{t - \tau} \, d\tau \right]$$

By definition this is the Cauchy principal part for

$$f_i(t) = \frac{1}{\pi} \int_{-\infty}^{\infty} \frac{f(\tau)}{t - \tau} \, d\tau$$

This is the explicit formula for the Hilbert transform of f.

Also, we have the explicit formulation of $\hat{f}$ in terms of f depicted in Figure 6-14 for real f. The impulse response corresponding to $-J(\omega)$ is obviously the negative of the impulse response corresponding to J. Therefore, the explicit formula for the inverse Hilbert transform is

$$f = -\frac{1}{\pi t} * f_i$$

The companion to Theorem 3 is the following.

Theorem 4. If f has no d-c component and f_i is the Hilbert transform of f, then

$$f_i(t) = \frac{1}{\pi}\int_{-\infty}^{\infty}\frac{f(\tau)}{t-\tau}\,d\tau \quad \text{and} \quad f(t) = -\frac{1}{\pi}\int_{-\infty}^{\infty}\frac{f_i(\tau)}{t-\tau}\,d\tau$$

when the integrals are taken as Cauchy principal parts.

In addition to the proof given above, Prob. 5 describes a proof under the gigantic assumption that f is an analytic function.

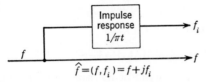

$$\hat{f}=(f,f_i)=f+jf_i$$

FIGURE 6-14.   Explicit formulation of $\hat{f}$ for real f.

If we generalize Fourier transform to Fourier-Stieltjes transform (or, better yet, to Wiener's generalized transform), all the notions in this section are generalized. Thus, any function of finite average power† can be treated with Hilbert transforms.

Example 4. Suppose $f(t) = \cos\omega_0 t$. Then

$$f_i(t) = \frac{1}{\pi}\int_{-\infty}^{\infty}\frac{\cos\omega_0\tau}{t-\tau}\,d\tau = \frac{1}{\pi}\int_{-\infty}^{\infty}\cos\left[\omega_0(t-\tau)-\omega_0 t\right]\,d\tau$$

$$= \frac{\cos\omega_0 t}{\pi}\int_{-\infty}^{\infty}\frac{\cos\left[\omega_0(t-\tau)\right]}{t-\tau}\,d\tau + \frac{\sin\omega_0 t}{\pi}\int_{-\infty}^{\infty}\frac{\sin\left[\omega_0(t-\tau)\right]}{t-\tau}\,d\tau$$

The first integral is zero since its integrand is odd about $\tau = t$; the second integral is π if $\omega_0 > 0$, which we can assume since cosine is an even function, and we have $\sin\omega_0 t$ as the Hilbert transform of $\cos\omega_0 t$. The same result is obtained more easily by using the frequency-response definition of the Hilbert transform. For if

$$f(t) = \tfrac{1}{2}(e^{j\omega_0 t} + \tfrac{1}{2}e^{-j\omega_0 t})$$

then

$$f_i(t) = \frac{-j}{2}e^{j\omega_0 t} + \frac{j}{2}e^{-j\omega_0 t}$$

† That is,

$$\lim_{T\to\infty}\frac{1}{2T}\int_{-T}^{T}|f(t)|^2\,dt < \infty$$

which is Euler's formula for $\sin \omega_0 t$. Also,

$$\hat{f} = e^{j\omega_0 t}$$

which is the output of a filter having frequency response

$$V(\omega) = \begin{cases} 2 & \text{for } \omega > 0 \\ 0 & \text{for } \omega < 0 \end{cases}$$

when $\frac{1}{2}(e^{j\omega_0 t} + e^{-j\omega_0 t})$

is the input.

We wish next to consider the use of Hilbert transforms (and other tools) in relating the real and imaginary parts of transfer functions.

6-4 RELATIONS BETWEEN COMPONENTS OF REALIZABLE TRANSFER FUNCTIONS

We first consider the problem of relating the real and imaginary parts as Hilbert transform pairs. This follows not too gracefully but simply from the work of preceding sections. The only difficulties involve signs, 2π's, and interchanging the roles of t and ω.

AS HILBERT TRANSFORM PAIRS

From Sec. 6-3 we have the following (among other things): Let $\hat{F}$ be the Fourier transform of $\hat{f}$, let $\hat{F}(\omega) = 0$ for $\omega < 0$, let $f = \operatorname{Re}\hat{f}$, and let $f_i = \operatorname{Im}\hat{f}$; then $f_i = 1/\pi t * f$ and $f = -1/\pi t * f_i$. In this result we can view $\hat{F}(\omega)$ as $V(\omega)F(\omega)$, where F is the Fourier transform of f, but such a point of view is not needed in this section. As a brief diversion, this last remark will be verified directly. Let $\hat{F} = \hat{u} + j\hat{v}$, and let F be the Fourier transform of f with $F = u + jv$. Since f is real, u is an even function and v is an odd function; that is, $F(-\omega) = \overline{F(\omega)}$ or $u(-\omega) + jv(-\omega) = u(\omega) - jv(\omega)$. Now

$$\hat{f}(t) = \frac{1}{2\pi} \int_0^\infty e^{j\omega t}\hat{F}(\omega)\, d\omega$$

and hence

$$f(t) = \operatorname{Re}\hat{f} = \frac{1}{2\pi} \int_0^\infty \hat{u}(\omega)\cos \omega t\, d\omega - \frac{1}{2\pi} \int_0^\infty v(\omega)\sin \omega t\, d\omega$$

On the other hand,

$$f(t) = \frac{1}{2\pi} \int_{-\infty}^\infty e^{j\omega t}[u(\omega) + jv(\omega)]\, d\omega = \frac{1}{2\pi} \int_{-\infty}^\infty u(\omega)\cos \omega t\, d\omega$$
$$- \frac{1}{2\pi} \int_{-\infty}^\infty v(\omega)\sin \omega t\, d\omega$$

where the imaginary part drops out because of the evenness of u and the oddness of v. Also, by these properties both of the remaining integrals are even functions of ω [since $v(\omega)$ and $\sin \omega t$ are both odd, their product is even]; hence,

$$f(t) = \frac{1}{2\pi} \int_0^\infty 2u(\omega) \cos \omega t \, d\omega - \frac{1}{2\pi} \int_0^\infty 2v(\omega) \sin \omega t \, d\omega$$

This, along with the other formula for f, gives $\hat{u} + j\hat{v} = 2(u + jv)$ for $\omega > 0$—by the uniqueness of Fourier transforms. That is, $\hat{F} = VF$, as was obvious from earlier considerations.

Returning to the first remark of this section, we shall write it with the roles of variables ω and t reversed: If $\hat{f}(t)$ is the Fourier transform of $\hat{F}(\omega)$,

$$\hat{f}(t) = \int_{-\infty}^\infty e^{-j\omega t} \hat{F}(\omega) \, d\omega$$

and $\hat{f}$ is zero for $t < 0$; and if $\hat{F}(\omega) = \hat{R}(\omega) + j\hat{I}(\omega)$, where $\hat{R}$ and $\hat{I}$ are the real and imaginary parts of $\hat{F}$, then $\hat{I}(\omega) = 1/\pi\omega * \hat{R}(\omega)$ and $\hat{R}(\omega) = -1/\pi\omega * \hat{I}(\omega)$. Now it is easy to see that the condition that a function of time be zero for negative t implies that its Fourier transform has real and imaginary parts which are Hilbert transform pairs. When we restrict our attention to realizable convoluting systems, functions of t which are zero for negative t arise quite naturally as the associated impulse-response functions. The Fourier transforms of said impulse responses are transfer functions, and relations between components of transfer functions are of some interest to us. The version obtained above by simply reversing the roles of ω and t is not quite what we want. This occurred because of the lack of perfect symmetry between the Fourier transform and its inverse. Slight additional modifications provide the final form.

Theorem 5. Let $H(\omega)$ be the transfer function of a realizable linear time-invariant convoluting system, let $R(\omega) = \text{Re } H(\omega)$, and let $I(\omega) = \text{Im } H(\omega)$; then

$$X(\omega) = \frac{1}{\pi} \int_{-\infty}^\infty \frac{R(\lambda)}{\lambda - \omega} \, d\lambda \qquad \text{and} \qquad R(\omega) = \frac{-1}{\pi} \int_{-\infty}^\infty \frac{I(\lambda)}{\lambda - \omega} \, d\lambda$$

The formula given here to obtain X from R is often called the Hilbert transform, but it differs in sign from the formula we use. Of course the proof involves simple modification of the relations we obtained between R and I above. If

$$\hat{f}(t) = h(t) = \frac{1}{2\pi} \int_{-\infty}^\infty e^{j\omega t} H(\omega) \, d\omega$$

then $(1/2\pi)H(-\omega) = \hat{F}(\omega)$, $R(\omega) = 2\pi\hat{R}(-\omega)$, and $I(\omega) = 2\pi\hat{I}(-\omega)$. In turn,

$$I(-\omega) = \frac{1}{\pi\omega} * R(-\omega) \qquad \text{or} \qquad I(-\omega) = \frac{1}{\pi} \int_{-\infty}^\infty \frac{R(-\theta)}{\omega - \theta} \, d\theta$$

If we set $-\theta = \lambda$ and replace ω with $-\omega$, we get

$$I(\omega) = \frac{1}{\pi} \int_{-\infty}^\infty \frac{R(\lambda)}{\lambda - \omega} \, d\lambda$$

as was to be shown.   Similarly,

$$R(\omega) = \frac{-1}{\pi} \int_{-\infty}^{\infty} \frac{I(\lambda)}{\lambda - \omega} \, d\lambda$$

follows from the formula for obtaining $\hat{R}$ from $\hat{I}$.

In view of Theorem 5 we see that the condition that the impulse response of a network be zero for negative time leads to the restriction on the transfer function that only one component can be selected arbitrarily.   For example, if we specify $R(\omega)$ and its inverse Fourier transform is $r(t)$, then the impulse response of a realizable network for which R is the real part of the transfer function is $h(t) = V(t)r(t)$, where

$$V(t) = \begin{cases} 2 & \text{for } t > 0 \\ 0 & \text{for } t < 0 \end{cases}$$

What amounts to the same thing, $I(\omega)$ is constrained to be the inverse Hilbert transform of $R(\omega)$.

Example 5.   Let us consider the *frequency-domain* version of Example 4. In this case we can take $R(\omega) = \cos T\omega$, where T is a positive constant.   Of course $I(\omega) = -1/\pi\omega * R(\omega)$; from the previous example this gives

$$I(\omega) = -\sin T\omega$$

In turn, $H(\omega) = \cos T\omega - j \sin T\omega$ or $H(\omega) = e^{-jT\omega}$, which is the transfer function of a delay line of delay T.   That is, for arbitrary input $f(t)$, if we take the output to be $f(t - T)$, the transfer function is $e^{-jT\omega}$.   Though $\cos T\omega$ is the real part of the nonrealizable frequency response $e^{jT\omega}$, Theorem 5 automatically leads to a realizable transfer function.   Note that in this example we are successfully applying the theory to functions of ω and t which are not Fourier-transformable even though Fourier transforms were used to develop the theory.   The success in applying the theory to certain functions which do not have a Fourier transform is no surprise if Fourier-Stieltjes or Wiener's generalized transforms are used in the development of the theory.

Example 6.   Suppose

$$R(\omega) = \frac{a}{a^2 + (\omega + b)^2}$$

is the real part of a realizable transfer function and we wish to find $I(\omega)$ and $H(\omega)$.   Of course,

$$I(\omega) = \frac{a}{\pi} \int_{-\infty}^{\infty} \frac{d\lambda}{(\lambda - \omega)[a^2 + (\lambda + b)^2]}$$

This integral can be evaluated if we expand the integrand in partial fractions:

$$\frac{1}{(\lambda - \omega)[a^2 + (\lambda + b)^2]} = \frac{\alpha(\lambda + b) + \beta}{a^2 + (\lambda + b)^2} + \frac{\gamma}{\lambda - \omega}$$

where α, β, and γ are constants yet to be determined. The manner in which the linear function of λ is written in the first term is merely a matter of convenience. If we multiply both sides by $\lambda - \omega$ and let λ approach ω, we get $\gamma = 1/[a^2 + (\omega + b)^2]$. If we set $\lambda = -b$, we get

$$\frac{\beta}{a^2} + \frac{\gamma}{-b-\omega} = \frac{1}{(-b-\omega)a^2}$$

which, with the known value of γ, gives

$$-\beta = \frac{\omega + b}{a^2 + (\omega + b)^2}$$

after a little manipulation. The value of α is not needed; but to obtain the proper behavior as $\lambda \to \infty$, it is clear that $\alpha = -\gamma$. The above expansion leads to three integrals; however,

$$\gamma \int_{-\infty}^{\infty} \frac{d\lambda}{\lambda - \omega} = 0 \quad \text{and} \quad \alpha \int_{-\infty}^{\infty} \frac{\lambda + b}{a^2 + (\lambda + b)^2}\, d\lambda = 0$$

since the first integrand is odd about $\lambda = \omega$ and the second one is odd about $\lambda = -b$ (recall that Cauchy-principal-part integrals are used and hence the integrals exist). Thus,

$$I(\omega) = \frac{a\beta}{\pi} \int_{-\infty}^{\infty} \frac{d\lambda}{a^2 + (\lambda + b)^2}$$

or, if we let $\theta = (\lambda + b)/|a|$,

$$I(\omega) = \frac{a|a|}{a^2} \frac{\beta}{\pi} \int_{-\infty}^{\infty} \frac{d\theta}{1 + \theta^2}$$

To be specific, let $a < 0$. Then

$$\frac{a|a|}{a^2} = -1$$

and we have

$$I(\omega) = -\frac{\beta}{\pi} \arctan \theta \Big]_{-\infty}^{\infty} = -\beta$$

Therefore,

$$I(\omega) = \frac{\omega + b}{a^2 + (\omega + b)^2}$$

Finally,

$$H(\omega) = \frac{a + j(\omega + b)}{a^2 + (\omega + b)^2} = \frac{1}{a - j(\omega + b)}$$

or

$$H(\omega) = \frac{1}{-j\omega + (a - jb)}$$

which corresponds to a realizable network since $a < 0$, that is, the pole is in the left half plane.

This last example can be extended to obtain simple rules for finding I from R (or R from I) when they are rational functions of ω. However, it is just as easy to attack this simple special case directly in terms of partial-fraction expansions. The method obtained in this way provides no new concepts, but it does provide a very practical approach to finding one component of a transfer function when the other component is specified (as a rational function).

IN TERMS OF PARTIAL-FRACTION EXPANSIONS†

We now consider the relationship between real and imaginary components of a transfer function under the restriction that the transfer function $H(p)$ is a rational function. The key ideas will be given as simple lemmas which lead up to the desired result.

Lemma 1. $H(p) = E(p) + O(p)$, where E is even and O is odd iff

$$E(p) = \frac{H(p) + H(-p)}{2} \qquad O(p) = \frac{H(p) - H(-p)}{2}$$

The *if* part of the theorem is easily seen by inspection. For the *only if* we have $H(p) = E(p) + O(p)$ with E even and O odd. In turn, $H(-p) = E(p) - O(p)$. Addition gives $E(p) = [H(p) + H(-p)]/2$ and subtraction gives $O(p) = [H(p) - H(-p)]/2$, as was to be shown.

Lemma 2. Let $H(p)$ be a proper rational function with poles only in the left half plane off the $j\omega$ axis; then (1) $E(p)$ can be written as $(PFL)_E + (PFR)_E$, where $(PFL)_E$ denotes the terms of the partial-fraction expansion for $E(p)$ which correspond to poles in the left half plane (PFR denoting terms in the right half of the p plane) and $H(p) = 2(PFL)_E$; (2) $O(p)$ can be written as $(PFL)_O + (PFR)_O$, where $(PFL)_O$ denotes the terms of the partial-fraction expansion of $O(p)$ which correspond to poles in the left half plane and $H(p) = 2(PFL)_O$.

This lemma is a trivial observation in that

$$E(p) = \frac{H(p)}{2} + \frac{H(-p)}{2}$$

where $H(p)$ has poles only in the left half plane and hence $H(-p)$ has poles only in the right half plane (we make use of the uniqueness of the partial-fraction expansion). Similar reasoning can be applied for $O(p)$. Note also that

$$(PFR)_E = \frac{H(-p)}{2} \qquad \text{and} \qquad (PFR)_O = -\frac{H(-p)}{2}$$

Lemma 3. If $H(\bar{p}) = \overline{H(p)}$, $R(\omega) = \text{Re } H(j\omega)$, and $I(\omega) = \text{Im } H(j\omega)$, then when $p = j\omega$, $E(p) = R(p/j)$ and $O(p) = jI(p/j)$, where E and O are the unique functions defined by Lemma 1.

For the proof we have $H(j\omega) = E(j\omega) + O(j\omega)$ and $H(-j\omega) = E(j\omega) - O(j\omega) = \overline{H(j\omega)}$. Addition gives $R(\omega) = E(j\omega)$, and subtraction gives $jI(\omega) = O(j\omega)$, as was to be shown.

----

† The remainder of the chapter is included partly as a matter of completeness rather than as a matter of meeting primary objectives.

If H is a rational function, $R(p/j)$ and $I(p/j)$ are rational and can readily be analytically continued to all complex p. In turn, $E(p) = R(p/j)$ and $O(p) = jI(p/j)$ for all complex p if the analytic continuations of R and I are used [note that $R(p/j)$ and $I(p/j)$ are complex-valued when p is off the $j\omega$ axis].

The last two lemmas provide a method for obtaining one component of a transfer function from the other component. Actually, they provide a method for obtaining $H(p)$ from $R(\omega)$ or $I(\omega)$, and once $H(p)$ is known the other component is easily found from its definition; however, in most applications we are actually interested in obtaining $H(p)$ from $R(\omega)$ or from $I(\omega)$. The method made available by Lemmas 2 and 3 will be summarized as a theorem.

Theorem 6. If $H(p)$ is a proper rational transfer function of a real system and H has its poles in the left half plane off the $j\omega$ axis, then $H(p)$ can be obtained from $R(\omega) = \operatorname{Re} H(j\omega)$ and from $I(\omega) = \operatorname{Im} H(j\omega)$ in the following way: (1) From $R(\omega)$, formulate $E(p) = R(p/j)$ and analytically continue to all complex p [the continuation is trivial since $R(\omega)$ is rational, and hence it simply involves letting p take on complex values]. Expand $E(p)$ in partial fractions, and then $H(p)/2$ is given by the terms of the partial-fraction expansion which correspond to poles in the left half plane. (2) From $I(\omega)$, formulate $O(p) = jI(p/j)$, and $H(p)/2$ is given by the terms of the partial-fraction expansion of $O(p)$ which correspond to poles in the left half plane as before.

The most interesting difference between Theorems 6 and 5 is that in Theorem 6 we required that the system be real such that $H(-j\omega) = \overline{H(j\omega)}$ and we could use Lemma 3, while in Theorem 5 we did not require that the system be real. That is, in Theorem 5 it was not necessary that

$$h(t) = \frac{1}{2\pi} \int_{-\infty}^{\infty} e^{j\omega t} H(j\omega) \, d\omega$$

be a real-valued function.

Example 7. Suppose $I(\omega) = \omega/(a^2 + \omega^2)$, where a is real and negative. Then

$$O(p) = j \frac{p/j}{a^2 + (p/j)^2} = \frac{-p}{p^2 - a^2} \qquad \text{or} \qquad O(p) = \frac{A}{p - a} + \frac{B}{p + a}$$

and we easily see that $A = -a/2a = -\tfrac{1}{2}$. Hence $H(p) = -1/(p - a)$, which agrees with Example 6 if b in said example is set equal to zero. Of course $R(\omega) = a/(a^2 + \omega^2)$ as before.

RELATIONS BETWEEN AMPLITUDE AND PHASE

The primary purpose of Sec. 6-4 has already been fulfilled; namely, the components of the transfer function of realizable systems have been shown to be Hilbert transform pairs. In addition, a practical way to go from a component of a rational transfer function to the entire transfer function has been described. The final task is to extend the work to relations between amplitude and phase. Integral formulas analogous to Hilbert transforms and practical computational methods can be developed.

For the integral formulas, we introduce the following notations:

$$W(p) = \log |H(p)| + j\phi(p)$$

where $H(p) = |H(p)|e^{j\phi(p)}$ and the $\log |H(p)|$ is the ordinary real logarithm. Also, let $\tilde{A}(p) = \log |H(p)|$, $A(\omega) = \tilde{A}(j\omega)$, and $\alpha(\omega) = \phi(j\omega)$. Of course, $A(\omega)$ is the amplitude-frequency response on a logarithmic basis [for example, $20 \log_{10} |H(j\omega)|$ is the *gain* in decibels] and $\alpha(\omega)$ is the phase response. The problem of interest here is that of obtaining formulas relating the real and imaginary parts of $W(j\omega)$, that is, formulas relating A and α.

Conditions commonly satisfied by $H(p)$ are not always satisfied by $W(p)$; this leads to the fact that the amplitude and phase of H are not quite so tightly tied as the real and imaginary parts of H. As illustrations of this, consider the following two modifications of phase response which leave the amplitude response unchanged:

1. Multiplication of $H(j\omega)$ by $e^{-j\omega T}$; this introduces a linear phase response.
2. Multiplication of $H(j\omega)$ by $[j\omega - (a + jb)]/[j\omega + (a + jb)]$, where $a > 0$. Note that

$$\left| \frac{j\omega - (a + jb)}{j\omega + (a + jb)} \right| = 1$$

The first illustration corresponds to following the system, which has transfer function $H(p)$, by a delay line; and the second corresponds to following said system by an "all-pass" network which introduces a phase shift of

$$-2 \arctan \frac{b + \omega}{a}$$

These examples make it clear that the assumption that $H(p)$ corresponds to a realizable system is not adequate to provide a unique relationship between amplitude and phase responses. This possible lack of uniqueness implies that $W(j\omega)$ may fail to satisfy the hypothesis of Theorem 5. Specifically, in the first illustration ωT is added to $\alpha(\omega)$ and this linear term would generally render $W(j\omega)$ not Fourier-transformable. In turn, the proof of Theorem 5, which was based on Fourier transforms, cannot be applied to $W(j\omega)$. In the second illustration, the factor $p - (a + jb)$ introduces a zero in $H(p)$ in the right half plane. This causes no difficulty in relating R and I of Theorem 5 since H still corresponds to a realizable system. However, a zero in H produces a pole in W ($\log z$ goes to infinity as z goes to zero), and this pole in the right half plane renders the inverse Fourier transform of $W(p)$ nonzero for negative t; that is, W cannot play the role of a realizable frequency-response function if H has zeros in the right half plane.

If
$$\lim_{p \to \infty} H(p) = 0$$

then
$$\lim_{p \to \infty} W(p) = \infty$$

Typically, $H(p)$ is asymptotic to C/p^n for $|p|$ large; in this case $|W(p)|$ is asymptotic to $-nC \log |p|$, which goes to ∞; however, it goes to infinity very slowly.† Thus to obtain α from A as an integral over the ω axis, a factor to provide convergence for the integral is needed. We shall guess the appropriate form by manipulating our Hilbert transform formula.

Recall that
$$I(\omega) = \frac{1}{\pi} \int_{-\infty}^{\infty} \frac{R(\lambda)}{\lambda - \omega} \, d\lambda$$

Since we are using the Cauchy principal part,
$$R(\omega) \int_{-\infty}^{\infty} \frac{d\lambda}{\lambda - \omega} = 0$$

and hence we can write I thus:
$$I(\omega) = \frac{1}{\pi} \int_{-\infty}^{\infty} \frac{R(\lambda) - R(\omega)}{\lambda - \omega} \, d\lambda$$

To obtain better behavior in the denominator for large λ, we now multiply the numerator and denominator by $\lambda + \omega$ to obtain
$$I(\omega) = \frac{1}{\pi} \int_{-\infty}^{\infty} \frac{\lambda R(\lambda) - \lambda R(\omega)}{\lambda^2 - \omega^2} \, d\lambda + \frac{\omega}{\pi} \int_{-\infty}^{\infty} \frac{R(\lambda) - R(\omega)}{\lambda^2 - \omega^2} \, d\lambda$$

Finally, if we assume that R is an even function (which is the case if H is the transfer function of a real parameter system), the integrand of the first integral is an odd function of λ; that is,
$$\frac{-\lambda R(-\lambda) - (-\lambda) R(\omega)}{(-\lambda)^2 - \omega^2} = -\frac{\lambda R(\lambda) - \lambda R(\omega)}{\lambda^2 - \omega^2}$$

if $R(-\lambda) = R(\lambda)$. Since we are integrating over the symmetrical interval $(-\infty, \infty)$, the integral of this odd function is zero. Hence as a somewhat interesting corollary to Theorem 5 we have
$$I(\omega) = \frac{\omega}{\pi} \int_{-\infty}^{\infty} \frac{R(\lambda) - R(\omega)}{\lambda^2 - \omega^2} \, d\lambda$$

when we append the assumption that R is an even function. We shall now show that the above formula can be applied to the real and imaginary parts of W, that is, to the "log-amplitude" and phase responses.

† In particular,
$$\lim_{p \to \infty} \frac{\log |p|}{|p|^{\delta}} = 0 \qquad \text{if } \delta > 0$$

This may be easier to see if we write $|p|$ as e^u and let $u \to \infty$; then the ratio is $u/e^{\delta u}$, which clearly goes to zero as u goes to ∞.

Theorem 7. Let $W(p)$ be a regular function for Re $p \geq 0$ [which is the case if $H(p)$ is regular for Re $p \geq 0$ and H has no zero in the right half plane]; let†

$$\lim_{\rho \to \infty} \int_C \frac{W(p) - A(\omega_0)}{p^2 + \omega_0{}^2} \, dp = 0$$

where C is the semicircle in the right half plane of radius ρ about $p = 0$; and let $H(-j\omega) = \overline{H(j\omega)}$. Then

$$\alpha(\omega) = \frac{\omega}{\pi} \int_{-\infty}^{\infty} \frac{A(\lambda) - A(\omega)}{\lambda^2 - \omega^2} \, d\lambda = \frac{2\omega}{\pi} \int_0^{\infty} \frac{A(\lambda) - A(\omega)}{\lambda^2 - \omega^2} \, d\lambda$$

PROOF: The technique used for this proof is the same as that used to prove Cauchy's formula (Theorem 28) in Sec. 2-4. Consider the following function, which is regular for Re $p \geq 0$ except at $p = \pm j\omega_0$:

$$F(p) = \frac{W(p) - A(\omega_0)}{p^2 + \omega_0{}^2}$$

We integrate this function around the contour indicated in Figure 6-15. Since $F(p)$ is regular on and inside the indicated contour, the integral is

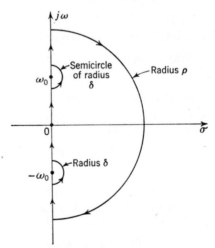

FIGURE 6-15.   Integration contour.

zero. As ρ goes to ∞, the integral on the semicircle of radius ρ goes to zero by hypothesis. Thus if we let $\rho \to \infty$, we have

$$\int_{|\omega \pm \omega_0| > \delta} F(j\omega) \, d(j\omega) = - \int_{\substack{\text{on small} \\ \text{semicircles}}} F(p) \, dp$$

† This is the case if
$$H(p) \to Cp^n$$
as $p \to \infty$, where n is an integer (positive, negative, or zero).

Consider the semicircle centered at $p = j\omega_0$ and view the integrand as

$$\frac{1}{2j\omega_0}\left[\frac{W(p) - A(\omega_0)}{p - j\omega_0} - \frac{W(p) - A(\omega_0)}{p + j\omega_0}\right]$$

Since the length of the path of integration is only $\pi\delta$ and the second term is bounded in the neighborhood of $p = j\omega_0$, the contribution of this second term to the "top" small semicircle goes to zero as δ goes to zero. Since $W(p)$ is regular (and hence continuous) at $p = j\omega_0$, the first term is approximately

$$\frac{1}{2j\omega_0}[W(j\omega_0) - A(\omega_0)]\int_{\substack{\text{top} \\ \text{semicircle}}}\frac{dp}{p - j\omega_0}$$

and if we let $p - j\omega_0 = \delta e^{j\theta}$, the indicated integral is

$$j\int_{-\pi/2}^{\pi/2}\frac{\delta e^{j\theta}\,d\theta}{\delta e^{j\theta}} = j\pi$$

In a similar fashion, the semicircle at $p = -j\omega_0$ gives

$$-\frac{j\pi}{2j\omega_0}[W(-j\omega_0) - A(\omega_0)]$$

If $H(-j\omega) = \overline{H(j\omega)}$, R is even and I is odd. Hence $|H| = \sqrt{R^2 + I^2}$ is even and in turn $A(\omega)$ is an even function. Also, $|H(-\omega)|e^{j\alpha(-\omega)} = |H(-\omega)|e^{-j\alpha(\omega)}$. Therefore, α is an odd function. Thus the contributions from the small semicircles can be written as

$$\frac{\pi}{2\omega_0}[j\alpha(\omega_0) - j\alpha(-\omega_0)] = j\frac{\pi\alpha(\omega_0)}{\omega_0}$$

We now have

$$j\frac{\pi}{\omega_0}\alpha(\omega_0) = -\int_{-j\infty}^{j\infty}\frac{A(\omega) + j\alpha(\omega) - A(\omega_0)}{-\omega^2 + \omega_0^2}\,d(j\omega)$$

Since $\alpha(\omega)$ is odd,

$$\int_{-\infty}^{\infty}\frac{\alpha(\omega)}{\omega_0^2 - \omega^2}\,d\omega = 0$$

The final form is

$$\alpha(\omega_0) = \frac{\omega_0}{\pi}\int_{-\infty}^{\infty}\frac{A(\omega) - A(\omega_0)}{\omega^2 - \omega_0^2}\,d\omega$$

as was to be proved if we replace ω with λ and ω_0 with ω. Of course the integrand is an even function and hence we can integrate from 0 to ∞ and multiply by 2.

The inverse form of Theorem 7 can be obtained by simply replacing $W(p)$ with $W_1(p) = [W(p) - A(0)]/p$. We define $W_1(0)$ as

$$\lim_{p\to 0}\frac{W(p) - A(0)}{p} = W'(0)$$

Of course the indicated limit is the definition of $W'(0)$ save for the fact that we wrote $A(0)$ in place of $W(0)$. However, $A(0) = W(0)$ since $\alpha(0) = 0$. This last condition, $\alpha(0) = 0$, follows from the fact that α is odd, which implies that $\alpha(0) = \alpha(-0) = -\alpha(0)$ and only zero is its own negative. In the above considerations it was implicitly assumed that $W(0)$ was finite. Problem 12 provides an inverse relation which can be used if W has a simple pole at $p = 0$ provided that

$$\lim_{p \to \infty} W(p)$$

is finite (which calls for a transfer function which does not approach zero as p goes to ∞).

Theorem 8.   Let the hypotheses of Theorem 7 hold for $W_1(p)$.   Then

$$A(\omega) - A(0) = -\frac{\omega^2}{\pi} \int_{-\infty}^{\infty} \frac{(1/\lambda)\alpha(\lambda) - (1/\omega)\alpha(\omega)}{\lambda^2 - \omega^2}\, d\lambda$$

To see this, observe that if $W = A + j\alpha$, then

$$W_1 = \frac{A + j\alpha - A(0)}{j\omega} = \frac{\alpha}{\omega} + j\frac{1}{\omega}[A(0) - A(\omega)]$$

where α/ω is even and $[A(0) - A(\omega)]/\omega$ is odd.   Applying Theorem 7 to W_1 gives

$$\frac{A(0) - A(\omega)}{\omega} = \frac{\omega}{\pi} \int_{-\infty}^{\infty} \frac{\alpha(\lambda)/\lambda - \alpha(\omega)/\omega}{\lambda^2 - \omega^2}\, d\lambda$$

as was to be shown.

In the above two theorems, we required that $H(p)$ have no zeros in the right half plane (zeros of H provide poles for W and W_1). If H corresponds to a realizable system, we call the system *minimum phase* iff H has no zeros and no poles in the right half plane.

If we restrict our attention to rational transfer functions, a simple method for computing the transfer function H (and in turn the phase of H) from its amplitude can easily be formulated. For this, let $M(\omega) = |H(j\omega)|^2$ and let $\phi(j\omega) = \alpha(\omega)$ be the phase response as before.

Theorem 9.   Let $H(p)$ be rational, let $H(p) = \overline{H(\bar{p})}$, and let all the zeros and poles of H be in the left half plane off the $j\omega$ axis; then if $M(p/j)$ is factored into two parts, one having all the zeros and poles of $M(p/j)$ which are in the left half plane and the other having all the zeros and poles of $M(p/j)$ which are in the right half plane, then the part which has the zeros and poles in the left half plane is $H(p)$ except possibly for sign (it is assumed that when M is written in factored form the constant C^2 introduced below in the proof is split between the factors, with $|C|$ going to each).

The proof is quite simple; however, there is a very elementary point to be mentioned first. If a is a zero of $H(p)$, clearly $\bar{a}$ is also a zero of $H(p)$. For consider the fact that $H(\bar{a}) = \overline{H(a)} = \bar{0} = 0$. Similarly, if b is a pole,

$$\lim_{p \to b} H(p) = \lim_{p \to b} \overline{H(\bar{p})} = \lim_{p \to \bar{b}} \overline{H(p)}$$

which does not exist if

$$\lim_{p \to b} H(p)$$

does not exist. Finally, if a is a zero of order K, $\bar{a}$ is a zero of order K. To see this, suppose $K = 2$. Then a is a zero of

$$H_1(p) = \frac{H(p)}{(p - a)(p - \bar{a})}$$

It is easy to see that $H_1(\bar{p}) = \overline{H_1(p)}$ and hence $\bar{a}$ is a zero of $H_1(p)$, which means that $\bar{a}$ is at least a second-order zero of H. The proof can be continued for arbitrary K by induction. A similar argument holds for poles. Thus we see that the zeros and poles of the transfer function of real parameter systems occur in conjugate pairs, with the members of any pair being of equal order.

We now write H in factored form:

$$H(p) = C \frac{\displaystyle\prod_{i=1}^{n} (p - a_i)}{\displaystyle\prod_{k=1}^{m} (p - b_k)}$$

where Re $a_i < 0$ and Re $b_k < 0$. As another detail, observe that C is real. To see this, let p have a real value σ which is not a pole or zero of H. Then $\overline{H(\sigma)} = H(\sigma)$ gives

$$\bar{C} \frac{\displaystyle\prod_{k=1}^{n} (\sigma - \bar{a}_i)}{\displaystyle\prod_{k=1}^{m} (\sigma - \bar{b}_k)} = C \frac{\displaystyle\prod_{i=1}^{n} (\sigma - a_i)}{\displaystyle\prod_{k=1}^{m} (\sigma - b_k)}$$

However, since poles and zeros occur in conjugate pairs (with equal orders) the same numbers appear in the products on the left and right (only the arrangement may be changed). Hence we can cancel and get $C = \bar{C}$; that is, C is real.

Since $M(\omega) = H(j\omega)\overline{H(j\omega)} = H(j\omega)H(-j\omega)$,

$$M(\omega) = C \frac{\Pi(j\omega - a_i)}{\Pi(j\omega - b_k)} C \frac{\Pi(-j\omega - a_i)}{\Pi(-j\omega - b_k)}$$

Obviously, if we analytically continue in p with $\omega = p/j$ we get

$$M\left(\frac{p}{j}\right) = C \frac{\Pi(p - a_i)}{\Pi(p - b_k)} C \frac{\Pi(-p - a_i)}{\Pi(-p - b_k)}$$

If a_i is a zero of H, $-a_i$ appears as a zero of the second factor in M. Clearly, all the zeros and poles of the second factor are in the right half plane while the zeros and poles of the first factor are in the left half plane. No cancellation is possible because of this separation; hence if one starts with $M(p/j)$ all the indicated zeros and poles appear, which proves the theorem except for one more trivial point. If we start with $M(p/j)$ and factor, only C^2 is available. But C can only be determined within a sign from C^2. In terms of finding phase response, we have an ambiguity of a constant factor of π in phase.

Example 8. Suppose

$$|H(j\omega)|^2 = 9\frac{\omega^2 + 1}{\omega^4 + 1}$$

Then $M\left(\dfrac{p}{j}\right) = 9\dfrac{1 - p^2}{p^4 + 1} = \dfrac{9(p + 1)(-p + 1)}{(p - u)(p - ue^{j\pi/2})(p - \bar{u})(p - \bar{u}e^{-j\pi/2})}$

where $u = e^{j\pi/4} = \frac{1}{2}(\sqrt{2} + j\sqrt{2})$. The factors which correspond to zeros and poles in the left half plane give

$$H(p) = \pm 3\frac{p + 1}{(p - ue^{j\pi/2})(p - \bar{u}e^{-j\pi/2})}$$

The denominator is

$$\left[p - \left(\frac{-1}{\sqrt{2}} + \frac{j}{\sqrt{2}}\right)\right]\left[p - \left(-\frac{1}{\sqrt{2}} - \frac{j}{\sqrt{2}}\right)\right]$$

which gives $H(p) = \dfrac{\pm 3(p + 1)}{p^2 + \sqrt{2}\,p + 1}$

This result is easily checked.

As the last straw, the problem of finding $H(p)$ from $\alpha(\omega)$ will be considered for rational H. Let $H = C(N/D)$, where N is the numerator polynomial and D is the denominator polynomial; and let the coefficient of the highest power of p be ± 1 for each of these polynomials. As usual, let H have zeros and poles only in the left half plane off the $j\omega$ axis; also let H be written in lowest terms. Since there is no hope for determining C from α (except for sign) we shall take $C = 1$ for this discussion. Recall that

$$E(p) = \frac{1}{2}\left[\frac{N(p)}{D(p)} + \frac{N(-p)}{D(-p)}\right] = \frac{N(p)D(-p) + N(-p)D(p)}{2D(p)D(-p)}$$

and, similarly,

$$O(p) = \frac{N(p)D(-p) - N(-p)D(p)}{2D(p)D(-p)}$$

With $R(\omega) = E(j\omega)$, $I(\omega) = (1/j)0(j\omega)$, and $H(\bar{p}) = \overline{H(p)}$, we have

$$\tan\alpha(\omega) = \frac{I(\omega)}{R(\omega)} = \frac{(1/j)0(j\omega)}{E(j\omega)}$$

In turn,

$$j\tan\alpha(\omega) = \frac{N(j\omega)D(-j\omega) - N(-j\omega)D(j\omega)}{N(j\omega)D(-j\omega) + N(-j\omega)D(j\omega)}$$

Of course we see that $j\tan\alpha$ is a rational function of ω. If we now analytically continue, $\alpha(p/j) = \phi(p)$, we obtain $j\tan\phi(p) = T(p)/B(p)$, where

$T + B = N(p)D(-p)$. Thus, if we are given the rational function $\tan \alpha(\omega)$ we can analytically continue to obtain a rational function the numerator of which has been called T and the denominator of which has been called B. Finally, $T + B$ is a polynomial which permits us to find the zeros and poles of H, and this determines H within a multiplicative constant. Specifically, the zeros of $T + B$ in the left half plane are the zeros of H, and the zeros of $T + B$ in the right half plane are the negative of the poles of H. That is, $N(p)$ provides the left-half-plane zeros of $T + B$, and $D(-p)$ provides the right-half-plane zeros of $T + B$. Of course $D(-b) = 0$ occurs only for certain $(-b)$'s in the left half plane, which puts b in the right half plane.

The above discussion overlooked one possible flaw. If the formula for $\tan \alpha$ in terms of N and D is not in lowest terms, the numerator and denominator, T and B, could not be identified in terms of N and D (assuming that $\tan \alpha$ is known in lowest terms). That is, we have overlooked the possibility of cancellation in the formula for $\tan \alpha$. Thus we are led to consider the possibility that $N(b)D(-b) - N(-b)D(b) = 0$ and $N(b)D(-b) + N(-b)D(b) = 0$. This will contradict our assumptions. Adding the equations, we get $N(b)D(-b) = 0$. Subtraction gives $N(-b)D(b) = 0$. In each of these, the product is zero iff at least one of the two factors is zero. Since b and $-b$ are in different half planes and N and D have zeros only in the left half plane, at most one factor in each equation is zero; and in fact only the factor for which the argument (b or $-b$) is in the left half plane can be zero. Thus either $N(b)$ and $D(b)$ are zero, or $N(-b)$ and $D(-b)$ are zero. In either case D and N have a zero in common, which simply means that H was not written in lowest terms. Thus our procedure for getting H from ϕ clearly "works" if the rational functions are written in lowest terms. Having come this far, we shall summarize the above discussion.

Theorem 10. Let $H(p)$ be rational with zeros and poles only in the left half plane, let $H(\bar{p}) = \overline{H(p)}$, and let $\alpha(\omega)$ be the phase response corresponding to H. Then $j \tan \alpha(\omega)$ is a rational function; and if $T(p)/B(p)$ is its analytic continuation in the variable $\omega = p/j$, the zeros of $T + B$ in the left half plane are the zeros of H and the zeros of $T + B$ in the right half plane are the negative of the poles of H.

Example 9. Suppose $\alpha(\omega) = \arctan \omega + \arctan (-\omega/2)$. Recall that $\tan (a + b) = (\tan a + \tan b)/(1 - \tan a \tan b)$, which gives

$$j \tan \alpha(\omega) = j \cdot \frac{\omega - \omega/2}{1 + \omega^2/2} = \frac{j\omega}{2 + \omega^2}$$

Thus $T/B = p/(2 - p^2)$ and $T + B = 2 + p - p^2 = (2 - p)(1 + p)$. The left-half-plane zero is $p = -1$. The right-half-plane zero is $p = 2$. Thus

$$H(p) = C \frac{p + 1}{p + 2}$$

Problems

1. In Sec. 6-1 a theory for the propagation of energy through linear time-invariant systems was described briefly.   The main conclusion was that if $g = h * f$ and f has finite total energy, then

$$\int_{-\infty}^{\infty} |g(t)|^2 \, dt$$

the energy of g, is given by

$$\frac{1}{2\pi} \int_{-\infty}^{\infty} |H(\omega)|^2 |F(\omega)|^2 \, d\omega$$

where capital letters denote Fourier transforms.   Suppose we define

$$R_f(\tau) \equiv \int_{-\infty}^{\infty} f(t + \tau)\bar{f}(t) \, dt$$

Then $R_f(0)$ is the total energy of f.   Without reference to Fourier transforms, prove that

$$R_g(\tau) = R_f(\tau) * h_c(\tau)$$

where

$$h_c(\tau) = \int_{-\infty}^{\infty} h(\tau - t)\bar{h}(-t) \, dt$$

2. Let $f_b(t) = S(t) \cos \omega_0 t$, where

$$S(t) = \begin{cases} 1 & \text{for } 0 < t < T \gg \dfrac{2\pi}{\omega_0} \\ -1 & \text{for } T < t < 2T \\ S(t + 2T) & \text{for arbitrary } t \end{cases}$$

Find the steady state g_b (using approximate low-pass analogy) for the circuit in the sketch.

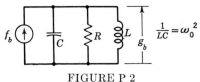

FIGURE P 2

3. In Example 3, an exact bandpass analysis was compared with the solution obtained by the approximate low-pass analogy.   Make the same kind of comparison for said circuit when the input is $i_b(t) = \cos \omega t \cos \omega_0 t$ with $\omega_0 \gg \omega$.

4. Sketch the bandpass network analogous to the low-pass network shown in the sketch.

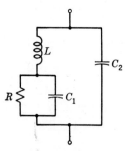

FIGURE P 4

5. Prove the following theorem by contour integration. If $H(p)$ is regular for $\text{Re } p \geq 0$, if

$$\lim_{p \to \infty} H(p) = 0$$

and if $R(\omega) = \text{Re } H(j\omega)$ and $I(\omega) = \text{Im } H(j\omega)$, then

$$I(\omega) = \frac{1}{\pi} \int_{-\infty}^{\infty} \frac{R(\tau)}{\lambda - \omega} \, d\lambda \quad \text{and} \quad R(\omega) = \frac{-1}{\pi} \int_{-\infty}^{\infty} \frac{I(\lambda)}{\lambda - \omega} \, d\lambda$$

HINT: Consider

$$\int_C \frac{H(p)}{p - j\omega_0} \, dp$$

where C is a path similar to that used in the proof of Theorem 7.

6. An all-pass-phase equalization network is shown in the sketch. Let $Z_a(\omega)Z_b(\omega) = R^2$ for all ω. If Z_a is pure reactance [that is, $\text{Re } Z_a(\omega) = 0$ for all ω], show that the amplitude response for this network is 1 for all $p = j\omega$. Show that the phase shift is twice the phase angle of $1 + Z_a/R$.

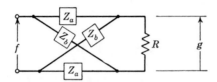

FIGURE P 6

7. If $R(\omega) = 6(1 - \omega^2)/(\omega^4 + 5\omega^2 + 4)$, find $H(p)$. Assume that H satisfies the conditions of Theorem 6.

8. If $I(\omega) = -2\omega/(\omega^4 + 2\omega^2 + 1)$, find $R(\omega)$.

9. If $|H(j\omega)|^2 = (\omega^2 + 1)/(\omega^4 + 4\omega^2 + 4)$, find $H(p)$ (the zeros and poles of H are in the left half plane).

10. If

$$\alpha(\omega) = \arctan \frac{\sqrt{2}\,\omega}{1 - \omega^2} - \arctan \frac{\omega}{3}$$

and $H(0) = \frac{1}{3}$, find $H(p)$. Assume that conditions of Theorem 10 hold.

11. (a) If $f(t) = 1/(t^2 + 1)$, find the Fourier transform of f.

(b) Find the Hilbert transform of $f(t)$ by taking the imaginary part of the inverse Fourier transform of $V(\omega)F(\omega)$.

12. An alternative to Theorem 8 is to assume that

$$A(\infty) = \lim_{p \to \infty} W(p)$$

is finite (now W may have a simple pole at $p = 0$) and take $W_1 = p[W(p) - A(\infty)]$. If W_1 satisfies the hypotheses of Theorem 7, show that

$$A(\omega) - A(\infty) = -\frac{1}{\pi} \int_{-\infty}^{\infty} \frac{\lambda \alpha(\lambda) - \omega \alpha(\omega)}{\lambda^2 - \omega^2} \, d\lambda$$

13. Show that the conclusion of Theorem 9 holds without the assumption $H(\bar{p}) = \overline{H(p)}$ except that H can now be found only within a complex multiplicative constant of unit modulus.

7

DISCRETE SYSTEMS AND $\mathcal{Z}$ TRANSFORMS

In Part I, operational analysis was developed for application to complex-valued functions of a real variable. There are numerous more or less obvious extensions to other kinds of functions. The following are typical types of functions covered by popular extensions: (1) vector-valued functions of a real variable, (2) complex-valued functions of n real variables, and (3) complex-valued functions of an integer variable. The following are corresponding typical applications: (1) systems with several real-valued functions of time as input (such an input can be viewed as a single vector-valued function); (2) systems for which the input is a complex-valued function of position (and possibly time as well); in this case $n = 1$, 2, 3, or 4 depending on the specific application; and (3) discrete systems. Extension 1 is readily handled by using matrix algebra, extension 2 is straightforward with multiple integrals appearing where single integrals appear in the book, and extension 3 is elementary but will be developed in this chapter. All the above extensions, as well as others suggested by them, are important; however, it is rather easy to develop the extensions as needs arise. Actually some special tools are required for the discrete case. Applications such as those in sampled-data servo systems justify a rather detailed look at the discrete case, and the fact that its development is not quite obvious as an extension of the continuous case makes it all the more necessary that the discrete case be given special attention.

7-1 DISCRETE SYSTEMS

By a discrete system is meant a system for which the input and output are complex-valued (or real-valued) functions defined only on the integers (usually all integers—positive, negative, and zero). By the way, a function having the integers as its domain is called a sequence. Often in applications of the theory a function of the real-variable time, say $\tilde{f}(t)$, is initially available; then the system samples $\tilde{f}$ at times . . . , $t_{-2}, t_{-1}, t_0, t_1, \ldots$ to form a sequence $f(n) = \tilde{f}(t_n)$. In view of this sampling often present in discrete systems, such systems are also called sampled-data systems. For example, in range-tracking pulsed radar the range of the target $\tilde{f}(t)$ is sampled with each transmitted pulse; if T is the pulse repetition period, the sequence which is the input to a range-tracking system is $f(n) = \tilde{f}(nT)$.

EXPLICIT DESCRIPTION

We restrict our analysis to linear time-invariant discrete systems. Of course if Φ denotes the transformation of input into output performed by the system, Φ is linear iff whenever f_1 and f_2 are acceptable inputs, $a_1f_1 + a_2f_2$ is an acceptable input, where a_1 and a_2 are complex constants, and

$$\Phi(a_1f_1 + a_2f_2) = a_1\Phi(f_1) + a_2\Phi(f_2)$$

Also, Φ is time-invariant iff shifting f in time† by an amount k on the n axis shifts the output in the same way; i.e., let $g = \Phi(f)$, where f is an arbitrary input. Then $\Phi[f(n + k)] = g(n + k)$ for arbitrary fixed k. Consider the discrete δ-function input

$$f(n) = \delta(n) = \begin{cases} 1 & \text{for } n = 0 \\ 0 & \text{for other } n \end{cases}$$

and let $h(n)$ denote the corresponding output; h is called the impulse response of the system. Note that if f is an arbitrary input we can write $f(n)$ as

$$\sum_{k=-\infty}^{\infty} f(k)\delta(n - k)$$

† It is convenient and often appropriate to view n as discrete time—like the ticking of a clock.

Now, by linearity,†

$$\Phi(f) = \Phi\left[\sum_k f(k)\delta(n - k)\right] = \sum_k f(k)\Phi[\delta(n - k)]$$

Finally, by time invariance, $\Phi[\delta(n - k)] = h(n - k)$; thus

$$\Phi(f) = \sum_k h(n - k)f(k)$$

Let the output produced by f be denoted by g. Then Figure 7-1 summarizes

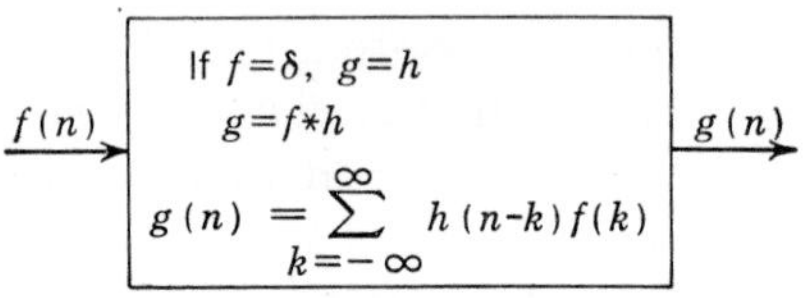

$$
\boxed{
\begin{array}{c}
\text{If } f=\delta, \ g=h \\
g=f*h \\
g(n) = \sum_{k=-\infty}^{\infty} h(n-k)f(k)
\end{array}
}
$$

$f(n) \longrightarrow \qquad \longrightarrow g(n)$

FIGURE 7-1.   Explicit formulation of output in terms of input.

the above discussion.   Of course we define the convolution of two sequences h and f as the sequence obtained thus:

$$\sum_{k=-\infty}^{\infty} h(n - k)f(k)$$

and we use the symbol

$$\sum_k \qquad \text{for} \qquad \sum_{k=-\infty}^{\infty}$$

The major mathematical distinction between discrete systems and *continuous systems* (previous chapters have been concerned with what might be called the continuous case) is that functions of a real variable can behave wildly but sequences cannot.   As a symptom of this, not all continuous systems can be characterized by a convolution integral; e.g., differentiation cannot be written as a convolution unless we resort to δ functions.   However, all discrete systems can be described with a convolution. Because sequences are mathematically much simpler objects than functions of a real variable, on a relative basis the discrete theory should be viewed as elementary and the continuous theory as advanced.   In turn, it is logical to study the discrete case first as a warm-up for the continuous case; however, in applications there is a larger market for the continuous theory, and at least in engineering literature the discrete case is left for an advanced course.   The urgency for the continuous theory simply crowds the discrete theory out of the early work.

† Linearity is defined in such a way that only finite superposition is guaranteed; hence the derivation is rigorous only if $f(n) = 0$ for all but a finite number of values of n.   However, we restrict the system and its inputs so that this infinite superposition is valid.

EXAMPLES

The above discussion provided an explicit *time-domain* description of linear time-invariant discrete systems in terms of (discrete) convolution. Throughout the discrete theory there is an obvious analogy to the continuous theory; and just as continuous systems are often described implicitly by a differential equation, discrete systems are often described by a difference equation. For example, consider a simple range-tracking servo which at time $n - 1$ has an output $g(n - 1)$ which is intended as an estimate of the true target range $f(n - 1)$. When the $(n - 1)$st pulse is received from

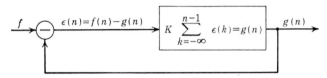

FIGURE 7-2. Block diagram of simple range tracker.

the point target, the difference in actual target range $f(n - 1)$ and indicated range $g(n - 1)$ can be found by the use of simple circuitry. It would seem reasonable to take $g(n)$ in such a way as to tend to drive the error $g - f$ to zero. The very simplest systems used change g by a constant times the error thus:

$$g(n) - g(n - 1) = K[f(n - 1) - g(n - 1)]$$

This is a first-order difference equation where f is the driving function and $g(n) - g(n - 1)$ is called the first difference of $g(n)$. A block diagram

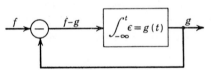

FIGURE 7-3. Continuous system analogous to the feedback system shown in Figure 7-2.

which depicts such a simple range tracker as a feedback system is shown in Figure 7-2. Note that

$$g(n) = K \sum_{k=-\infty}^{n-1} \epsilon(k)$$

$$g(n - 1) = K \sum_{k=-\infty}^{n-2} \epsilon(k)$$

and hence $g(n) - g(n - 1) = K\epsilon(n - 1) = K[f(n - 1) - g(n - 1)]$ as given before. The analogous continuous case is $g' = K(f - g)$, and the analogous diagram is shown in Figure 7-3.

To develop some familiarity with discrete systems, we shall consider some simple problems for the system shown in Figure 7-2. First the impulse response corresponding to the above difference equation will be found. Here we take

$$f(n) = \delta(n) = \begin{cases} 1 & \text{if } n = 0 \\ 0 & \text{if } n \neq 0 \end{cases}$$

We shall assume zero initial conditions, that is, $g(0) = 0$—for that matter, let $g(n) = 0$ for $n \leq 0$. Then if we let $n = 1$ in $g(n) - g(n - 1) = K[f(n - 1) - g(n - 1)]$, we get

$$g(1) - g(0) = K[1 - g(0)] \qquad \text{or} \qquad g(1) = K$$

$n = 2$ gives

$$g(2) - g(1) = K[0 - g(1)] \qquad \text{or} \qquad g(2) = K(1 - K)$$

$n = 3$ gives

$$g(3) - g(2) = K[0 - g(2)] \qquad \text{or} \qquad g(3) = K(1 - K)^2$$

and, finally,

$$g(n) - g(n - 1) = K[0 - g(n - 1)] \qquad \text{or} \qquad g(n) = K(1 - K)^{n-1}$$

Thus we have the following impulse response:

$$h(n) = \begin{cases} K(1 - K)^{n-1} & \text{for } n > 0 \\ 0 & \text{for } n \leq 0 \end{cases}$$

As a second simple example suppose $f(n) = Ae^{pn}$ (for all n), where A and p are fixed complex numbers, and we wish to find the *steady-state* solution to the above difference equation. More precisely, we wish to find a $g(n)$ of the form Be^{pn} if such a solution exists. With the above functions the difference equation is

$$Be^{pn} - Be^{p(n-1)} = K(Ae^{p(n-1)} - Be^{p(n-1)}) \qquad \text{or} \qquad B(e^p - 1) = KA - KB$$

In turn,

$$Be^{pn} = \frac{K}{e^p - (1 - K)} Ae^{pn}$$

provides a steady-state solution.

One more exercise is in order. The impulse response will be used to find the step response of the system. Here we are interested in

$$f(n) = \begin{cases} 1 & \text{for } n \geq 0 \\ 0 & \text{for } n < 0 \end{cases}$$

However, it is nearly as easy to consider

$$f(n) = \begin{cases} e^{pn} & \text{for } n \geq 0 \\ 0 & \text{for } n < 0 \end{cases}$$

and obtain the step response as the special case $p = 0$.   Recall that

$$g(n) = \sum_k h(n - k)f(k)$$

since for the input of interest $f(k) = 0$ for $k < 0$; and since $h(n) = 0$ for $n \leq 0$, we have (for $n > 0$)

$$g(n) = \sum_{k=0}^{n-1} h(n - k)f(k)$$

or

$$g(n) = \sum_{k=0}^{n-1} K(1 - K)^{n-k-1}e^{pk}$$

$$= K(1 - K)^{n-1} \sum_{k=0}^{n-1} \left(\frac{e^p}{1 - K}\right)^k$$

This last sum is a finite geometric series; hence

$$g(n) = K(1 - K)^{n-1} \frac{1 - [e^p/(1 - K)]^n}{1 - e^p/(1 - K)}$$

or

$$g(n) = K \frac{(1 - K)^n - e^{pn}}{(1 - K) - e^p}$$

The step response is $g(n) = 1 - (1 - K)^n$.   Note that if $|1 - K| < 1$ and n is large,

$$g(n) \cong \frac{K}{e^p - (1 - K)} e^{pn}$$

as expected from the steady-state calculation.   Observe that the step response is bounded if $0 \leq K \leq 2$; Figure 7-4 depicts the step response. The "ringing" phenomenon obtained for $1 < K < 2$ is peculiar to the discrete case for the equation under consideration.   That is, there is no value of K which yields a ringing solution to $g' = K(f - g)$ in the continuous case.

It is not worthwhile to take the time to develop everything for the discrete case which was developed for the continuous case, and we shall not display all similarities and differences. However, a few more observations along these lines will be made in con-

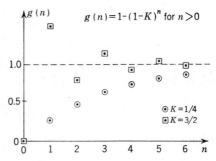

FIGURE 7-4.   Step response of range-tracking radar.

nection with the above examples.   Consider the difference equation with K very small.   Then $g(n) - g(n - 1)$ will be small.   We might try to approximate $g(n)$ with samples of a function of a real variable $\tilde{g}(t)$ thus: $g(n) \cong \tilde{g}(n)$ in such a way that $g(n) - g(n - 1) \cong \tilde{g}(n) - \tilde{g}(n - 1)$ is approximately the derivative of $\tilde{g}$ times the increment of time $n - (n - 1) = 1$. If this is done we get $\tilde{g}' = K(\tilde{g} - \tilde{f})$, where we take

$$\tilde{f}(t) = \begin{cases} 1 & \text{for } t \geq 0 \\ 0 & \text{for } t < 0 \end{cases}$$

to correspond to a step input. The solution to this differential equation is the familiar $\tilde{g}(t) = 1 - e^{-Kt}$. The question is the following: For K small, does $\tilde{g}(n) \cong g(n)$? For K small, $e^{-K} \cong 1 - K$, and we get $\tilde{g}(t) \cong 1 - (1 - K)^t$ or $\tilde{g}(n) = 1 - (1 - K)^n$, as expected.

Finally, we shall illustrate a technique used in the analysis of real parameter systems in the continuous case. Recall the steady-state solution

$$g(n) = \frac{K}{e^p - (1 - K)} e^{pn} \qquad \text{if } f(n) = e^{pn}$$

Now suppose $f(n) = \cos \omega n = \text{Re } e^{j\omega n}$ and we wish to find the steady-state response. If K is real, we can use the discrete version of Theorem 4, Chap. 3. That is, the response to the real part of $e^{j\omega n}$ is the real part of the response to $e^{j\omega n}$. Thus if the input is a discrete cosine wave of frequency ω and if K is real, the output is

$$g(n) = K \text{ Re } \frac{e^{j\omega n}}{e^{j\omega} - (1 - K)}$$

Some manipulation gives

$$g(n) = K[1 + (1 - K)^2 - 2(1 - K) \cos \omega]^{-\frac{1}{2}} \cos (\omega n + \phi)$$

where ϕ is the angle (argument) of the complex number $\cos \omega - (1 - K) - j \sin \omega$. For comparison, the amplitude response for the analogous continuous system is

$$\frac{1}{\sqrt{1 + (\omega/K)^2}}$$

Observe that if ω is small, the amplitude frequency response of the discrete system can be simplified by using the approximation $\cos \omega = 1 - \omega^2/2$, which leads to a response of

$$\frac{1}{\sqrt{1 + (\omega/\omega_c)^2}}$$

where $$\omega_c = \frac{K}{(1 - K)^{\frac{1}{2}}} \cong K$$

as one might expect. Similarly, the phase responses for the discrete and continuous cases are approximately equal when K and ω are small.

7-2 Z TRANSFORMS

In Sec. 7-1 the notion of a discrete system was given, and it was shown that convolution could be used to characterize such systems mathematically. Also, to compensate for the possible lack of experience with simple discrete problems, several examples were given and analogies to the continuous case were made. In this section operational analysis for the discrete case will be developed. As with other aspects of the discrete case, its operational theory is mathematically somewhat simpler than that developed for the continuous case. However, there are several notational conventions in use, and they all have attractive features. If we start with the approach of Chap. 3, the problem is to find a universal set of eigensequences for linear time-invariant discrete systems; the various ways of denoting these eigenfunctions lead to the various versions of Z transforms. Specifically, $f(n) = Az^n$ (all n) is an eigenfunction for arbitrary complex z. We can also write $|z| = e^\sigma$ and $\omega =$ angle of z. Then $f(n) = Ae^{pn}$, where $p = \sigma + j\omega$; and if we choose, we can always take $|\omega| \leq \pi$. It develops that $f(n) = Az^{-n}$ and $f(n) = Ae^{-pn}$ are also somewhat useful ways to denote the eigenfunctions. There will be no attempt to carry all the above notations in this section; in Sec. 7-4 a slight modification of the Ae^{pn} notation will be used, and in this section z^{-n} notation will be used.

Theorem 1. If Φ is a linear time-invariant discrete system and $f(n) = Az^{-n}$ is in its domain of definition (that is, Az^{-n} is an acceptable input), then $\Phi(Az^{-n}) = HAz^{-n}$, where H is a constant in that H does not depend on n. Of course, H may depend on z; the transfer function is defined as H as a function of z.

PROOF: Let $\Phi(z^{-n}) = g(n)$. Then $g(n + k) = \Phi(z^{-n-k}) = z^{-k}g(n)$ for all (n, k). In particular, $g(k) = g(0)z^{-k}$. Let $H = g(0)$. By linearity, $G(Az^{-n}) = HAz^{-n}$.

Theorem 2. Functions of the form Az^{-n}, and only such functions (the other notations clearly cover the same class of functions), are eigenfunctions to all linear time-invariant discrete systems. The proof is similar to that of Theorem 3, Chap. 3, except that no continuity argument is needed.

Example 1. $g(n) = \sum_k h(n - k)f(k)$. Find $H(z)$. If we change the summation variable to $r = n - k$, we get

$$g(n) = \sum_r h(r)f(n - r)$$

and if $f(n) = z^{-n}$,

$$g(n) = \sum_r h(r)z^{-n+r}$$

or

$$g(n) = \left[\sum_{r=-\infty}^{\infty} h(r)z^r \right] z^{-n}$$

That is, the transfer function is given in terms of the impulse response by

$$H(z) = \sum_n h(n)z^n$$

The approach used in Chap. 3 will now be dropped, and the theory analogous to two-sided Laplace transforms will be developed directly. The key to the direct development of Z transforms is to observe that the convolution of two sequences is what appears when two power (or Laurent) series are multiplied. That is,

$$\left[\sum_n f(n)z^n\right]\left[\sum_n h(n)z^n\right] = \sum_n \left[\sum_k f(k)h(n-k)\right] z^n$$

The Z transform of f will be denoted by F and by $Z(f)$ and is defined thus:

$$F(z) = \sum_{n=-\infty}^{\infty} f(n)z^n$$

Of course the Z transform† of a sequence is the Laurent series obtained by using the sequence as coefficients in a Laurent series. With the theory of regular functions available, the theory of Z transforms consists in restating old results (Sec. 2-4). Generally,

$$\sum_n f(n)z^n$$

converges inside an angular ring in the z plane; this ring will be assumed to be of positive area, and the inside (excluding the boundary) will be called the ring of convergence of $Z(f)$.

Theorem 3 (Linearity). Let the rings of convergence of $Z(f_1)$ and of $Z(f_2)$ have some points in common; then for constants C_1 and C_2,

$$Z(C_1f_1 + C_2f_2)$$

exists and equals $C_1Z(f_1) + C_2Z(f_2)$ in a ring in the z plane.

Theorem 4 (Inversion Theorem). Let C be a simple closed path in the ring of convergence of $Z(f) = F(z)$, and let $z = 0$ be inside C; then

$$f(n) = \frac{1}{2\pi j} \int_C \frac{F(z)}{z^{n+1}}\, dz$$

This is simply Theorem 32, Chap. 2.

Theorem 5 (Convolution Theorem). Let the rings of convergence of $H(z) = Z(h)$ and $F(z) = Z(f)$ have points in common; then

$$g = f * h = \sum_k h(n-k)f(k)$$

exists, $G(z) = Z(g)$ exists, and $G(z) = H(z)F(z)$ in a ring in the z plane.

PROOF:‡ At common points of convergence

$$H(z)F(z) = \left[\sum_s h(s)z^s\right]\left[\sum_r f(r)z^r\right]$$

or

$$H(z)F(z) = \sum_r \sum_s h(s)f(r)z^{s+r}$$

---

† Called *generating function* in mathematical literature.

‡ This discussion is a *derivation* rather than a proof; however, the steps involved are valid as shown in nearly any book on theory of function of a complex variable (cf. Ref. 5).

We make the change of summation variables

$$r + s = n$$
$$r = k$$

Then $\quad HF = \sum_n \sum_k h(n - k)f(k)z^n = \sum_n \left[\sum_k h(n - k)f(k) \right] z^n$

Corollary 1. Let $D(f)$ be the first difference of f; that is, if $g \equiv D(f)$, $g(n) = f(n) - f(n - 1)$; then $Z(Df) = (1 - z)F(z)$.

PROOF: Let

$$h(n) = \begin{cases} 1 & \text{for } n = 0 \\ -1 & \text{for } n = 1 \\ 0 & \text{for other } n \end{cases}$$

Then $D(f) = h * f$, that is,

$$\sum_k f(k)h(n - k) = f(n) - f(n - 1)$$

Thus $Z(Df) = HF$ and $H(z) = 1 - z$, as was to be shown.

Corollary 2. Let Σf be defined thus: $g = \Sigma f$ iff

$$g(n) = \sum_{k=-\infty}^{n} f(k)$$

Then $\quad\quad Z(\Sigma f) = \dfrac{1}{1 - z} F(z)$

if $Z(f)$ converges at some points inside the unit circle $|z| = 1$.

Here we take

$$h(n) = \begin{cases} 1 & \text{for } n \geq 0 \\ 0 & \text{for } n < 0 \end{cases}$$

Then $\Sigma f = h * f$ and $H(z) = 1 + z + z^2 + \cdots = 1/(1 - z)$ if $|z| < 1$.

Corollary 3 (Shift Theorem). Let $f_r(n) = f(n + r)$ for all n and arbitrary fixed r. Then $Z(f_r) = z^{-r}F(z)$.

The direct proof is

$$\sum_n f(n + r)z^n = \sum_s f(s)z^{s-r} = z^{-r}F(z)$$

As a corollary, take

$$h(n) = \begin{cases} 1 & \text{for } n = -r \\ 0 & \text{for other } n \end{cases}$$

Then $f_r = f * h$.

Example 2. We shall recompute the step response corresponding to the difference equation

$$g(n) - g(n - 1) = K[f(n - 1) - g(n - 1)]$$

We take the Z transform of both sides, using Theorems 3 and 5 to obtain

$$(1 - z)G = KzF - KzG \quad \text{or} \quad G = \frac{KzF}{1 - (1 - K)z}$$

For the step response we take

$$f(n) = \begin{cases} 1 & \text{for } n \geq 0 \\ 0 & \text{for } n < 0 \end{cases}$$

Then $F(z) = 1 + z + z^2 + \cdots = 1/(1 - z)$ for $|z| < 1$.   Thus

$$G(z) = \frac{Kz}{[1 - (1 - K)z](1 - z)}$$

We now wish to find the inverse Z transform of G.   Of course, Theorem 4 can be used; however, when rational functions of z are under consideration we can always expand the function in partial fractions from which the inverse transform will be obvious from our knowledge of the geometric series (this is shown in Example 3).

Let $K \neq 1$.   Then we consider

$$G(z) = \frac{Kz}{[1 - (1 - K)z](1 - z)} = \frac{A}{1 - z} + \frac{B}{1 - (1 - K)z}$$

Multiply G by $1 - z$ and let z approach 1.   Then

$$\frac{K}{1 - (1 - K)} = A \quad \text{or} \quad A = 1$$

Similarly,

$$\frac{K[1/(1 - K)]}{1 - 1/(1 - K)} = B \quad \text{or} \quad B = -1$$

Thus

$$G(z) = \frac{1}{1 - z} - \frac{1}{1 - (1 - K)z}$$

For $|z|$ small (F converged for $|z|$ small),

$$\frac{1}{1 - z} = 1 + z + z^2 + \cdots$$

and

$$\frac{1}{1 - (1 - K)z} = 1 + (1 - K)z + (1 - K)^2 z^2 + \cdots$$

Clearly, for $n < 0$ the coefficient of z^n is 0 and for $n \geq 0$ the coefficient is $1 - (1 - K)^n$; that is,

$$g(n) = \begin{cases} 1 - (1 - K)^n & \text{for } n \geq 0 \\ 0 & \text{for } n < 0 \end{cases}$$

which agrees with the step response found without the use of transforms.

Example 3.   Inverse of Rational Transforms.   As with Laplace transforms, there is no (conceptual) difficulty in computing the inverse transform of rational functions of z. Let $F(z)$ be a proper rational function of z which we expand into partial fractions. Let the circle for inversion be $|z| = r$, that is,

$$f(n) = \frac{1}{2\pi j} \int_{|z|=r} \frac{F(z)\, dz}{z^{n+1}}$$

With F expanded into partial fractions, let $A/(a - z)^k$ denote a typical term in the expansion. The problem is to find the inverse transform of this term. There are two cases: $r/|a| < 1$ and $r/|a| > 1$.

Suppose $r/|a| < 1$ and consider $k = 1$ (the A will now be dropped):

$$\frac{1}{a - z} = \frac{1/a}{1 - z/a} = \frac{1}{a}\left(1 + \frac{z}{a} + \frac{z^2}{a^2} + \cdots\right)$$

That is,
$$\frac{1}{a - z} = \frac{1}{a} + \left(\frac{1}{a}\right)^2 z + \frac{1}{a^3} z^2 + \cdots$$

Thus we have what is by now a familiar inverse Z transform:

$$Z^{-1}\left(\frac{1}{a - z}\right) = \begin{cases} \left(\dfrac{1}{a}\right)^{n+1} & \text{for } n \geq 0 \\ 0 & \text{for } n < 0 \end{cases}$$

The big dividend is that k differentiations of the series for $1/(a - z)$ provides the inverse transform of $[1/(a - z)]^k$. Consider one differentiation of the equation

$$\frac{1}{a - z} = \frac{1}{a} + \frac{1}{a^2} z + \frac{1}{a^3} z^2 + \cdots$$

This yields

$$\left(\frac{1}{a - z}\right)^2 = \frac{1}{a^2} + \frac{2}{a^3} z + \frac{3}{a^4} z^2 + \cdots$$

The next differentiation gives

$$2\left(\frac{1}{a - z}\right)^3 = \frac{2}{a^3} + \frac{2 \times 3}{a^4} z + \frac{3 \times 4}{a^5} z^2 + \cdots$$

In general,

$$(k - 1)!\left(\frac{1}{a - z}\right)^k = \frac{(k - 1)(k - 2) \cdots 1}{a^k} + \frac{k(k - 1) \cdots 2}{a^{k+1}} z + \cdots$$
$$+ \frac{(k + n - 1) \cdots (n + 1)}{a^{k+n}} z^n + \cdots$$

This last general result can be proved (by induction) by simply differentiating the equation. The conclusion is that, for $r < |a|$,

$$Z^{-1}\left[\frac{1}{(a - z)^k}\right] = \begin{cases} \dfrac{(k + n - 1)!}{n!(k - 1)!} \dfrac{1}{a^{k+n}} & \text{for } n \geq 0 \\ 0 & \text{for } n < 0 \end{cases}$$

Now suppose $r > |a|$. Then the above result provides the following series if we interchange the roles of a and z:

$$\left(\frac{1}{z-a}\right)^k = \sum_{n=0}^{\infty} \frac{(k+n-1)!}{n!(k-1)!} \frac{1}{z^{k+n}} a^n$$

The summation variable is now changed to $s = n + k$ to give

$$\left(\frac{1}{z-a}\right)^k = \sum_{s=k}^{\infty} \frac{(s-1)!a^{-k}}{(s-k)!(k-1)!} a^s z^{-s}$$

From this we have the following inverse Z transform for $r > |a|$:

$$Z^{-1}\left[\left(\frac{1}{z-a}\right)^k\right] = \begin{cases} \dfrac{(-n-1)!a^{-k-n}}{(-n-k)!(k-1)!} & \text{for } n \leq -k \\ 0 & \text{for } n > -k \end{cases}$$

Example 4.   In Example 3 a procedure for finding the inverse transform of any proper rational function of z was given.   Here two rational transforms of some mild interest will be mentioned.   If

$$f(n) = \begin{cases} vn & \text{for } n \geq 0 \\ 0 & \text{for } n < 0 \end{cases}$$

f is a discrete ramp function or constant-velocity function for $n \geq 0$.   In this case

$$Z(f) = v \sum_{n=0}^{\infty} nz^n$$

Recall that in the first part of Example 3 we had

$$\left(\frac{1}{z-a}\right)^2 = \frac{1}{a^2} + \frac{2}{a^3} z + \frac{3}{a^4} z^2 \cdots$$

Thus $$z\left(\frac{1}{1-z}\right)^2 = z + 2z^2 + 3z^3 + \cdots = \sum_{n=0}^{\infty} nz^n$$

That is, $zv/(1-z)^2$ is the Z transform of a discrete ramp.   If only discrete theory is considered,† the natural definition of a constant velocity for $n \geq 0$ would probably be that

$$Df = \begin{cases} v & \text{for } n \geq 0 \\ 0 & \text{for } n < 0 \end{cases}$$

---

† $f(n) = vn$ is probably motivated by sampling $\tilde{f}(t) = \tilde{v}t$ to obtain $f(n) = \tilde{v}(nT) = (\tilde{v}T)n = vn$.

This gives $F(z) = v/(1 - z)^2$ and $f(n) = (n + 1)v$ for $n \geq 0$. The two agree for large n in the sense that

$$\lim_{n \to \infty} \frac{n}{n + 1} = 1$$

That is, the per cent difference goes to zero. Of course the definition of D could be changed to $DF = f(n + 1) - f(n)$ to eliminate the slight difference.

Along the same lines, constant acceleration, jerk, and snap functions will now be considered, mostly for illustrative purposes. The notion of constant-acceleration ramp suggested by sampling a continuous function is

$$f(n) = \begin{cases} \frac{1}{2}an^2 & \text{for } n \geq 0 \\ 0 & \text{for } n < 0 \end{cases}$$

Now
$$Z(f) = \frac{1}{2}a \sum_{n=0}^{\infty} n^2 z^n$$

Differentiation of both sides of

$$\frac{z}{(1 - z)^2} = z + 2z^2 + 3z^3 + \cdots$$

gives

$$\frac{2z}{(1 - z)^3} + \frac{1}{(1 - z)^2} = 1 + 4z + 9z^2 + \cdots$$

Therefore
$$\frac{z(1 + z)}{(1 - z)^3} = z + 4z^2 + 9z^3 + \cdots + n^2z^n + \cdots$$

That is,
$$Z(\tfrac{1}{2}an^2) = \frac{a}{2} \frac{z(1 + z)}{(1 - z)^3}$$

One can continue in the same way to obtain $Z(\frac{1}{6}Jn^3)$, $Z(\frac{1}{24}sn^4)$, etc.

The above two examples illustrate the fact that if the original sequence is simply some power of n (greater than, say, 1) the transform is rather involved, while if the transform is a simple (negative) power of $z - a$ the original sequence is rather involved. However, for large n

$$f(n) = Z^{-1}\left[\frac{1}{(1 - z)^{k+1}}\right] \cong \frac{1}{k!}n^k$$

in the sense that

$$\lim_{n \to \infty} \frac{f(n) - (1/k!)n^k}{(1/k!)n^k} = 0$$

Of course, in Corollary 1 it became more or less obvious that $1 - z$ often plays a role in Z transforms analogous to the role played by p in Laplace transforms. With this in mind the above remarks are no surprise in view of the fact that

$$L^{-1}\left(\frac{1}{p^{k+1}}\right) = \begin{cases} \dfrac{1}{k!}\, t^k & \text{for } t > 0 \\ 0 & \text{for } t < 0 \end{cases}$$

(the inversion taken with Re $p > 0$).

In the case of Laplace transforms we made occasional use of initial-value and final-value theorems; there are analogous theorems for Z transforms. If we think of z as being analogous to $e^{-\sigma}$ it is seen that

$$\lim_{\sigma \to \infty} \quad \text{and} \quad \lim_{z \to 0}$$

correspond.   Also,

$$\lim_{\sigma \to 0+} \quad \text{and} \quad \lim_{z \to 1-}$$

correspond.   The following theorems are analogous to Theorems 21 and 22, Chap. 2.

Theorem 6.   Let $f(n) = 0$ for $n < 0$.   Then

$$f(0) = \lim_{z \to 0} (1 - z)F(z) = F(0,$$

Of course, this is trivial since

$$F(z) = f(0) + f(1)z + f(2)z^2 + \cdots$$

Theorem 7.   Let $F(z)$ converge for z real with $z < 1$, let $f(n) = 0$ for $n < 0$, and let

$$\lim_{n \to \infty} f(n) = f(\infty)$$

exist (finite for now).   Then

$$\lim_{z \to 1-} (1 - z)F(z)$$

exists and is equal to $f(\infty)$.

PROOF: Since

$$F(z) = \sum_{n=0}^{\infty} f(n)z^n$$

$$(1 - z)F(z) = \sum_{n=0}^{\infty} f(n)z^n - \sum_{r=0}^{\infty} f(r)z^{r+1}$$

or

$$(1 - z)F(z) = \sum_{n=0}^{\infty} [f(n) - f(n - 1)]z^n$$

To see the idea in the theorem, assume that we can interchange

$$\lim_{z \to 1-}$$

and the sum on n; then

$$\lim_{z \to 1-} (1 - z)F(z) = \sum_{n=0}^{\infty} [f(n) - f(n - 1)]$$

This is a telescoping sum:

$$\sum_{n=0}^{N} [f(n) - f(n - 1)] = f(0) - f(-1) + f(1) - f(0) + f(2) - f(1)$$

$$+ \cdots + f(N) - f(N - 1) = f(N)$$

In turn $$\sum_{n=0}^{\infty} [\quad] = \lim_{N \to \infty} f(N) = f(\infty)$$

Justifying the interchange is not a trivial matter; the following method uses tools which are a bit large for the job.

For z real with $z < 1$, let $z = e^{-\sigma}$. Then

$$(1 - z)F(z) = \sum_{n=0}^{\infty} (1 - e^{-\sigma})f(n)e^{-\sigma n}$$

Let $\tilde{f}(t) \equiv f(n)$ for $n \le t < n + 1$.   Note that

$$\int_{n}^{n+1} e^{-\sigma t}\, dt = \frac{e^{-\sigma n} - e^{-\sigma n}e^{-\sigma}}{\sigma}$$

Therefore $$e^{-\sigma n} = \frac{\sigma}{1 - e^{-\sigma}} \int_{n}^{n+1} e^{-\sigma t}\, dt$$

In turn $$(1 - e^{-\sigma})f(n)e^{-\sigma n} = \sigma \int_{n}^{n+1} \tilde{f}(t)e^{-\sigma t}\, dt$$

On the interval of integration $f(n) = \tilde{f}(t)$.   Thus

$$(1 - z)F(z) = \int_{0}^{\infty} \tilde{f}(t)e^{-\sigma t}\sigma\, dt = \int_{0}^{\infty} \tilde{f}\left(\frac{\theta}{\sigma}\right) e^{-\theta}\, d\theta$$

We are now faced with exactly the same problem presented by the continuous case:

$$\lim_{\sigma \to 0^+} \int_{0}^{\infty} \tilde{f}\left(\frac{\theta}{\sigma}\right) e^{-\theta}\, d\theta$$

Let $|f(n)| \le M$.   Then $Me^{-\theta}$ provides an integrable dominating function and

$$\lim_{\sigma \to 0^+} \tilde{f}\left(\frac{\theta}{\sigma}\right) = f(\infty) \qquad \text{for } 0 < \theta < \infty$$

That is, $$\lim_{z \to 1^-} (1 - z)F(z) = f(\infty) \int_{0}^{\infty} e^{-\theta}\, d\theta = f(\infty)$$

as was to be shown.

If

$$\lim_{n \to \infty} f(n) = \infty \ (\text{or} -\infty)$$

$F(z)$ converges for $z < 1$, and $f(n) = 0$ for $n < 0$; it is easy to see that

$$\lim_{z \to 1^-} (1 - z)F(z) = \infty \quad (\text{or} - \infty)$$

Since

$$(1 - z)F(z) = \int_0^\infty \hat{f}\left(\frac{\theta}{\sigma}\right) e^{-\theta}\, d\theta$$

the details for the ∞ cases here can be treated in exactly the way they were treated in the proof of Theorem 21, Chap. 2.

Since sequences are mathematically much simpler than functions of a real variable, it is somewhat annoying that we use our knowledge of the continuous case to lead our way in the discrete case, and in the proof of Theorem 7 a major tool from the theory of functions of a real variable was used on a rather simple infinite series. The role of real-variable theory can be avoided by use of a theorem due to Abel (see Ref. 5, p. 120).

Example 5. Recall the range-tracking servo which was discussed in Sec. 7-1. The open-loop operation was

$$K \sum_{k = -\infty}^{n-1} \epsilon(k) = g(n)$$

The transfer function corresponding to this is $Kz/(1 - z)$, and the difference equation was

$$g(n) - g(n - 1) = K[f(n - 1) - g(n - 1)]$$

If for some reason the echo (from the target being tracked) fades away, the system is usually designed in such a way that the output from the error detector, normally $K[f(n - 1) - g(n - 1)]$, is made (approximately) zero. In this event $g(n) - g(n - 1) = 0$; that is, the output (indicated target position) remains constant. Because of this feature such a range-tracking system is sometimes called a position-memory system. Let us apply Theorem 7 to this position-memory system, as shown in Figure 7-5.

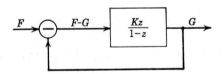

FIGURE 7-5. Block diagram of position-memory tracker.

Recall that if f is a step input, the error $\epsilon = f - g$ approaches zero as n goes to infinity. The limiting behavior will now be computed for constant-velocity and constant-acceleration inputs. From the block diagram, $G = KEz/(1 - z) = F - E$, where E is the Z transform of the error. Thus

$$E = \frac{1 - z}{1 - (1 - K)z}\, F$$

For a constant-velocity input,

$$F(z) = \frac{zv}{(1-z)^2} \quad \text{and} \quad (1-z)E(z) = \frac{zv}{1-(1-K)z}$$

In the limit as $z \to 1$, we have

$$\lim_{n \to \infty} \epsilon(n) = \frac{v}{K}$$

For a constant-acceleration input,

$$(1-z)E(z) = (1-z)\frac{(1-z)}{1-(1-K)z}\frac{a}{2}\frac{z(1+z)}{(1-z)^3}$$

Now as $z \to 1$,

$$\lim_{n \to \infty} \epsilon(n) = \infty$$

There are advantages to operating on the error in more elaborate ways to correct the output of range-tracking systems; the difference equation

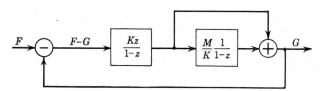

FIGURE 7-6.   Velocity-memory tracker.

and block diagram of Figure 7-6 depict a system often used:

$$g(n+1) - g(n) = K[\epsilon(n)] + M\sum_{k=-\infty}^{n}\epsilon(k)$$

As we shall soon show, if we have a constant-velocity target, $\epsilon(n) \to 0$ as $n \to \infty$, which implies that the proper correction $g(n+1) - g(n) = v$ is obtained from "old" terms in

$$\sum_{k=-\infty}^{n}\epsilon(k)$$

when n is large.   In turn, if the echo from a target fades, $g(n+1) - g(n)$ will remain constant.   That is, the output will coast at a constant velocity. For this reason the system of Figure 7-6 is sometimes called a velocity-memory system.

As for limiting error calculations with this system, we have

$$G = E\left[\frac{Kz}{1-z} + \frac{Mz}{(1-z)^2}\right] = F - E$$

Therefore

$$E = F\frac{(1-z)^2}{(1-z)^2 + Mz + Kz(1-z)}$$

If $F(z) = vz/(1 - z)^2$, we get

$$\lim_{n \to \infty} \epsilon(n) = \lim_{z \to 1} \frac{vz(1 - z)}{(1 - z)^2 + Mz + Kz(1 - z)} = 0$$

If
$$F(z) = \frac{a}{2} \frac{z(1 + z)}{(1 - z)^3}$$

then $\lim_{n \to \infty} \epsilon(n) = \lim_{z \to 1} \frac{a}{2} \frac{z(1 + z)(1 - z)^2(1 - z)}{(1 - z)^2 + Mz + Kz(1 - z)} \frac{1}{(1 - z)^3} = \frac{a}{M}$

For a constant jerk (snap, etc.) target,

$$\lim_{n \to \infty} \epsilon(n)$$

is ∞ for the above system.

7-3 DIFFERENCE EQUATIONS, HOMOGENEOUS SOLUTIONS, AND INITIAL CONDITIONS

A general difference equation of order m can be written as $a_m D^m(g) + a_{m-1} D^{m-1}(g) + \cdots + a_1 D(g) + a_0 g = f$ or as

$$b_m g(m + n) + b_{m-1} g(m - 1 + n) + \cdots + b_1 g(n + 1) + b_0 g(n) = f(n)$$

We have worked with some simple difference equations in some of the examples. Obviously, difference equations should have homogeneous solutions just as differential equations do. Of course, such is the case; and similar techniques can be used to find homogeneous, particular, and general solutions. Typically, to find the homogeneous solutions we set $g(n) = z^n$ and get

$$b_m z^{n+m} + b_{m-1} z^{n+m-1} + \cdots + b_1 z^{n+1} + b_0 z^n = 0$$
or
$$b_m z^m + b_{m-1} z^{m-1} + \cdots + b_0 = 0$$

This equation is solved to obtain as many as m values of z which provide homogeneous solutions. Two-sided Z transforms can be used to find a particular solution.

In the case of Laplace transforms we were able to solve for the particular plus homogeneous solution which met desired initial conditions. This can be done for difference equations; however, a one-sided Z_1 transform should be used. Suppose the following equation is to hold for $n = 0, 1, 2, \ldots$:

$$b_m g(n + m) + \cdots + b_1 g(n + 1) + b_0 g(n) = f(n)$$

Of course we define

$$G(z) = \sum_{n=0}^{\infty} g(n) z^n \quad \text{and} \quad F(z) = \sum_{n=0}^{\infty} f(n) z^n$$

A modified version of Corollary 3 is now of interest:

$$Z_1[f(n + m)] \equiv \sum_{n=0}^{\infty} f(n + m)z^n = \sum_{r=m}^{\infty} f(r)z^{r-m} = \sum_{r=0}^{\infty} f(r)z^{r-m} - \sum_{r=0}^{m-1} f(r)z^{r-m}$$

That is, for the right-sided Z transform,

$$Z[f(n + m)] = z^{-m}F(z) - z^{-m} \sum_{r=0}^{m-1} f(r)z^r$$

To obtain a unique solution to the difference equation under consideration it is assumed that $g(0)$, $g(1)$, . . . , $g(m - 1)$ are specified. Then the right-sided Z transform permits us to solve for g with the initial conditions incorporated.

Example 6. For $n \geq 0$, let $g(n + 1) - g(n) = K[f(n) - g(n)]$, let

$$f(n) = \begin{cases} 1 & \text{for } n \geq 0 \\ 0 & \text{for } n < 0 \end{cases}$$

and let $g(0) = A$. This is a very simple case, but it illustrates the method discussed for incorporating initial conditions. We multiply both sides by z^n and sum over n. The interesting term is

$$\sum_{n=0}^{\infty} g(n + 1)z^n = \sum_{n=1}^{\infty} g(n)z^{n-1} = z^{-1} \sum_{n=0}^{\infty} g(n)z^n - g(0)z^{-1}$$

We get

$$(z^{-1} - 1)G - z^{-1}A = \frac{K}{1 - z} - KG$$

That is,

$$G = \frac{Kz}{(1 - z)[1 - (1 - K)z]} + \frac{A}{1 - (1 - K)z}$$

The first term is the same as that found in Example 2, and the second term has an inverse Z transform well known by now. Thus

$$g(n) = 1 - (1 - K)^n + A(1 - K)^n$$

for $n > 0$ and $g(n) = 0$ for $n < 0$. Clearly, $g(0) = A$.

7-4 SEQUENCES CREATED BY SAMPLING

As mentioned at the beginning of the chapter, the sequences involved in discrete systems are often created by sampling a function of a real variable. This is the case in a pulsed range-tracking radar; if T is the pulse repetition period and $\tilde{f}(t)$ is the range of the target as a function of time, then the input to the tracking system is $f(n) = \tilde{f}(nT)$, where nT is the time of the nth transmitted pulse. A number of interesting questions suggest themselves in the presence of sampling. We shall consider only a few simple questions, all of which are related to the question: Given $f(n)$ (and some properties of $\tilde{f}$), what are the prospects for finding $\tilde{f}$, or if $\tilde{f}$ cannot be found, in what way is $\tilde{f}$ free to vary? Partly because of the limited tools available to us, there is no attempt here to cover most of the important questions in sampling theory. What is given here should be viewed as only an introduction to sampling theory; one point illustrated in this section is the advantage of one of the other notations for Z transforms in certain applications.

One very important result was given in Sec. 2-5, namely, Theorem 36 (the sampling theorem). It will simply be restated here (not in detail).

Theorem 8. If $\tilde{f}(t)$ is bandwidth-limited (limited to $|\omega| < B$) in the sense that

$$\tilde{f}(t) = \frac{1}{2\pi} \int_{-B}^{B} e^{j\omega t} F(\omega) \, d\omega$$

then $\tilde{f}(t)$ can be reconstructed from $f(n) \equiv \tilde{f}(nT)$, where $T = \pi/B$, in the following way:

$$\tilde{f}(t) = \sum_{n=-\infty}^{\infty} f(n) \frac{\sin (Bt - n\pi)}{Bt - n\pi}$$

Put briefly, $\tilde{f}$ can be reconstructed by interpolating with the function $(\sin Bt)/Bt$.

Before proceeding further, the notation will be changed. Since a function of a real variable will be under consideration, $f(t)$ will now be used rather than $\tilde{f}$. The sequence of interest is $f(nT)$, and no separate notation will be introduced for this sequence.

Obviously, for an arbitrary function $f(t)$, given $f(nT)$, the values of $f(t)$ can be found only for $t = nT$. This trivial remark leads one to think that the bandwidth-limit assumption of Theorem 8 is very restricting.

Suppose we consider an exponential function $f(t) = Ae^{(\sigma+j\omega)t}$, where A and $p = \sigma + j\omega$ are complex constants. The sequence obtained by sampling with period T is

$$f(nT) = Ae^{\sigma Tn}e^{j\omega Tn}$$

Suppose we know only these sample values; can we determine $f(t)$ (that is, determine A and p) uniquely from these sample values? The amplitude is no problem since at $n = 0$, $f(0) = A$. Also, σ is easily determined from $|f(nT)|$. However, given $f(nT)$, ω is not unique. The point is that $\exp j\omega_1 Tn$ can equal $\exp j\omega_2 Tn$ for all integer n if ω_1 and ω_2 are related in a special way but not necessarily equal. Consider

$$\exp j\omega_1 Tn = \exp j\omega_2 Tn$$

or $\qquad \exp [j(\omega_1 - \omega_2) Tn] = 1 \qquad$ for all n

This is the case iff $(\omega_1 - \omega_2)Tn$ is an integer multiple of 2π for all n. The latter is true iff $(\omega_1 - \omega_2)T = k(2\pi)$ for some integer k. Thus we might say that after periodic sampling with period T, ω_1 and ω_2 are equivalent iff they differ by an integer times $2\pi/T$. Though the above observation about sampling of exponentials is very simple, it will be recorded here as a theorem.

Theorem 9. If $f(t)$ is an exponential function, then the sequence $f(nT)$ determines $|f(t)|$ uniquely, but the sequence determines the frequency of f only within an integer multiple of $2\pi/T$.

When concerned with periodic sampling with period T and a given frequency ω, the set of frequencies $\omega_k = \omega + (2\pi/T)k$ obtained for all integer k is called the aliases of ω. Of course, any particular ω_k is called an alias of ω.

We shall now develop a relation between the Z transform of $f(nT)$ and the Fourier transform of $f(t)$. With both the continuous case and the discrete case under consideration simultaneously, it is natural to employ notation which makes analogies between the two cases easy to formulate. For this reason a modified Z transform will now be defined for use in the next theorem. Only the *Fourier case* will be discussed. For Z transforms this corresponds to taking $z = e^{-j\omega}$ (that is, $|z| = 1$).

Recall that the Fourier transform of $f(t)$ is defined thus:

$$F(\omega) = \int_{-\infty}^{\infty} \exp\,(-j\omega t)\,f(t)\,dt$$

The natural discrete analogy to this is to define the Z_m transform of $f(nT)$ thus:

$$F_m(\omega) = \sum_{n=-\infty}^{\infty} \exp\,(-j\omega nT)\,f(nT)\,T$$

The factor T is analogous to dt, and it makes F and F_m have the same dimensions. Note that $F_m(\omega)$ is simply the function obtained by using $Tf(nT)$ as coefficients in a Fourier series. The inversion formula for the Z_m transform is the formula which provides the coefficients of a Fourier series; since $F_m(\omega)$ is periodic with period $2\pi/T$,

$$\int_{-\pi/T}^{\pi/T} F_m(\omega)\,\exp\,(j\omega nT)\,d\omega = 2\pi f(nT)$$

That is, the inverse Z_m transform is

$$f(nT) = \frac{1}{2\pi}\int_{\pi/T}^{\pi/T} F_m(\omega)e^{j\omega nT}\,d\omega$$

This can be obtained from Theorem 4 by assuming $Z[f(nT)]$ converges for $|z| = 1$ and making the substitutions

$$z = \exp\,(-j\omega T)\qquad dz = -jTe^{-j\omega T}\,d\omega\qquad TF(e^{-j\omega T}) = F_m(\omega)$$

which yields

$$f(nT) = \frac{-1}{2\pi}\int_{\pi/T}^{-\pi/T} F_m(\omega)e^{j\omega(n+1)T}e^{-j\omega T}\,d\omega = \frac{1}{2\pi}\int_{-\pi/T}^{\pi/T} F_m(\omega)\,\exp\,(j\omega nT)\,d\omega$$

The following important theorem gives $F_m(\omega) = Z_m[f(nT)]$ in terms of the Fourier transform of $f(t)$.

Theorem 10.   If $F(\omega)$ is the Fourier transform of $f(t)$, that is, if

$$F(\omega) = \int_{-\infty}^{\infty} \exp{(-j\omega t)}\, f(t)\, dt$$

then the Z_m transform of $f(nT)$ is given by

$$F_m(\omega) = \sum_{k=-\infty}^{\infty} F\left(\omega + \frac{2\pi k}{T}\right)$$

Note that $F_m(\omega)$ is the sum of the values of F where the summation is over all the aliases of the frequency ω.   In view of Theorem 7, this "clumping" or "folding" is about what was expected.

PROOF: By the inversion formula for Fourier transforms†

$$f(nT) = \frac{1}{2\pi} \int_{-\infty}^{\infty} \exp{(j\omega nT)}\, F(\omega)\, d\omega$$

The trick is to rewrite this as an inverse Z_m transform; to this end the ω axis is divided into intervals of length $2\pi/T$, and we obtain

$$f(nT) = \frac{1}{2\pi} \sum_{k=-\infty}^{\infty} \int_{2\pi k/T - \pi/T}^{2\pi k/T + \pi/T} \exp{(j\omega nT)}\, F(\omega)\, d\omega$$

For fixed k, let $\omega = \lambda + 2\pi k/T$.   Then

$$f(nT) = \frac{1}{2\pi} \sum_{k=-\infty}^{\infty} \int_{-\pi/T}^{\pi/T} F\left(\lambda + \frac{2\pi k}{T}\right) e^{j\lambda nT} e^{jk2\pi n}\, d\lambda$$

Since both k and n are integers, $\exp{j2\pi kn} = 1$; thus

$$f(nT) = \frac{1}{2\pi} \sum_{k=-\infty}^{\infty} \int_{-\pi/T}^{\pi/T} F\left(\omega + \frac{2\pi k}{T}\right) \exp{(j\omega nT)}\, d\omega$$

We now wish to interchange the sum over k and the integral over ω; a sufficient condition for this is that

$$\int_{-\infty}^{\infty} |F(\omega)|\, d\omega$$

† The function $f(t)$ is assumed to satisfy the conditions of Theorem 11, Chap. 2.   Of particular importance, it is assumed that $f(nT) = \frac{1}{2}[f(nT + 0) + f(nT - 0)]$ for all n.

be finite.   If the interchange is made, we get

$$f(nT) = \frac{1}{2\pi} \int_{-\pi/T}^{\pi/T} \sum_{k=-\infty}^{\infty} F\left(\omega + \frac{2\pi k}{T}\right) \exp{(j\omega nT)}\, d\omega$$

However, by the inversion formula of Z_m transforms,

$$f(nT) = \frac{1}{2\pi} \int_{-\pi/T}^{\pi/T} F_m(\omega) \exp{(j\omega nT)}\, d\omega$$

Obviously we have two functions

$$F_m \qquad \text{and} \qquad \sum_k F\left(\omega + \frac{2\pi k}{T}\right)$$

which have the same Fourier coefficients; but this is possible iff the two functions are equal (at least almost everywhere), which completes the proof.

If $F(\omega) = 0$ for $|\omega| > \pi/T$, it is clear that F, and hence $f(t)$, can be determined uniquely from F_m.   In turn, the sampling theorem can be viewed as a corollary to Theorem 10.   The proof of the sampling theorem (Theorem 8) would then go in the following way:

$$f(t) = \frac{1}{2\pi} \int_{-\pi/T}^{\pi/T} F(\omega) \exp{(j\omega t)}\, d\omega = \frac{1}{2\pi} \int_{-\pi/T}^{\pi/T} F_m(\omega) \exp{(j\omega T)}\, d\omega$$

$$= \frac{1}{2\pi} \int_{-\pi/T}^{\pi/T} \left[\sum_{n=-\infty}^{\infty} f(nT) \exp{(-j\omega nT)}\, T \right] \exp{(j\omega t)}\, d\omega$$

Granting an interchange,

$$f(t) = \sum_{n=-\infty}^{\infty} f(nT)\, \frac{\sin{\left[(\pi/T)(t - nT)\right]}}{(\pi/T)(t - nT)}$$

since
$$\frac{1}{2} \int_{-\pi/T}^{\pi/T} \exp{(j\omega t - j\omega nT)}\, d\omega = \frac{\sin{\left[(\pi/T)(t - nT)\right]}}{t - nT}$$

As the final consideration here, the isomorphism between discrete and continuous convolutions, which exists in the bandwidth-limited case, will be mentioned.   In terms of the notation in this section, discrete convolution of $h(nT)$ and $f(nT)$ is defined by

$$\sum_{k=-\infty}^{\infty} h(nT - kT)f(kT)T$$

which is analogous to

$$\int_{-\infty}^{\infty} h(t - \tau)f(\tau)\, d\tau$$

Theorem 11.   Let $f(t)$ and $h(t)$ be bandwidth-limited to $B = \pi/T$ and let

$$g(t) = \int_{-\infty}^{\infty} h(t - \tau)f(\tau)d\tau$$

Then
$$g(nT) = \sum_{k=-\infty}^{\infty} h(nT - kT)f(kT)T$$

To let Theorem 10 play the key role in relating the discrete and continuous cases, Theorem 11 will be proved by assuming that the following modified form of Theorem 5 is available.

Theorem 5_m.   Let

$$g(nT) = \sum_{k} h(nT = kT)f(kT)T$$

Then $G_m = H_m F_m$ (see Prob. 7 for proof of this).

We have $G = HF$ (convolution theorem of Fourier transforms) and, by Theorem 10,

$$G_m = G \qquad \text{since } G(\omega) = 0 \text{ for } |\omega| > \frac{\pi}{T}$$

However, $H_m = H$ and $F_m = F$; therefore,

$$G_m = H_m F_m$$

and by Theorem 5_m it follows that

$$g(nT) = \sum_{k} h(nT - kT)f(kT)T$$

which proves Theorem 11.

Problems

1. Suppose you deposit money in a savings account at the first of each year.   Let the dividend be paid at the same time in the amount of K times the amount present prior to your deposit.   Suppose you open the account with B dollars at $n = 0$ and then deposit $f(n)$ dollars each year (i.e., at $n = 1, 2, \ldots$).   Formulate the balance $g(n)$ after the nth deposit as a difference equation and solve with $f(n) = b$ (a constant).   It is pleasant that this system is unstable; i.e., if $K > 0$, $g(n)$ is unbounded even though $f(n)$ is bounded.

2. Find the homogeneous solutions to $D^2(g) + \omega^2 g = 0$, where g is a sequence.   Compare these homogeneous solutions with those for $g'' + \omega^2 g = 0$ when g is a function of a real variable.   In particular, consider the comparison for $|\omega| \ll 1$.

3. Suppose that $g(n + 2) + g(n + 1) + g(n) = 1$ for $n \geq 0$ and that $g(0) = 1$ and $g(1) = 2$.   Find $g(n)$ for $n \geq 0$.

4. In the sketch, let

$$f(n) = \begin{cases} vn & \text{for } n \geq 0 \\ 0 & \text{for } n < 0 \end{cases}$$

Find $g(n)$. Assume that $g(n) = 0$ for $n \leq 0$.

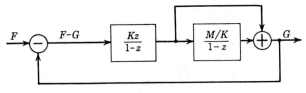

FIGURE P 4

5. Just as a theory of response time was developed for continuous systems, a similar theory for discrete systems can be developed. Consider response time measured in terms of the equivalent rectangle thus:

$$\rho \equiv \frac{\sum_{n=-\infty}^{\infty} |h(nT)|^2 T}{|h(0)|^2}$$

where it is assumed that $|h(0)|$ is the peak value of $|h(nT)|$. By using Z_m transforms and the Fourier-series version of Parseval's theorem, prove that ρ is a minimum iff $H(\omega) =$ constant for $|\omega| < \pi/T$. Show that this minimum is T and that

$$h(nT) = \begin{cases} \text{const} & \text{for } n = 0 \\ 0 & \text{for } n \neq 0 \end{cases}$$

corresponds to the minimizing H. If the bandwidth is restricted more, say $H(\omega) = 0$ for $|\omega| > k\pi/T$, where $0 < k < 1$, what is the minimum response time?

6. The theory sketched in Prob. 5 does not apply directly to discrete antennas. This is due to the lack of symmetry between the Z_m transform and the inverse Z_m transform. Consider a linear antenna array with adjacent elements spaced a distance T from one another. Let $f(nT)$ be the phasor of a sinusoidal illumination for the nth element. A derivation nearly identical to that given in Chap. 5 shows that the resulting antenna pattern is a constant times

$$F_m(\omega) = \sum_{n=-\infty}^{\infty} \exp(-j\omega nT) f(nT) T$$

where ω is the angle measured (in special units) from the normal to the array. The equivalent-rectangle resolution of the antenna is obviously

$$\rho = \frac{\int_{-\alpha}^{\alpha} |F_m(\omega)|^2 \, d\omega}{|F_m(0)|^2}$$

where we assume that side lobes at angles $|\omega| > \alpha$ do not have any harmful effects on the systems (2α can be taken as a full circle in most systems). To obtain simple results, assume that we can take $\alpha = \pi/T$. Show that the minimum value of ρ is $2\pi/T(2N + 1)$ if $f(nT) = 0$ for $|n| > N$ (of course $2NT$ is the aperture of the antenna) and that this minimum is obtained with $f(nT) = $ constant for $|n| \leq N$.

7. Let H_m and F_m be the Z_m transforms of $h(nT)$ and $f(nT)$. Write $H_m F_m$ as a double sum and change the summation variable to obtain a Z_m transform from this double sum.

Show that the Z_m transform of

$$\sum_{k=-\infty}^{\infty} h(nT - kT)f(kT)T$$

is so obtained, thus proving the convolution theorem for Z_m transforms.

8. Derive a sampling theorem under the assumption that the Fourier transform of $f(t)$ is zero for $|\omega_0 - \omega| > B$.

9. How do the sampled versions $f_1(nT)$ and $f_2(nT)$ of the functions $f_1(t)$ and $f_2(t)$ compare if

$$F_1(\omega) = \int_{-\infty}^{\infty} \exp(-j\omega t) f_1(t) \, dt$$

$$= \begin{cases} 1 & \text{for } |\omega| < \frac{\pi}{T} \\ 0 & \text{for } |\omega| > \frac{\pi}{T} \end{cases}$$

and $F_2(\omega)$ is as shown in the sketch?

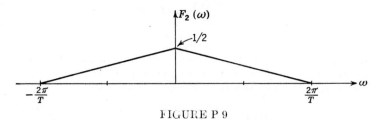

FIGURE P 9

10. Under the hypothesis of Theorem 11, show that

$$\sum_{n=-\infty}^{\infty} h(nT)f(nT)T = \int_{-\infty}^{\infty} h(t)f(t) \, dt$$

and that

$$\sum_{n=-\infty}^{\infty} |f(nT)|^2 T = \int_{-\infty}^{\infty} |f(t)|^2 \, dt$$

11. Complete the following theorem: F can be determined from F_m, and hence f can be determined from its sample values iff $F(\omega) = 0$ except on a set of ω's of measure $2\pi/T$, where the exceptional set has no two frequencies which are. . . .

8

INTRODUCTION TO POWER SPECTRA, AUTOCORRELATION FUNCTIONS, AND OPTIMUM LINEAR SYSTEMS

It is dangerous to study the theory of power spectra and autocorrelation functions without probability theory and the notion of a random process available as background. However, the interesting manipulational aspects of the theory can be given here and then exploited by applying the results to some exciting optimization problems for radar and communication systems. This chapter and the next provide a glimpse of the wonderful world of statistical systems analysis.

The danger mentioned above is not too great if it is kept in mind that the most important version of the theory is conceptually quite different from what will be given here, and that the notion of optimization that should be used requires a probabilistic framework which will be neither described nor adequately referred to.

The theory to be developed is an important version, but not the only version. It is very easily modified to obtain the theory usually of interest in connection with random processes; only the initial definitions need be changed. Then the development of the theory goes in exactly the same way. The material of this chapter should serve as a warm-up for a more complete treatment in the study of random processes, and it permits us to analyze finally rather large systems; the overall transmitting and receiving system for radar and communications is analyzed in Chap. 9. In these applications much of the material in previous chapters is utilized; in particular, practical applications of complex parameter circuits evolve and the theory of resolution (response time) is used.

8-1   INTRODUCTION

From the theory of Fourier transforms we can obtain a theory of energy-density spectra for functions which are square-integrable; this was mentioned briefly in Sec. 6-1. In this chapter we develop an analogous theory for functions having finite average power; specifically, the notion of power-density spectra is developed. The theory involving energy has application to functions which are square-integrable, i.e., to functions for which

$$\int_{-\infty}^{\infty} |f(t)|^2 \, dt < \infty$$

Of course the value of

$$\int_{-\infty}^{\infty} |f|^2$$

is defined as the total energy of f; typical motivation for this definition of energy is the fact that if f is the current in a resistor of R ohms,

$$R \int_{-\infty}^{\infty} |f|^2$$

is the total energy dissipated in the resistor. The theory involving average power has application to functions which have finite (normally positive) mean-square value, i.e., to functions for which

$$\lim_{T \to \infty} \frac{1}{2T} \int_{-T}^{T} |f(t)|^2 \, dt < \infty$$

Of course if the mean-square value of f is positive, f has infinite total energy.

Given any function of t, say $Q(t)$,

$$\lim_{T \to \infty} \frac{1}{2T} \int_{-T}^{T} Q(t) \, dt$$

will be called the time average of Q, and the following shorter notation will be used: $A[Q(t)]$. If Q is a function of several variables, say $Q(x, t, y)$, then a subscript will be attached to A to indicate over which variable the average is to be taken. For example,

$$A_y[Q(x, t, y)] = \lim_{T \to \infty} \frac{1}{2T} \int_{-T}^{T} Q(x, t, y) \, dy$$

As will be discussed shortly, there is a slight flaw in the above definition for time average, and the expression

$$\lim_{T \to \infty} \frac{1}{2T} \int_{-T}^{T} Q(t) \, dt$$

should be considered a formula for $A(Q)$ rather than the definition.

There is no need to discuss the theory involving energy prior to developing the theory of power correlation functions and power spectra; however, the energy theory has value of its own and it will now be summarized.

ENERGY SPECTRA AND CORRELATIONS

Let

$$\int_{-\infty}^{\infty} |f(t)|^2 \, dt < \infty$$

and let

$$F(\omega) = \int_{-\infty}^{\infty} e^{-j\omega t} f(t) \, dt$$

Let $J_f(\omega) \equiv |F(\omega)|^2$ be defined as the energy-density spectrum of f. Let

$$C_f(t) = \frac{1}{2\pi} \int_{-\infty}^{\infty} e^{j\omega t} J_f(\omega) \, d\omega$$

be defined as the energy autocorrelation function of f. Of course $C_f(t)$ and $J_f(\omega)$ form a Fourier transform pair. Recall that $\bar{f}(-t)$ is the inverse Fourier transform of $\bar{F}(\omega)$. In turn, since $J_f = F\bar{F}$, the convolution theorem gives $C_f(t) = f(t) * \bar{f}(-t)$. That is,

$$C_f(t) = \int_{-\infty}^{\infty} f(u)\bar{f}[-(t-u)] \, du = \int_{-\infty}^{\infty} f(u)\bar{f}(u-t) \, du$$

Let $u - t = v$. Then

$$C_f(t) = \int_{-\infty}^{\infty} f(t+v)\bar{f}(v) \, dv$$

This is the usual definition of the energy autocorrelation function.

Note that $C_f(0)$ is the total energy of f, that is,

$$C_f(0) = \int_{-\infty}^{\infty} |f|^2$$

It is customary to denote the variable of C_f by τ rather than t and to define C_f thus:

$$C_f(\tau) = \int_{-\infty}^{\infty} f(t+\tau)\bar{f}(t) \, dt$$

By Parseval's theorem $J_f(\omega)$ is indicative of total energy in that

$$\frac{1}{2\pi} \int_{-\infty}^{\infty} J_f(\omega)\, d\omega = \frac{1}{2\pi} \int_{-\infty}^{\infty} |F(\omega)|^2\, d\omega = \int_{-\infty}^{\infty} |f(t)|^2\, dt$$

Also, J_f is the distribution of energy with frequency in that if $H(\omega)$ is the transfer function of a circuit for which f is the input and g is the output, then G, the Fourier transform of the output, is given by $G = HF$. In turn, $J_g = |G|^2 = |H|^2|F|^2 = |H|^2 J_f$. In particular, if

$$H(\omega) = \begin{cases} 1 & \text{for } a < \omega < b \\ 0 & \text{for other } \omega \end{cases}$$

$\int |g|^2$ should be thought of as the energy of f in the frequency band $a < \omega < b$. We see that this is equal to

$$\frac{1}{2\pi} \int_{-\infty}^{\infty} J_g(\omega)\, d\omega = \frac{1}{2\pi} \int_{a}^{b} J_f(\omega)\, d\omega$$

Let $h_c(t)$ be the inverse Fourier transform of $|H|^2$. Then by the convolution theorem we get

$$h_c(t) = \int_{-\infty}^{\infty} h(v + t)\bar{h}(v)\, dv$$

just as we got

$$C_f(\tau) = \int_{-\infty}^{\infty} f(t + \tau)\bar{f}(t)\, dt$$

Since $J_g = |H|^2 J_f$, the convolution theorem gives the following relation between the energy correlations:

$$C_g(\tau) = h_c(\tau) * C_f(\tau)$$

The above is simply a frantic sketch of the mathematical theory of energy correlation and spectra. Since the theory of (power) correlation and spectra is very similar, it will be clear that the applications we develop in terms of power could be viewed in terms of energy as well. Also, the above sketch can serve to guide the development in the power case.

TIME AVERAGE

A few properties of time average will now be given. The properties are nearly obvious and hence this section can be skipped. We want a theorem which renders time average independent of shift on the t axis; i.e., we want

$$A[f(t + a)] = A[f(t)]$$

The formula

$$\lim_{T \to \infty} \frac{1}{2T} \int_{-T}^{T} f(t)\, dt$$

is "Cauchy principal partish," and it lets certain time averages exist which we could well do without. Some of the functions f which take advantage of the "locked limits" $(-T, T)$ do not have time averages which are independent of shift on the t axis. For example, let $f(t) = t$; then

$$A(f) = \lim_{T \to \infty} \frac{1}{2T} \int_{-T}^{T} t \, dt = \lim_{T \to \infty} \frac{1}{2T} (0) = 0$$

However,

$$A[f(t + a)] = \lim_{T \to \infty} \frac{1}{2T} \int_{-T}^{T} (t + a) \, dt = \lim_{t \to \infty} \frac{1}{2T} (2Ta) = a$$

To see how the Cauchy-principal-part feature is eliminated, we write

$$\frac{1}{2T} \int_{-T}^{T} f(t) \, dt = \frac{1}{2T} \int_{-T}^{0} f(t) \, dt + \frac{1}{2T} \int_{0}^{T} f(t) \, dt$$

Now to unlock the limits we define $A(f)$ thus:

$$A(f) \equiv \lim_{T_1 \to \infty} \frac{1}{2T_1} \int_{-T_1}^{0} f(t) \, dt + \lim_{T_2 \to \infty} \frac{1}{2T_2} \int_{0}^{T_2} f(t) \, dt$$

With this definition, $A(f)$ does not exist if $f(t) = t$.

In the definition of $A(f)$, $t = 0$ seems to be a special point; but such is not actually the case since

$$\frac{1}{2T_1} \int_{-T_1}^{c} f = \frac{1}{2T_1} \int_{-T_1}^{0} f + \frac{1}{2T_1} \int_{0}^{c} f$$

and

$$\lim_{T_1 \to \infty} \frac{1}{2T_1} \int_{0}^{c} f = 0$$

In turn,

$$\lim_{T_1 \to \infty} \frac{1}{2T_1} \int_{-T_1}^{c} f = \lim_{T_1 \to \infty} \frac{1}{2T_1} \int_{-T_1}^{0} f$$

Theorem 1. If $A(f)$ exists, then

$$\lim_{T \to \infty} \frac{1}{2T} \int_{-T}^{T} f(t) \, dt$$

exists and equals $A(f)$. Of course this theorem is trivial, but it is useful in that the Cauchy-principal-part formula is simpler than the expression for the definition of $A(f)$. For the formal proof we write

$$\frac{1}{2T} \int_{-T}^{T} f = \frac{1}{2T} \int_{-T}^{0} f + \frac{1}{2T} \int_{0}^{T} f$$

and use the fact that the limit of the sum equals the sum of the limits if the limit on each term exists. These individual limits exist since $A(f)$ exists. Thus

$$\lim_{T \to \infty} \frac{1}{2T} \int_{-T}^{T} f = \lim_{T \to \infty} \frac{1}{2T} \int_{-T}^{0} f + \lim_{T \to \infty} \frac{1}{2T} \int_{0}^{T} f$$

but this last expression is clearly $A(f)$.

Theorem 2. A is a linear operator. This follows from the linearity of integrals and the linearity of limits.

Theorem 3. $A[f(t + a)] = A[f(t)]$ in the sense that if either exists, the other exists and they are equal.

PROOF: Consider, say, the "right half" of the definition for $A[f(t + a)]$:

$$\frac{1}{2T} \int_0^T f(t + a)\, dt = \frac{1}{2T} \int_a^{T+a} f(t)\, dt$$

$$= \frac{T + a}{T} \frac{1}{2(T + a)} \int_0^{T+a} f(t)\, dt - \frac{1}{2T} \int_0^a f(t)\, dt$$

Now if $A[f(t)]$ exists,

$$\lim_{T \to \infty} \frac{1}{2(T + a)} \int_0^{T+a} f(t)\, dt$$

exists, and since

$$\lim_{T \to \infty} \frac{T + a}{T} = 1 \qquad \text{and} \qquad \lim_{T \to \infty} \frac{1}{2T} \int_0^a f(t)\, dt = 0$$

we get

$$\lim_{T \to \infty} \frac{1}{2T} \int_0^T f(t + a)\, dt = \lim_{T \to \infty} \frac{1}{2(T + a)} \int_0^{T+a} f(t)\, dt$$

$$= \lim_{T \to \infty} \frac{1}{2T} \int_0^T f(t)\, dt$$

which proves that $A[f(t + a)]$ then exists.

If we are given that $A[f(t + a)]$ exists, consider

$$\frac{1}{2(T + a)} \int_0^{T+a} f(t)\, dt = \frac{T}{T + a} \left[\frac{1}{2T} \int_0^T f(t + a)\, dt + \frac{1}{2T} \int_0^a f(t)\, dt \right]$$

Then as $T \to \infty$, the right obviously goes to

$$\lim_{T \to \infty} \frac{1}{2T} \int_0^T f(t + a)\, dt$$

That is,

$$\lim_{T \to \infty} \frac{1}{2(T + a)} \int_0^{T+a} f(t)\, dt = \lim_{T \to \infty} \frac{1}{2T} \int_0^T f(t + a)\, dt$$

which completes the proof except for similar arguments for the "left half" of the definition of A.

8-2 BASIC THEORY OF CORRELATION FUNCTIONS AND SPECTRA

We now turn to the finite-average-power case (with infinite total energy); i.e., let $A(|f|^2) < \infty$. Recall that in the finite-energy case we were able to obtain the desired results quickly by taking the Fourier transform of f, and the energy spectrum was then defined in terms of said transform. However, we now face an f which does not tend to die as t goes to infinity, and f does not have a Fourier transform. One might be tempted to develop a generalized notion of transform for functions of finite average power, and then proceed in the same way. This can be done; however, the mathematics involved in obtaining Wiener's generalized harmonic analysis is too advanced† for this book. By developing the theory in another way we can avoid the problem of defining a transform for f itself. The key is to develop an all-time-domain theory first and then to use the Fourier transform on the autocorrelation of f rather than on f itself.

CORRELATION FUNCTIONS

Let f have finite (normally positive) average power. Then the autocorrelation function of f is defined thus:

$$R_f(\tau) = A_t[f(t + \tau)\bar{f}(t)] = \lim_{a \to \infty} \frac{1}{2a} \int_{-a}^{0} f(t + \tau)\bar{f}(t) \, dt$$

$$+ \lim_{b \to \infty} \frac{1}{2b} \int_{0}^{b} f(t + \tau)\bar{f}(t) \, dt$$

Theorem 4. If $A(|f|^2) < \infty$, R_f exists and $|R_f(\tau)| \leq R_f(0) = A(|f|^2)$.

The second part of the theorem, $|R_f(\tau)|$ is bounded by $R_f(0)$, will be proved by Schwarz inequality (see Chap. 5, Theorem 6) with an assist from Theorems 1 and 3. The first part can be proved with Schwarz inequality along with some manipulations similar to those used to prove Theorem 3, but this part of the proof will be omitted. Consider

$$\left| \frac{1}{2a} \int_{-a}^{a} f(t + \tau)\bar{f}(t) \, dt \right|^2 \leq \frac{1}{2a} \int_{-a}^{a} |f(t + \tau)|^2 \, dt \, \frac{1}{2a} \int_{-a}^{a} |f(t)|^2 \, dt$$

by Schwarz inequality. As a goes to infinity we get $|R_f(\tau)|^2 \leq A(|f|^2)A(|f|^2)$, where we use the fact that $A[|f(t + \tau)|^2] = A[|f(t)|^2]$. Since $R_f(0) = A(|f|^2)$, $|R_f(\tau)| \leq R_f(0)$.

It may be advisable to append more "adjectives" to the name of R_f; for example, $A[f(t + \tau)\bar{f}(t)]$ is the power autocorrelation function of f over time. However, we shall use the *correlation of f* to mean $A[f(t + \tau)\bar{f}(t)]$ for the rest of the chapter.

Example 1. Let $f(t) = C \cos(\omega t + \alpha)$. To find R_f we consider

$$\frac{|C|^2}{2T} \int_{-T}^{T} \cos(\omega t + \omega\tau + \alpha) \cos(\omega t + \alpha) \, dt = \frac{|C|^2}{2(2T)} \int_{-T}^{T} \cos \omega\tau \, dt$$

$$+ \frac{C^2}{2(2T)} \int_{-T}^{T} \cos(2\omega t + \omega\tau + 2\alpha) \, dt$$

As $T \to \infty$, we get $R_f(\tau) = \frac{1}{2}|C|^2 \cos \omega\tau$ (for $\omega \neq 0$) since

$$A_t \cos(2\omega t + \omega\tau + 2\alpha) = 0$$

† Some aspects of this theory are given in Chap. 10, but the value of Wiener's transform of a finite-average-power function is mostly conceptual. The more useful results are obtained in this chapter.

That is, the d-c level of a "pure sinusoid" is zero. As a similar example, if $f(t) = Ce^{j\omega t}$, $R_f(\tau) = |C|^2 A[\exp{(j\omega t + j\omega \tau)} \exp{(-j\omega t)}] = |C|^2 \exp{j\omega \tau}$.

The problem now is to find the correlation function of the output of a linear-time-invariant system in terms of the correlation of the input. It is not obvious that this is possible. The conjugate of the reflection of a function occurs rather often; so a special notation will be introduced for it: $\tilde{h}(t) \equiv \bar{h}(-t)$, that is, $\tilde{h}$ is the conjugate of the reflection of h.

Theorem 5 (For Convoluting Systems). Let $g = h * \tilde{h}$. Then we have $R_g = h * \tilde{h} * R_f$.

PROOF: Consider

$$g(t + \tau) = \smallint h(u)f(t + \tau - u)\, du \quad \text{and} \quad \bar{g}(t) = \smallint \bar{h}(v)\bar{f}(t - v)\, dv$$

Hence
$$g(t + \tau)\bar{g}(t) = \smallint\smallint h(u)\bar{h}(v)f(t + \tau - u)\bar{f}(t - v)\, du\, dv$$

We now average over t and assume that the (u, v) integration and averaging over t can be interchanged:

$$R_g(\tau) = \smallint\smallint h(u)\bar{h}(v)A_t[f(t + \tau - u)\bar{f}(t - v)]\, du\, dv$$

Recall that $A_t[Q(t + a)] = A_t[Q(t)]$; hence we can add v to t if we like without changing the value of the time average of the bracketed term:

$$R_g(\tau) = \smallint\smallint h(u)\bar{h}(v)A_t[f(t + v + \tau - u)\bar{f}(t)]\, du\, dv$$

However, $A_t[f(t + v - u + \tau)\bar{f}(t)] = R_f(\tau - u + v)$ by the definition of R_f; hence $R_g(\tau) = \smallint\smallint h(u)\bar{h}(v)R_f(\tau - u + v)\, du\, dv$. Finally, we make the change of variable $v = -r$. Then

$$R_g(\tau) = \smallint\smallint h(u)\bar{h}(-r)R_f(\tau - u - r)\, du\, dr$$

This is clearly a triple convolution,

$$\smallint \bar{h}(-r)R_f(\tau - u - r)\, dr = (R_f * \tilde{h})$$

evaluated at $\tau - u$; then the integral of $(R_f * \tilde{h})_{\tau - u}h(u)$ is the convolution of $(R_f * \tilde{h})$ and h evaluated at τ.

There was nothing put in the hypothesis to justify the interchange of the (u, v) integration and taking the time average; it is easy to formulate a modified version of Fubini's theorem for this, but this is hardly worth detailed attention.

There exist linear time-invariant systems which cannot be described with convolution; in particular, derivative and delay should be considered. From Theorem 3, delay does not change the correlation function; that is,

$$A_t[f(t - a + \tau)\bar{f}(t - a)] = A[f(t + \tau)\bar{f}(t)]$$

Theorem 6 (For Derivative). If $R_{f'}$ is the correlation of the derivative of f' and R_f is the correlation of f, then

$$R_{f'}(\tau) = -\frac{d^2}{d\tau^2} R_f(\tau)$$

PROOF: Consider

$$\frac{d}{d\tau} R_f(\tau) = \frac{d}{d\tau} A[f(t + \tau)\bar{f}(t)]$$

and assume that we can interchange differentiation with respect to τ and time average over t; then

$$R_f'(\tau) = A\left[\bar{f}(t) \frac{d}{d\tau} f(t + \tau)\right] = A[f'(t + \tau)\bar{f}(t)]$$

Before differentiating again, replace t with $t - \tau$ [this does not change $R_f'(\tau)$, by virtue of Theorem 3] thus:

$$R_f'(\tau) = A[f'(t)\bar{f}(t - \tau)]$$

Now differentiate both sides with respect to τ and interchange $d/d\tau$ and A_t:

$$R_f''(\tau) = A\left[f'(t) \frac{d}{d\tau} \bar{f}(t - \tau)\right]$$

Of course the derivative of the conjugate is equal to the conjugate of the derivative; hence we want

$$\frac{d}{d\tau} f(t - \tau) = f'(t - \tau) \frac{d(t - \tau)}{d\tau} = -f'(t - \tau)$$

Thus we get $R_f''(\tau) = -A[f'(t)\overline{f'}(t - \tau)] = -A[f'(t + \tau)\overline{f'}(t)] = R_{f'}(\tau)$, as was to be shown.

Example 2. Suppose $R_f(\tau) = C (\sin B\tau)/B\tau$ with $R_f(0) = C = A(|f|^2)$. The correlation function of the derivative of f is found by differentiating the above twice:

$$R_f'(\tau) = -C \frac{\sin B\tau}{B\tau^2} + C \frac{\cos B\tau}{\tau}$$

$$R_f''(\tau) = 2C \frac{\sin B\tau}{B\tau^3} - C \frac{\cos B\tau}{\tau^2} - C \frac{\cos B\tau}{\tau^2} - CB \frac{\sin B\tau}{\tau}$$

$$R_{f'}(\tau) = \frac{2C}{\tau^2}\left(\cos B\tau + \frac{B\tau}{2} \sin B\tau - \frac{\sin B\tau}{B\tau}\right)$$

If we want the mean-square value of the derivative, this can be found by letting τ go to zero (we should return to R_f and differentiate at $\tau = 0$ by using the definition of derivative). For $B\tau$ small,

$$R_{f'}(\tau) = \frac{2C}{\tau^2}\left[1 - \frac{(B\tau)^2}{2} + \frac{(B\tau)^2}{2} - \frac{1}{B\tau}\left(B\tau - \frac{(B\tau)^3}{3!}\right)\right] \simeq \frac{2C}{\tau^2} \frac{(B\tau)^2}{3!} = \frac{CB^2}{3}$$

Thus $A(|f'|)^2 = \frac{1}{3}CB^2$.

It is better to start with

$$R_f(\tau) = C\left[1 - \frac{(B\tau)^2}{3!} + \frac{(B\tau)^4}{5!} - \cdots\right]$$

Then $\quad R_f''(\tau) = C\left[-\dfrac{B^2}{3} + \dfrac{(B\tau)^2}{10}B^2 - \cdots\right] \quad$ and $\quad -R_f''(0) = \tfrac{1}{3}CB^2$

as found above.

Example 3.   Suppose a circuit has the rectangular impulse response shown in the sketch:

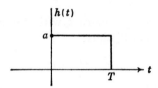

Then $h_c(t) = h * \tilde{h}$ is easily found to be the following:

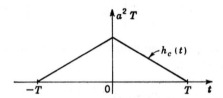

Suppose the input has a correlation of $R_f(\tau) = Ce^{-\alpha|\tau|}$ and we wish to find the mean-square output of the circuit.   By Theorem 5,

$$R_g(\tau) = \int_{-\infty}^{\infty} R_f(\tau - u)h_c(u)\,du$$

and

$$A(|g|^2) = R_g(0) = \int_{-\infty}^{\infty} R_f(-u)h_c(u)\,du = C\int_{-T}^{T} e^{-\alpha|u|}h_c(u)\,du$$

$$= 2Ca^2\int_0^T e^{-\alpha u}(T - u)\,du$$

This gives

$$A(|g|^2) = 2Ca^2\left[\frac{T}{\alpha} - \frac{1}{\alpha^2}(1 - e^{-\alpha T})\right]$$

POWER-DENSITY SPECTRA

In view of Theorem 5 it is natural to introduce the Fourier transform of the correlations to obtain a simple product in place of the triple convolution. Even though f does not have a Fourier transform, there is some chance that R_f is Fourier-transformable.   In Example 1, neither f nor R_f has a Fourier transform; periodic components in f are the usual cause for R_f not having a Fourier transform.   Without now going deeper into the existence of the Fourier transform of correlation functions, we define the power-density spectrum of f as the Fourier transform of its correlation function, and this spectrum will be denoted by S_f:

$$S_f(\omega) \equiv \int_{-\infty}^{\infty} e^{-j\omega\tau} R_f(\tau) \, d\tau$$

An obvious question is the following: Does power-density spectrum as just defined have any properties which justify its name? The following two properties would justify the name: (1) the average power of f is given by the integral over all ω of S_f (possibly times a constant); and (2) the variable ω is tied to the notion of frequency developed for linear time-invariant systems in that if f is the input to a system having the frequency response

$$H(\omega) = \begin{cases} 1 & \text{for } a < \omega < b \\ 0 & \text{for other } \omega \end{cases}$$

then the mean-square output (average power out) when f is the input is given by

$$\frac{1}{2\pi} \int_a^b S_f(\omega) \, d\omega$$

That S_f as defined (the transform of R_f) has the above properties is implied by the next two theorems.

Theorem 7. If S_f is the power-density spectrum of f, the average power of f is given thus:

$$A(|f|^2) = \frac{1}{2\pi} \int_{-\infty}^{\infty} S_f(\omega) \, d\omega$$

PROOF: By the inversion theorem of Fourier transforms,

$$R_f(\tau) = \frac{1}{2\pi} \int_{-\infty}^{\infty} e^{j\omega\tau} S_f(\omega) \, d\omega$$

and at $\tau = 0$,

$$R_f(0) = A(|f|^2) = \frac{1}{2\pi} \int_{-\infty}^{\infty} S_f(\omega) d\omega$$

Theorem 8. Let f be the input to a linear time-invariant system having a transfer function $H(\omega)$, let g be the output, and let S_f and S_g be corresponding power-density spectra; then

$$S_g(\omega) = |H(\omega)|^2 S_f(\omega)$$

PROOF: If the system is a convoluting system, Theorem 5 gives $R_g = R_f * h * \tilde{h}$; the convolution theorem gives $S_g = S_f H[\mathfrak{F}(\tilde{h})]$, where $\mathfrak{F}$ denotes the Fourier transform operator. Recall (Chap. 2, Lemma 1) that the Fourier transform of the conjugate of the reflection is equal to the conjugate of the transform, that is, $\mathfrak{F}(\tilde{h}) = \bar{H}$. Thus $S_g = S_f H \bar{H}$ or $S_g(\omega) = S_f(\omega)|H(\omega)|^2$. There is a bit more to the proof since not all linear time-invariant systems are convoluting systems. However, the remark about time translation and Theorem 6 nearly complete the proof. Specifically, if $g(t) = f(t + a)$, $R_g = R_f$ and in turn $S_g = S_f$. But in this case, $H(\omega) = e^{j\omega a}$ and $|H|^2 = 1$, so that $S_g = |H|^2 S_f$. If $g = f'$, $R_g = -R_f''$. By the differentiation theorem of Fourier transforms $S_g = -(j\omega)^2 S_f = \omega^2 S_f$, but in this case $H(\omega) = j\omega$ and $|H|^2 = \omega^2$, as desired.

The way is now open for solving numerous example problems and for considering significant applications of the theory. However, somewhat more can now be said about the nature of autocorrelation functions and about the existence of the notion of power spectra. Note that in view of the second property mentioned earlier,

$$A(|g|^2) = \frac{1}{2\pi} \int_b^a S_f(\omega) \, d\omega$$

but $A(|g|^2) \geq 0$; hence for arbitrary (a, b),

$$\int_a^b S_f(\omega) \, d\omega$$

is real and nonnegative. The fact that S_f is real can be seen directly. Observe that (by Theorem 3)

$$A[f(t - \tau)\bar{f}(t)] = A[\bar{f}(t + \tau)f(t)]$$

but since $A[\bar{Q}(t)] = \overline{A[Q(t)]}$, $A[\bar{f}(t + \tau)f(t)] = \bar{R}_f(\tau)$; thus $R_f(-\tau) = \bar{R}_f(\tau)$. This implies that the Fourier transform of R_f is real. Since

$$\int_a^b S_f(\omega) \, d\omega \geq 0 \qquad \text{for arbitrary } (a, b)$$

it follows that $S_f(\omega) \geq 0$, save possibly for a set of ω of measure zero, but this does not matter since only integral properties of S_f are of interest.

It is hardly obvious from the definition of autocorrelation that such functions always have nonnegative Fourier transforms (if they have transforms at all). However, the following (related) property is obvious: Consider arbitrary complex numbers $a_1, \ldots, a_n$ and arbitrary times $t_1, \ldots, t_n$ and take the time average of

$$\left| \sum_{k=1}^n a_k f(t + t_k) \right|^2$$

This can be written as

$$A\left[\sum_{k=1}^n \sum_{r=1}^n a_k \bar{a}_r f(t + t_k) \bar{f}(t + t_r) \right]$$

By linearity (Theorem 2) we get

$$\sum_{k=1}^n \sum_{r=1}^n a_k \bar{a}_r R_f(t_k - t_r)$$

since in $A[f(t + t_k)\bar{f}(t + t_r)]$ we can replace t with $t - t_r$. The original quantity on which the time average was being formulated was nonnegative, and hence its time average is nonnegative. Thus we obtain the following curious result: If $R_f(\tau)$ is an autocorrelation function, then for arbitrary complex $a_1, \ldots, a_n$ and arbitrary real $t_1, \ldots, t_n$

$$\sum_{k=1}^{n} \sum_{r=1}^{n} a_k \bar{a}_r R_f(t_k - t_r) \geq 0$$

To put it briefly, we shall say R_f has the nonnegative quadratic-form property. The good in the above observation is that it can be used to establish the existence of the Fourier (Stieltjes) transform of R_f.

Theorem 9. (Wiener-Kinchin theorem; given earlier as Theorem 3, Chap. 5.) A function $R_f(\tau)$ has the quadratic-form property and $R_f(\tau)$ is continuous iff there exists a real monotone nondecreasing function $\mathcal{S}_f(\omega)$ such that

$$R_f(\tau) = \frac{1}{2\pi} \int_{-\infty}^{\infty} e^{j\omega\tau} d\mathcal{S}_f(\omega)$$

The *if* part of the proof is trivial and was given in Chap. 5; again we omit the *only if*.

If $\mathcal{S}_f$ has a derivative, more precisely, if $\mathcal{S}_f$ is absolutely continuous or, equivalently, if

$$\mathcal{S}_f(\omega) - \mathcal{S}_f(0) = \int_0^{\omega} \mathcal{S}_f'(\omega) \, d\omega$$

this derivative is defined as the power-density spectrum of f. Since $\mathcal{S}_f$ is nondecreasing, clearly $S_f = \mathcal{S}_f'$ is nonnegative. In the general case we normalize thus:

$$\lim_{\omega \to -\infty} \mathcal{S}_f(\omega) = 0$$

Then we call $\mathcal{S}_f(\omega)$ the cumulative power spectrum of f and $\mathcal{S}_f(\omega_0)$ is equal to the power in f at all frequencies $\omega \leq \omega_0$. The obvious difficulty with power density arises when f has a periodic component, in which case a positive amount of power will "reside" at certain isolated frequencies. In this case $\mathcal{S}_f$ will have a jump discontinuity and S_f will not exist (properly) at these frequencies. To take care of this, it is convenient to let S_f have δ functions at such frequencies. It should probably be pointed out that δ functions will not cover all cases. Specifically, there exists what is called the singular case where $\mathcal{S}(\omega)$ is not constant, but $\mathcal{S}$ is continuous with $\mathcal{S}'(\omega) = 0$ wherever the derivative exists (and it exists almost everywhere). Here the power-density spectrum is zero (where it exists), there are no jumps to which we can assign δ functions, yet f has positive power. The existence of the singular case (an exciting pathology) is the major reason that δ-function conventions cannot always be used as a solid crutch.   Nevertheless the crutch provided by δ-function conventions is quite convenient and rather useful.

Example 4.   Of course all Fourier transform pairs in which one of the functions is nonnegative are obviously *correlation-function–power-spectrum pairs.*   Let the input $f(t)$ to a system have a power-density spectrum $S_f(\omega)$ which is constant out to very high frequencies.   To be specific, let the frequency response of the system be $H(\omega) = 1/(Tj\omega + 1)$.   The power-density spectrum of the output is

$$S_g(\omega) = \frac{1}{T^2\omega^2 + 1} S_f(\omega)$$

If we set $S_f(\omega) = C$, a constant, this is improper in that

$$A(|f|^2) = \frac{1}{2\pi} \int_{-\infty}^{\infty} C \, d\omega = \infty$$

However, if $S_f(\omega) \cong C$ for $0 \le |\omega| \le \Omega \gg 1/T$, the input f produces about the same output spectrum as a slightly fictitious input having a constant power-density spectrum.   In some applications the primary source of noise has a power-density spectrum which is constant over a very large part of the frequency spectrum.   We refer to such a noise as "white noise"; the term white is motivated by the fact that white light contains radiation of all frequencies.   If f is white noise,

$$S_g(\omega) = \frac{C}{(T\omega)^2 + 1}$$

The mean-square value of g is easily found:

$$A(|g|^2) = \frac{C}{2\pi} \int_{-\infty}^{\infty} \frac{d\omega}{(T\omega)^2 + 1}$$

$$= \frac{C}{2\pi T} \int_{-\infty}^{\infty} \frac{d\theta}{\theta^2 + 1} = \frac{C}{2\pi T} \arctan\theta \Big]_{-\infty}^{\infty} = \frac{C}{2T}$$

The correlation of g is also easily found:

$$\frac{1}{2\pi} \int_{-\infty}^{\infty} e^{j\omega t} \frac{1}{(\omega T)^2 + 1} \, d\omega = \frac{1}{2\pi j} \int_{-j\infty}^{j\infty} e^{pt} \frac{1}{1 - p^2 T^2} \, dp$$

$$= \frac{1}{2\pi j} \int_{-j\infty}^{j\infty} e^{pt} \left(\frac{\frac{1}{2}}{1 + pT} + \frac{\frac{1}{2}}{1 - pT} \right) dp = \frac{1}{2T} e^{-|t|/T}$$

Thus $R_g(\tau) = (C/2T)e^{-|\tau|/T}$.   Of course $R_g(0) = C/2T$, as expected.

We now have the basic tools to treat the optimization of linear time-invariant systems.   Before taking up the detailed theory, a few remarks about *noise* are in order.   When noise is present in a system, we seldom know the actual noise voltage as a function of time.   However, we often know certain averages such as the average power.   We shall usually assume that the autocorrelation function of the noise is known: $A_t[n(t + \tau)\bar{n}(t)] = R_n(\tau)$. Note that fixing $R_n(\tau)$ does not fix $n(t)$. To see this, observe that $n(t)$ can be passed through a network having a constant-amplitude response of 1 and having arbitrary phase response. This changes the noise waveform, but it does not change its power-density spectrum (Theorem 8). In turn, a phase-only filter does not change the autocorrelation function of the noise. Thus if we assume that only the correlation (or spectrum) of a noise is known, such knowledge of the noise is far short from knowing the actual waveform of the noise. It amounts to assuming that we know how, on the average, the power of the noise is distributed with frequency. Many common sources of noise have a power-density spectrum which is nearly constant over a frequency band much greater than the bandwidth occupied by the desired signals.

In the following sections we shall assume that signal plus noise is available as the input of a linear time-invariant system, as indicated in Figure 8-1.

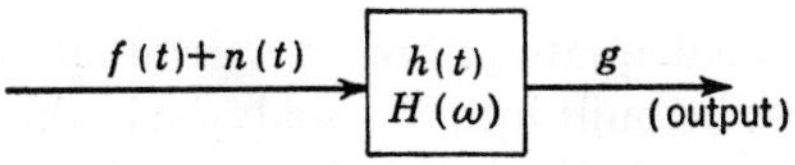

FIGURE 8-1. System to operate on signal and noise.

If the actual waveform of the noise were known, we could generate this waveform and subtract it to eliminate the effects of noise.

Two types of signals will be considered, specifically a known pulselike signal and a persisting noiselike signal. More precisely, the following two types of signals will be considered:

1. The waveform $f(t)$ known, with

$$\int_{-\infty}^{\infty} |f(t)|^2 \, dt < \infty$$

(finite total energy pulse)

2. The waveform $f(t)$ not known, with $0 < A(|f|^2) < \infty$ (positive finite average signal power), and the power spectrum (or correlation) of f known

The noise will be assumed to have positive finite average power, and the power-density spectrum of the noise is assumed to be known.

8-3 MATCHED FILTER FOR PULSE SIGNAL

The problem we treat here is the following: Find the filter, $h(t)$ or $H(\omega)$, which maximizes the ratio of the |peak signal out|² to the mean-square noise out. The signal out of the filter is $h * f$ and the noise out is $n * h$. If the filter maximizes said output signal-to-noise ratio, it would seem that the presence of the signal at the input would be most easily detected by observing the output. It turns out that the filter we find is optimum in a detection-theory sense, but this is beyond the scope of the book.

No realizability constraint will be placed on the filter in this section.

If a realizability constraint exists in a system to which the analysis is to be applied, it is often satisfactory to approximate a nonrealizable filter with a realizable filter which contains considerable time delay, as shown.   If

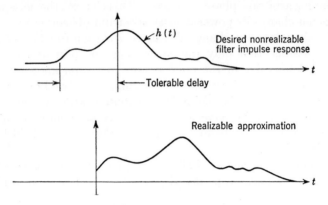

the tolerable delay is inadequate to obtain a good approximation, the realizability constraint must be built into the analysis; in this case the problem can be solved by variational methods (cf. Ref. 10), but the solution is not so attractive as the one we shall now derive.

The time at which the output $f * h$ takes on its peak value can be changed (without changing the waveshape) by incorporating delay or anticipation in the filter; this introduces a linear phase shift in $H(\omega)$.   This linear phase shift has no effect on the mean-square noise out.   Thus it is seen that the time at which the peak value occurs can be assigned arbitrarily; we shall select the time $t = 0$.   The Fourier transform of the signal out of the filter is $H(\omega)F(\omega)$.   The signal out is

$$\frac{1}{2\pi} \int_{-\infty}^{\infty} e^{j\omega t} H(\omega)F(\omega) \, d\omega$$

and the value at $t = 0$ is

$$\frac{1}{2\pi} \int_{-\infty}^{\infty} H(\omega)F(\omega) \, d\omega$$

The mean-square noise out is

$$\frac{1}{2\pi} \int_{-\infty}^{\infty} S_n(\omega)|H(\omega)|^2 \, d\omega$$

The problem is to find the $H(\omega)$ which maximizes

$$\frac{\text{Signal}}{\text{Noise}} \equiv \frac{|(1/2\pi)\int HF \, d\omega|^2}{(1/2\pi)\int S_n|H|^2 \, d\omega}$$

This maximization can be done by using the Schwarz inequality (Chap. 5, Theorem 6).   For example, consider the special case of white noise; i.e., let $S_n(\omega)$ be a constant, say $S_n(\omega) = N$. By the Schwarz inequality the numerator satisfies the following:

$$|\int HF\, d\omega|^2 \leq \int |H|^2 \int |F|^2$$

with equality iff $H = C\bar{F}$, where C is any nonzero complex constant. In turn, we have the following relation for the signal-to-noise ratio:

$$\frac{\text{Signal}}{\text{Noise}} \leq \frac{1}{2\pi N} \frac{\int |H|^2 \int |F|^2\, d\omega}{\int |H|^2\, d\omega} \quad \text{or} \quad \frac{\text{Signal}}{\text{Noise}} \leq \frac{1}{N}\left(\frac{1}{2\pi}\int |F|^2\, d\omega\right)$$

Thus the maximum signal-to-noise ratio is obtained with a filter frequency response $H(\omega)$ which is the complex conjugate of the Fourier transform of the signal. In terms of impulse response $h(t) = \bar{f}(-t)$, that is, $h = \bar{f}$. The value of the maximum possible signal-to-noise ratio is

$$\frac{1}{N}\frac{1}{2\pi}\int |F|^2$$

and, by Parseval's theorem,

$$\frac{1}{2\pi}\int |F(\omega)|^2\, d\omega = \int |f(t)|^2\, dt$$

which is the total energy of the signal. This is a rather striking observation; as far as $|\text{peak signal}|^2$ to mean-square noise ratio is concerned (in the white-noise case), only the total energy of the signal is important. The final expression for signal-to-noise ratio is

$$\frac{\text{Signal energy}}{\text{Power density of noise}}$$

The dimensions of the numerator and denominator are the same; in the case of voltage the numerator is in volts squared–seconds and the denominator is in volts squared per radian per second. However, the two quantities have different physical meaning. In the following example the ratio is written in terms of quantities which are more easily compared.

Example 5. Suppose $f(t)$ is bandwidth-limited to $|\omega| < B$; in fact, let $f(t) = f(0)(\sin Bt)/Bt$. If we are interested in a filter which passes the signal while rejecting the noise, it should reject all frequencies $|\omega| > B$, for only noise occupies such frequencies. The average noise power in the band occupied by the signal (in the white-noise case) is $(1/2\pi)N(2B)$. The peak signal power is $|f(0)|^2$. The point of this simple example is to observe that the ratio of these two powers,

$$\frac{|f(0)|^2}{(1/\pi)NB}$$

is equal to the ratio found above; i.e.,

$$\frac{\text{Signal energy}}{\text{Noise density}} = \frac{\pi|f(0)|^2}{NB}$$

One easy way to see this is to recall that the Fourier transform of the signal is

$$F(\omega) = \begin{cases} \dfrac{\pi}{B} f(0) & \text{for } |\omega| < B \\ 0 & \text{for } |\omega| > B \end{cases}$$

In turn, the total energy of the signal is

$$\int |f|^2 = \frac{1}{2\pi} \frac{\pi^2}{B^2} |f(0)|^2 \int_{-B}^{B} d\omega = \frac{\pi}{B} |f(0)|^2$$

Thus the ratio of signal energy to noise density is

$$\frac{(\pi/B)|f(0)|^2}{N}$$

as was to be shown.

Before removing the assumption of white noise, note that, if $H(\omega) = \bar{F}(\omega)$, then the signal out of the filter is $f * \bar{f}$, which is equal to

$$\int_{-\infty}^{\infty} f(t + \tau)\bar{f}(\tau) \, d\tau$$

For this reason the use of such a filter is often referred to as correlation filtering (or correlation detection). The filter $H = \bar{F}$ is also called the matched filter for f.

It is no strain to remove the assumption of white noise; we simply use the Schwarz inequality with the weight function $S_n(\omega)$. Recall that the ratio to be maximized is

$$\frac{|(1/2\pi)\int FH \, d\omega|^2}{(1/2\pi)\int |H|^2 S_n \, d\omega}$$

Since $S_n(\omega) \geq 0$, it is a perfectly good weight function. If $S_n(\omega) = 0$ on some interval of the ω axis and $F(\omega) \neq 0$ on this interval, it is obvious that the ratio in question can be made infinite. That is, if there is an interval of frequencies at which the signal has positive energy and at which there is no noise, we can pass this interval with a filter and obtain signal response with no noise. Hence we now assume $S_n(\omega) = 0$ implies that $F(\omega) = 0$, and we integrate over only those ω for which $S_n(\omega) > 0$. We can now put the weight function into the numerator thus:

$$\left| \frac{1}{2\pi} \int \frac{F}{S_n} H S_n \, d\omega \right|^2$$

Now, by the Schwarz inequality, the numerator is not greater than

$$\left(\frac{1}{2\pi} \right)^2 \left(\int \left| \frac{F}{S_n} \right|^2 S_n \, d\omega \right) \left(\int |H|^2 S_n \, d\omega \right)$$

with equality iff $H = C(\bar{F}/S_n)$. In turn, the ratio satisfies

$$\frac{\text{Signal}}{\text{Noise}} \leq \frac{1}{2\pi} \int_\Omega \frac{|F|^2}{S_n} \, d\omega$$

where Ω is the set of frequencies where $S_n(\omega) \neq 0$. The optimum filter is $H = C(\bar{F}/S_n)$, and an infinite ratio can be obtained iff

$$\int_{-\infty}^\infty \frac{|F|^2}{S_n} \, d\omega$$

diverges where we agree in particular that the integral diverges if $F(\omega) \neq 0$ on an interval of frequencies where $S_n = 0$.

Of course, if S_n is constant we return to the special results obtained for white noise. Note that $H = C(\bar{F}/S_n)$ implies that frequencies where S_n is small tend to be weighted more heavily than frequencies where the noise power is high.

Of course, the signals may be complex-valued and in view of the discussion of general complex filtering of Chap. 4 we are led to the following question: How much improvement is there if we optimize the output signal-to-noise ratio with a general complex filter instead of restricting ourselves to an "ordinary" complex filter? This question will be left for later. In the next chapter important (and exciting) applications of complex-valued signals and complex parameter systems are described; these applications provide the incentive for going further with the complex case.

8-4 LEAST-SQUARES FILTERING

As a brief preliminary, cross correlations and cross spectra should be mentioned. The (time average) cross correlation of f and g evaluated at τ is

$$R_{fg}(\tau) \equiv A_t[f(t + \tau)\bar{g}(t)]$$

and the cross spectrum is

$$S_{fg}(\omega) = \int_{-\infty}^\infty e^{-j\omega\tau} R_{fg}(\tau) \, d\tau$$

For some (and possibly all) values of τ, $f(t + \tau)\bar{g}(t)$ may have a time average of zero. If f and g have no physical dependence (for example, if f is the internal noise of one resistor and g the noise of another resistor), the following relationship is common:

$$R_{fg}(\tau) = A[f(t + \tau)\bar{g}(t)] = A[f(t + \tau)]A[\bar{g}(t)]$$
$$= (\text{d-c level of } f)(\text{d-c level of } \bar{g}) \qquad \text{for all } \tau$$

When the cross correlation of f and g is equal to the product of the indicated mean values (for all τ), we say that f and g are uncorrelated. Of course if f and g are uncorrelated and $A(f)$ or $A(g) = \overline{A(\bar{g})}$ is zero, then $R_{fg}(\tau) = 0$.

In this section the means will be assumed to be zero. The slight modification of the theory for nonzero means is covered in the problems at the end of the chapter. There is a theory for finding the cross correlation (cross spectrum) of the outputs of two filters in terms of the cross correlation (cross spectrum) of the inputs; this theory is quite similar to that given in Sec. 8-2. This extension of the theory will not be described as a separate item, but will be incorporated with the development of the theory of least-squares filtering. It is handy to observe the relationship between the cross correlation of f and g and the cross correlation of g and f: $R_{gf}(\tau) = A_t[g(t + \tau)\bar{f}(t)]$. Replace t with $t - \tau$ (Theorem 3); then

$$R_{gf}(\tau) = A[\bar{f}(t - \tau)g(t)] = \overline{A[f(t - \tau)\bar{g}(t)]} = \overline{R_{fg}(-\tau)} = \tilde{\bar{R}}_{fg}(\tau)$$

Thus, the cross correlation of g and f is equal to the conjugate of the reflection of the cross correlation of f and g. In turn, $S_{gf}(\omega) = \overline{S_{fg}(\omega)}$.

NATURE OF THE PROBLEM AND SOLUTION WITHOUT CONSTRAINTS

Suppose that f is a signal and we wish to obtain some linear time-invariant transformation of f. Let $P(\omega)$ be the frequency response corresponding to said linear time-invariant transformation. If f were available noise-free,

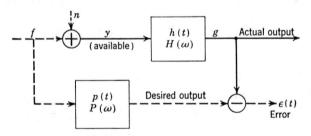

FIGURE 8-2.   Least-squares filtering problem.

we should simply pass f through a system having the transfer function $P(\omega)$. If P is too difficult (or impossible) to synthesize, we should use a transfer function which approximates P. Let only $y = f + n$ be available with the actual "waveshapes" of f and n unknown but with their correlations known.

The problem to be solved here is the following: Find the linear time-invariant transformation of $y = f + n$ which provides the best estimate of the desired transformation of f. Let $p(t)$ be the impulse response corresponding to $P(\omega)$; if there is no impulse response in the proper sense, δ function will be permitted for the sake of generality. A diagram of the problem is shown in Fig. 8-2.

Best estimate is taken to mean the estimate which minimizes the mean-square value of ϵ; that is, we wish to find the $H(\omega)$ which minimizes $A|\epsilon|^2$. Also we wish to find the minimum value as a measure of system performance.

There may be constraints on the problem in that not all $H(\omega)$ are permitted. The most popular constraint is to insist that H correspond to a realizable system $[h(t) = 0$ for $t < 0]$. We shall solve the problem with and without the realizability constraint. Note that if $n = 0$ and the desired transformation is not realizable, the problem may still be quite interesting. Specifically, if $P(\omega) = e^{j\omega T}$, the transformation desired is prediction by an amount of T in time which obviously is not realizable; here $p(t) = \delta(t + T)$. This pure prediction problem has been given considerable emphasis in the literature.

To solve the problem we start by formulating the correlation function of $\epsilon(t)$ rather than only its mean-square value. Recall that $R_\epsilon(0) = A(|\epsilon|^2)$. The error is given thus (subscript denotes where evaluated):

$$\epsilon(t) = (p * f)_t - (h * y)_t$$

In turn,

$$\epsilon(t + \tau)\bar{\epsilon}(t) = (p * f)_{t+\tau}(\bar{p} * \bar{f})_t + (h * y)_{t+\tau}(\bar{h} * \bar{y})_t$$
$$- (p * f)_{t+\tau}(\bar{h} * \bar{y})_t - (h * y)_{t+\tau}(\bar{p} * \bar{f})_t$$

We now average over t to obtain $R_\epsilon(\tau)$. The first two terms correspond to Theorem 5; they give $R_f * p * \bar{p} + R_y * h * \bar{h}$. The first two terms can be viewed as special cases of either of the last two terms. The time average of the third term will now be derived. This term can be written as a double integral thus:

$$\iint p(u)\bar{h}(v)f(t + \tau - u)\bar{y}(t - v) \, du \, dv$$

The time average is now taken, and we interchange the time-average operator and the integrals on u and v. Since $A[f(t + \tau - u)\bar{y}(t - v)] = R_{fy}(\tau - u + v)$, we get

$$\iint p(u)\bar{h}(v)R_{fy}(\tau - u + v) \, du \, dv = \iint p(u)\bar{h}(-v)R_{fy}(\tau - u - v) \, du \, dv$$

That is, the time average of the third term is $p * \bar{h} * R_{fy}$. Similarly, the fourth term gives

$$h * \bar{p} * R_{yf} = h * \bar{p} * \tilde{R}_{fy}$$

Note that if we put $y = f$ and $h = p$ in the third term it serves as a check for the first term.

With all the convolutions appearing it is natural to take the Fourier transform of R_ϵ to obtain the power-density spectrum of the error. We now have the following two equations:

$$R_\epsilon = R_f * p * \bar{p} + R_y * h * \bar{h} - R_{fy} * p * \bar{h} - \tilde{R}_{fy} * \bar{p} * h$$
$$S_\epsilon = S_f|P|^2 + S_y|H|^2 - S_{fy}P\bar{H} - \bar{S}_{fy}\bar{P}H$$

We wish to find the H (or h) which minimizes

$$R_\epsilon(0) = \frac{1}{2\pi} \int_{-\infty}^{\infty} S_\epsilon(\omega) \, d\omega$$

This is easily done in terms of the equation for S_ϵ. Everything is known except H; the trick is to put all the terms involving H into a perfect square, namely,

$$\left| S_y^{\frac{1}{2}} H - \frac{P S_{fy}}{S_y^{\frac{1}{2}}} \right|^2 = S_y |H|^2 - H \bar{P} \bar{S}_{fy} - \bar{H} P S_{fy} + \frac{|P S_{fy}|^2}{S_y}$$

Hence

$$S_\epsilon = \left| S_y^{\frac{1}{2}} H - \frac{P S_{fy}}{S_y^{\frac{1}{2}}} \right|^2 + S_f |P|^2 - \frac{|S_{fy}|^2}{S_y} |P|^2$$

and we wish to choose H to minimize

$$\int_{-\infty}^{\infty} S_\epsilon(\omega) \, d\omega$$

Since the term involving H is nonnegative, the best we could do is make it zero. This calls for

$$H = \frac{S_{fy}}{S_y} P \tag{8-1}$$

which is the optimum H (subject to no constraints). With the optimum H, the mean-square error is

$$A\left(|\epsilon|^2\right)_{\min} = \frac{1}{2\pi} \int_{-\infty}^{\infty} \frac{S_f S_y - |S_{fy}|^2}{S_y} |P|^2 \, d\omega \tag{8-2}$$

Suppose the signal and noise are uncorrelated, as is usually the case. Then

$$R_{fy}(\tau) = A\{f(t + \tau)[\bar{f}(t) + \bar{n}(t)]\} = A[f(t + \tau)\bar{f}(t)] + A[f(t + \tau)\bar{n}(t)]$$

but now $A[f(t + \tau)\bar{n}(t)] = A(f)A(\bar{n}) = 0$ since the means are assumed to be zero. Thus if the signal and noise are uncorrelated, $R_{fy} = R_f$. Similarly, in this case $R_y = A[(f + n)_{t+\tau}(\bar{f} + \bar{n})_t] = R_f + R_n + A(f\bar{n}) + A(n\bar{f}) = R_f + R_n$. We now get

$$H = \frac{S_f}{S_f + S_n} P \tag{8-3}$$

and

$$A\left(|\epsilon|^2\right) = \frac{1}{2\pi} \int_{-\infty}^{\infty} \frac{S_f(S_f + S_n) - S_f^2}{S_f + S_n} |P|^2 \, d\omega$$

or

$$A\left(|\epsilon|^2\right) = \frac{1}{2\pi} \int_{-\infty}^{\infty} \frac{S_f S_n}{S_f + S_n} |P|^2 \, d\omega \tag{8-4}$$

Example 6.   The theory of least-squares filtering without constraints is beautifully simple, and examples consist in direct substitution. The following case will be considered so that it will be available for comparison when the realizability constraint is imposed. We wish to predict $f(t + \alpha T)$; let $S_f = S/[1 + (\omega T)^2]$, where S is a constant indicative of signal strength. Let $S_n(\omega) = N$ (a constant) with signal and noise uncorrelated. Then the optimum transfer function is

$$H(\omega) = \frac{S}{S + N + N(\omega T)^2} e^{j\omega \alpha T}$$

and $\quad A(|\epsilon|^2) = \frac{SN}{2\pi} \int_{-\infty}^{\infty} \frac{d\omega}{S + N + N(\omega T)^2} = \frac{S}{2T} \sqrt{\frac{N}{S + N}}$

Observe that

$$A(|f|^2) = \frac{1}{2\pi} \int_{-\infty}^{\infty} \frac{S}{1 + (\omega T)^2} d\omega = \frac{S}{2T}$$

Therefore, we have

$$A(|\epsilon|^2) = \sqrt{\frac{N}{S + N}} \, A(|f|^2)$$

If $S/N \gg 1$, $\qquad A(|\epsilon|^2) = A(|f|^2) \sqrt{\frac{N}{S}}$

If $S/N \ll 1$, $\qquad A(|\epsilon|^2) \cong A(|f|^2)$

OPTIMIZATION WITHIN THE REALIZABILITY CONSTRAINT

Reconsider the expression obtained for the power density

$$S_\epsilon = \left| S_y H^{\frac{1}{2}} - \frac{PS_{fy}}{S_y^{\frac{1}{2}}} \right|^2 + S_f |P|^2 - \frac{|S_{fy}|^2 |P|^2}{S_y}$$

If H is constrained, it is not generally possible to make the first term zero. The integral of the last two terms might be viewed as the mean-square error due to noise and the integral of the first term as error due to constraints placed on the filter response $H(\omega)$. The key to dealing with the realizability constraint is to "factor" the power-density spectrum S_y so that

$$S_y(\omega) = Q(\omega)\bar{Q}(\omega) = |Q|^2 = |\bar{Q}|^2$$

where the inverse Fourier transform of Q is zero for negative argument. We can view $Q(\omega)$ as the frequency response of a realizable filter in that

$$q(t) = \frac{1}{2\pi} \int_{-\infty}^{\infty} e^{j\omega t} Q(\omega) \, d\omega = 0 \qquad \text{for } t < 0$$

As usual, the inverse Fourier transform of $\bar{Q}(\omega)$ is $\bar{q}(-t)$, which is zero for $t > 0$. We shall not make use of the idea, but note that S_y can be viewed as the power-density spectrum of the noise out of a filter which has impulse response $q(t)$ and which has a white-noise input of unit power-density spectrum. Given $S_y(\omega)$, the problem of finding q (or Q) is often referred to as the Wiener-Hoff factorization problem. If S_y is a rational function, Theorem 9, Chap. 6, solves the problem. The factorization problem will be discussed more later; for now, let us see how the factorization provides the key to optimization of H within the realizability constraint.

With any constraint, optimization consists in finding the H which satisfies the constraint and which minimizes the integral of

$$\left| S_y^{\frac{1}{2}} H - \frac{PS_{fy}}{S_y^{\frac{1}{2}}} \right|^2$$

or of

$$S_y \left| H - \frac{PS_{fy}}{S_y} \right|^2$$

Rewrite this as

$$S_y \left| \frac{QH - (PS_{fy}/\bar{Q})}{Q} \right|$$

and finally as

$$\frac{S_y}{|Q|^2} \left| HQ - \frac{PS_{fy}}{\bar{Q}} \right|^2 = \left| HQ - \frac{PS_{fy}}{\bar{Q}} \right|^2$$

since $|Q|^2 = S_y$.

Let $r(t)$ be the inverse Fourier transform of $R(\omega) = PS_{fy}/\bar{Q}$ and let $v(t)$ be the inverse Fourier transform of $V(\omega) = H(\omega)Q(\omega)$. Of course $v = q * h$. Recall that Q, P, and S_{fy} are known fixed functions and we wish to find the H (or h) which minimizes

$$\frac{1}{2\pi} \int_{-\infty}^{\infty} \left| HQ - \frac{PS_{fy}}{\bar{Q}} \right|^2 d\omega$$

subject to the constraint that $h(t) = 0$ for $t < 0$.   Since

$$q(t) = 0 \qquad\qquad\qquad \text{for } t < 0$$

then $\qquad v(t) = \int_0^t h(t - \tau)q(\tau)\, d\tau = 0 \qquad \text{for } t < 0$

Thus as h runs through realizable impulse-response functions, v runs through realizable impulse-response functions.   Now, the inverse Fourier transform of

$$HQ - \frac{PS_{fy}}{Q}$$

is $v(t) - r(t)$, and by Parseval's theorem

$$\frac{1}{2\pi} \int_{-\infty}^{\infty} |HQ - R|^2\, d\omega = \int_{-\infty}^{\infty} |v(t) - r(t)|^2\, dt$$

Since $v(t) = 0$ for $t < 0$, the corresponding mean-square error is

$$\int_{-\infty}^{0} |r(t)|^2\, dt + \int_0^{\infty} |v(t) - r(t)|^2\, dt$$

The best possible $v(t)$ for $t > 0$ is $v(t) = r(t)$ for $t > 0$.   The realizability constraint forces us to accept $v(t) = 0$ for $t < 0$.   Let

$$U(t) = \begin{cases} 1 & \text{for } t > 0 \\ 0 & \text{for } t < 0 \end{cases}$$

Then the optimum $v(t)$ is $v(t) = U(t)r(t)$. Thus $q * h = U(t)r(t)$. In turn,

$$QH = \int_{-\infty}^{\infty} e^{-j\omega t} U(t)r(t) \, dt = \int_{0}^{\infty} e^{-j\omega t} r(t) \, dt$$

Therefore, the optimum realizable transfer function is

$$H(\omega) = \frac{1}{Q(\omega)} \int_{0}^{\infty} e^{-j\omega t} \left[\frac{1}{2\pi} \int_{-\infty}^{\infty} e^{j\theta t} \frac{P(\theta) S_{fy}(\theta)}{\bar{Q}(\theta)} \, d\theta \right] dt \qquad (8\text{-}5)$$

The corresponding mean-square error is

$$A(|\epsilon|^2)_r = \int_{-\infty}^{0} |r(t)|^2 \, dt + A(|\epsilon|^2)_{\text{no constraint}}$$

As may have been noticed, the above derivation certainly provides a realizable $v(t)$, but this can happen with h not realizable. In particular, suppose S_y, P, and Q are rational functions of ω; then to have $q(t) = 0$ for $t < 0$ we shall insist that $Q(p/j)$ have no poles for Re $p \geq 0$. The other requirement we make is that $Q(p/j)$ have no zeros† for Re $p \geq 0$. The reason for this is that zeros of Q appear as poles of $H = 1/Q$ [inverse transform of $U(t)r(t)$]. Theorem 9, Chap. 6, provides that Q have neither zeros nor poles in the right half plane.

REMARKS ON FACTORIZATION

Before giving an example of optimization within the realizability constraint, a few more words about factorization are in order. First consider rational power-density spectra. Let $S(\omega)$ be a power-density spectrum which is a rational function of ω. Of course S is real and nonnegative. Since $S(\omega)$ is real for all real ω, the coefficients of this rational function are all real (more precisely, if S is written in lowest terms, the coefficients in the numerator and denominator can be made real by dividing the numerator and denominator by a complex constant). The realness of the coefficients is obvious. In view of the real coefficients, the zeros and poles of $S(\omega)$ appear in conjugate pairs; thus we can write

$$S(\omega) = C \frac{(\omega - a_1)(\omega - a_2) \cdots (\omega - a_n)}{(\omega - b_1)(\omega - b_2) \cdots (\omega - b_m)} C \frac{(\omega - \bar{a}_1) \cdots (\omega - \bar{a}_n)}{(\omega - \bar{b}_1) \cdots (\omega - \bar{b}_m)}$$

It is assumed that

$$\int_{-\infty}^{\infty} S(\omega) \, d\omega < \infty$$

and hence the poles (b's) are never real (therefore always available in pairs). Since $S(\omega) \geq 0$, if S has any real zeros (real a's), such zeros must be of even order since, in the neighborhood of an odd-order zero, $S(\omega) \cong K(\omega - a)^{2k+1}$, which goes negative. Split the even-order zeros evenly between the two factors. Finally, factor such that each b_k has a positive imaginary part and

† Zeros at Re $p = 0$ can be handled but should be given special attention.

each a_k has a nonnegative imaginary part.   Now take

$$Q(\omega) = C \frac{(\omega - a_1) \cdot \cdot \cdot (\omega - a_n)}{(\omega - b_1) \cdot \cdot \cdot (\omega - b_m)}$$

Of course $S(\omega) = \bar{Q}(\omega)Q(\omega)$ for real ω.   It is not difficult to see that

$$q(t) = \frac{1}{2\pi} \int_{-\infty}^{\infty} e^{j\omega t} Q(\omega) \, d\omega = 0 \qquad \text{for } t < 0$$

As an inverse Laplace transform,

$$q(t) = \frac{1}{2\pi j} \int_{-j\infty}^{j\infty} e^{pt} Q\left(\frac{p}{j}\right) dp$$

and the typical pole of $Q(p/j)$ is $p/j - b_k = 0$ or $p = jb_k$.   Since the imaginary part of b_k is positive, the real part of jb_k is negative.   That is, all the poles of $Q(p/j)$ are in the left-half p plane (off the $j\omega$ axis).   In turn (see Sec. 2-4), the inverse transform of $Q(p/j)$ is zero for $t < 0$.   By the way, if $\int S < \infty$, S is a proper rational function.   In turn, Q is a proper rational function and hence Q has an inverse transform.   The above discussion puts the factorization problem to rest for rational $S_y(\omega)$.   The content is about the same as Theorem 9, Chap. 6.

The general case requires some more work.   Recall that $R_y(-\tau) = \overline{R_y(\tau)}$; and if y is real, R_y is real and in this case $R_y(-\tau) = R_y(\tau)$.   In turn, $S_y(\omega)$ is an even function if y is real-valued.   In order to use the results of Sec. 6-4 without modification, we shall restrict the following discussion to even power spectra for the moment.   In view of Theorem 7, Chap. 6, we hope to be able to find $Q(\omega)$ thus:

1. Find $\alpha(\omega) = \dfrac{2\omega}{\pi} \displaystyle\int_0^{\infty} \dfrac{\log \sqrt{S(\omega)} - \log \sqrt{S(\lambda)}}{\omega^2 - \lambda^2} \, d\lambda$.

2. Let $Q(\omega) = \sqrt{S(\omega)} \, e^{j\alpha(\omega)}$.

To obtain a Q in this fashion, of course the indicated integral over λ must converge.   If $S(\omega)$ is smooth, the integral will converge iff

$$\int_{-\infty}^{\infty} \frac{\log S(\omega)}{\omega^2 + 1} \, d\omega$$

converges.   The danger is that $S(\omega)$ may get small too fast (as ω goes to $\pm \infty$ or at points on the ω axis); in this event†

$$\int_{-\infty}^{\infty} \frac{\log S(\omega)}{1 + \omega^2} \, d\omega = -\infty$$

† If

$$\int_{-\infty}^{\infty} S(\omega) \, d\omega < \infty$$

it follows that

$$\int_{-\infty}^{\infty} \log S(\omega) \, d\omega < \infty$$

so that only $-\infty$ is a threat.

In view of these remarks, the following famous mathematical result may seem reasonable.

Theorem 10 (*Paley-Wiener Condition for Factorization*). Let $S(\omega) \geq 0$ with

$$\int_{-\infty}^{\infty} S(\omega)\, d\omega < \infty$$

Then there exists a realizable frequency-response function $Q(\omega)$ such that $S(\omega) = |Q(\omega)|^2$ iff

$$\int_{-\infty}^{\infty} \frac{\log S(\omega)}{1 + \omega^2} > -\infty$$

The proof is difficult and will be omitted.

Example 7.   As in Example 6, let the noise be white so that its power-density spectrum is a constant N. Let the power-density spectrum of the signal be $S_f(\omega) = S/[(T\omega)^2 + 1]$, where S is a constant. We wish to find the realizable filter which provides the best (least squares) estimate of $f(t + \alpha T)$. Let the signal and noise be uncorrelated; hence,

$$S_y(\omega) = N + \frac{S}{(T\omega)^2 + 1} \quad \text{and} \quad S_{fy} = \frac{S}{(T\omega)^2 + 1}$$

The transfer function required to provide the desired transformation of f is $P(\omega) = e^{j\omega\alpha T}$. The problem is to find the $H(\omega)$ which minimizes the integral of $|HQ - PS_f/\bar{Q}|^2$, where Q provides the factorization of S_y. Let $a^2 = (N + S)/N$. Then

$$S_y = N \frac{\omega^2 + a^2/T^2}{\omega^2 + 1/T^2}$$

Since
$$S_y = N \frac{(\omega + ja/T)(\omega - ja/T)}{(\omega + j1/T)(\omega - j1/T)}$$

$$Q(\omega) = \sqrt{N}\, \frac{\omega - ja/T}{\omega - j1/T}$$

Our concern is with

$$R(\omega) = \frac{PS_f}{\bar{Q}} = \frac{e^{j\omega\alpha T}}{\sqrt{N}} \frac{S/T^2}{\omega^2 + 1/T^2} \frac{\omega + j1/T}{\omega + ja/T}$$

$$= \frac{S}{T^2\sqrt{N}}\, e^{j\omega\alpha T}\, \frac{1}{(\omega + ja/T)(\omega - j1/T)}$$

The inverse transform of this is easily found; in terms of p we want the inverse Laplace transform (along Re $p = 0$) of

$$\frac{-1}{(p - a/T)(p + 1/T)} = -\frac{T/(a + 1)}{p - a/T} + \frac{T/(1 + a)}{p + 1/T}$$

Save for the factor $T/(1 + a)$ the inverse is $e^{-t/T}$ for $t > 0$ and $e^{at/T}$ for

$t \leq 0$. The optimum transfer function is the following ($e^{j\omega \alpha T}$ causes a translation of the inverse transform):

$H(\omega) =$

$$\frac{S}{NT(1+a)} \frac{\omega - j(1/T)}{\omega - j(a/T)} \int_{-\infty}^{\infty} e^{-j\omega t} U(t) \left[\begin{array}{ll} \exp\left(-\dfrac{t + \alpha T}{T}\right) & \text{for } t > -\alpha T \\[2mm] \exp\dfrac{at + a\alpha T}{T} & \text{for } t < -\alpha T \end{array} \right] dt$$

If actual prediction is involved, $\alpha > 0$. If αT represents delay permitted in estimating f, $\alpha < 0$. In either case it is easy to solve for H in closed form; it is particularly easy when $\alpha > 0$. In this case we want

$$\int_0^\infty \exp\left(-j\omega t - \frac{t}{T} - \alpha\right) dt = e^{-\alpha} \frac{1}{j\omega + 1/T} = -je^{-\alpha} \frac{1}{\omega - j(1/T)}$$

Thus if $\alpha > 0$,

$$H(\omega) = \frac{Se^{-\alpha}}{NT(1+a)(j\omega + a/T)}$$

The mean-square error is also of interest. For comparison with Example 6, let $\alpha = 0$. The mean-square error is given by that found without the realizability constraint plus the integral over the negative t axis of the square of the inverse transform of $PS_f/\bar{Q}$. That is,

$$\int_{-\infty}^0 |r(t)|^2 \, dt = \frac{S^2}{T^4 N} \left(\frac{T}{1+a}\right)^2 \int_{-\infty}^0 \exp\left(2\frac{at}{T}\right) dt$$

Thus the mean-square error in the presence of the realizability constraint is

$$A|\epsilon|^2 = \frac{S}{2T} \left[\frac{S/N}{a(1+a)^2} + \sqrt{\frac{N}{N+S}} \right] \qquad \text{where } A(|f|^2) = \frac{S}{2T}$$

With or without the realizability constraint the mean-square error approaches the mean-square signal $A(|f|^2)$ as N/S goes to infinity. It is interesting to compare the errors with and without the realizability constraint when N/S is very small (hi-fi case). For small N/S, $a^2 = 1 + S/N \cong S/N$ and $a \gg 1$. In turn, $1 + a \cong a$ and we get

$$A|\epsilon|^2 \cong A(|f|^2) \left(\sqrt{\frac{N}{S}} + \sqrt{\frac{N}{S}}\right) = 2\sqrt{\frac{N}{S}} A(|f|^2)$$

In the nonrealizable case with $S/N \gg 1$,

$$A|\epsilon|^2 \cong \sqrt{\frac{N}{S}} A(|f|^2)$$

Thus for the pure filtering problem ($\alpha = 0$) under consideration, the realizability constraint increases the mean-square error by a factor of 2 when the *input signal-to-noise ratio* is high.

Problems

1. Suppose there is white noise at the input to the feedback system shown (see Sec. 2-5, Example 11, for some properties of this control system). If the power density of n is N (constant), find $A(|g|^2)$.   *Ans.* $(Na/2)(1 + b/a^2)$.

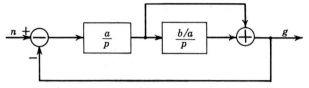

FIGURE P 1

2. Consider a pulse

$$f(t) = \frac{A}{\sqrt{2\pi}\,\sigma}\, e^{-t^2/2\sigma^2}$$

in the presence of additive white noise of density N. Find the signal waveform out of a matched filter. Find the mean-square noise out of such a matched filter. Verify that the ratio of $|\text{peak signal}|^2$ to mean-square noise is equal to

$$\frac{1}{N}\int_{-\infty}^{\infty} |f|^2\, dt$$

3. For the signal of Prob. 2, let the noise be colored with

$$S_n(\omega) = B\beta \exp\left(-\frac{\omega^2\beta^2}{2}\right)$$

Find the relation between σ and β for which the maximum $|\text{signal out}|^2$ to mean-square noise is infinite.

4. Find the optimum (least squares) realizable filter for the prediction of $f(t + \alpha T)$ if $\alpha > 0$ and

$$S_f(\omega) = \frac{1}{(T\omega)^4 + 1}$$

where $f(t)$ is available noise-free.

5. Let $f(t)$ and $n(t)$ be uncorrelated with mean zero. Let

$$S_f(\omega) = \frac{S}{(T\omega)^2 + 1}$$

where S is a constant. Let the noise spectrum be $S_n(\omega) = N - S_f(\omega)$, where N is a constant greater than S. Find the filter for $y = f + n$ which minimizes $A(|f - h * y|^2)$ with and without the realizability constraint. Compare the mean-square errors in the two cases if $S/N \gg 1$.

6. Solve Prob. 5 with the following spectra in place of those used in that problem:

$$S_f(\omega) = \frac{S}{(T\omega)^4 + 1} \qquad \text{and} \qquad S_n = N$$

(as usual, S and N are constants).

7. Consider the filtering problem of estimating $f(t)$ if the mean of f is $a_f = A(f)$ and the mean of n is a_n. Suppose we first subtract the mean of $f + n$ from the available data to obtain y, which is then filtered as shown in the diagram. In addition to filtering y

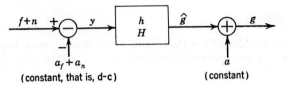

FIGURE P 7

to obtain an estimate of f, we permit the insertion of direct current of level a. Note that $A(y) = 0$ since

$$y = f + n - a_f - a_n$$

(a) Show that $A(\hat{g}) = 0$ for any impulse response h.

(b) Let $\hat{f} = f - a_f$; that is, let $\hat{f}$ be the a-c part of f. If g is to be an estimate of f, the error in the system is $\epsilon = h * y + a - f - a_f$. Show that the mean-square error is

$$A(|\epsilon|^2) = A(|h * y - \hat{f}|^2) + |a - a_f|^2$$

(c) For any filter h, what value of a minimizes the mean-square error? Note that the problem of optimizing h is now identical to that solved in Sec. 8-4 (zero mean values) except that f is replaced by $\hat{f}$ and $f + n$ is replaced by $f + n - a_f - a_n$.

8. In Chap. 7 it was made obvious that in almost every way the theory of the continuous case (functions of a real variable) and the theory of the discrete case (sequences) are analogous. The detailed development of the discrete theory corresponding to the continuous theory in this chapter is a reasonable exercise.

In this problem let n denote an integer variable and consider the case where the sequence is obtained by sampling a function of a real variable $f(t)$ to obtain $f(nT)$. The autocorrelation function of this sequence is defined thus:

$$R_f(nT) = \lim_{N \to \infty} \frac{1}{2N} \sum_{k=-N}^{N} f(nT + kT)\bar{f}(kT)$$

The power-density spectrum of said sequence is

$$S_f(\omega) = \sum_{n=-\infty}^{\infty} \exp\,(-j\omega nT)R_f(nT)T$$

(a) If

$$g(nT) \equiv h * f]_{nT} = \sum_{k=-\infty}^{\infty} h(nT - kT)f(kT)T$$

show that

$$R_g(nT) = h(nT) * \bar{h}(nT) * R_f(nT)$$

where $\bar{h}(nT) = \bar{h}(-nT)$.

(b) Show that $S_g = |H|^2 S_f$ if

$$H(\omega) = \sum_{n=-\infty}^{\infty} e^{-j\omega nT}h(nT)T$$

(H is the modified Z transform of the sequence h).

(c) Formulate and solve the matched filtering and least-squares filtering problems for a sample sequence $f(nT)$ in the presence of additive noise $r(nT)$.

9. The problem of relating the (discrete) power-density spectrum of $f(nT)$ to the (continuous) power-density spectrum of $f(t)$ is quite interesting. What is desired is a result similar to Theorem 10, Chap. 7, but for power spectra.　Let

$$R_f(\tau) = \lim_{D \to \infty} \frac{1}{2D} \int_{-D}^{D} f(t + \tau)\bar{f}(t)\, dt$$

and let

$$R_{fd}(nT) \equiv \lim_{N \to \infty} \frac{1}{2N} \sum_{k=-\infty}^{\infty} f(nT - kT)\bar{f}(kT)$$

That is, R_{fd} is the correlation of the sequence $f(nT)$.　If R_f and R_{fd} happen to be related thus: $R_{fd}(nT) = R_f(nT)$, then Theorem 10, Chap. 7, can be applied to obtain

$$S_{fd}(\omega) \equiv Z_m(R_{fd}) = \sum_{k=-\infty}^{\infty} S_f\!\left(\omega + \frac{2\pi k}{T}\right)$$

where $S_f(\omega)$ is the power-density spectrum of $f(t)$.

Show that, if

$$\lim_{N \to \infty} \frac{1}{2N} \sum_{k=-N}^{N} f(nT + kT + \alpha)\bar{f}(kT + \alpha)$$

is constant in α for $0 \le \alpha \le T$, then $R_{fd}(nT) = R_f(nT)$.

HINT: Integrate the indicated sum over α from 0 to T to obtain $R_f(nT)$; assume that integration on α and the limit on N can be interchanged.　Note that if the indicated sum is constant in α, it must be constant at $R_{fd}(nT)$ since this is its value at $\alpha = 0$.

The result of this problem can be summarized thus:　If the autocorrelation of the sample sequence is independent of the *starting phase of the sampling*, then the power density of the sample sequence is related to the power density of the original function $f(t)$ in the way one would hope in the light of Theorem 10, Chap. 7.

9

INTRODUCTION TO ANALYSIS AND OPTIMIZATION OF RADAR AND COMMUNICATION SYSTEMS[†]

In Chap. 8 it was demonstrated that in the presence of additive noise, there exist performance limitations on linear time-invariant systems. In this chapter these performance limitations (and corresponding optimum transmitters and receivers) will be derived for communication and radar systems. The additive noises considered will be antenna noise (radio noise from our

[†] The material in this chapter consists of an elaboration on part of the contents of Ref. 11.

galaxy) and receiver noise. Among other things, practical (in fact, important) applications of complex parameter systems are illustrated.

The examples discussed in other chapters were concerned with subsystems such as pulse amplifiers, bandpass amplifiers, pulse (range) tracking systems, and antennas. Here we finally come to grips with the analysis of what might properly be called systems rather than subsystems. The approach to analysis and optimization started in this section grows into something of an academic discipline when pursued in depth and with attention to other types of systems. As will be illustrated here for radar and communications, the discipline rests on a simple mathematical model (applicable to many types of systems) which displays the entire system along with the role played by major subsystems such as the transmitter. With the model available, analytical techniques such as those developed in Chap. 8 can be applied for optimization of design and for determination of the best possible system performance. The thorough development of said discipline is not given here since a solid background in the theory of random processes is a prerequisite. It is hoped that the topics covered here provide an exciting glimpse of *statistical systems analysis*.

The general mathematical models and the analytical techniques to be discussed are applicable to communications, radar, sonar, infrared, and antenna systems. In connection with radar (and sonar) the theory can handle continuously distributed targets, while most of the previously available work on radar has considered only point targets. As far as applications are concerned, there will be some emphasis on the range channel of coherent radars with particular attention to pulse-compression radars.

The mathematical model we shall employ involves linear time-invariant operations, and hence the model can be thought of as cascaded filters. In the case of a communication system the circuits will in fact be electrical filters. However, in the radar and sonar one of the filters depicts the role of the transmitted pulse, and the model provides insight not previously available.

9-1 MODEL OF RADAR SYSTEM

For simplicity we shall restrict our attention to the range channel of the radar, but analogous derivations are possible for the angle channels or for all channels simultaneously; when channels are considered simultaneously, the theory involves functions of more than one variable. The performance of the system will be investigated for a single range sweep, and of course the antenna will be considered stationary during the sweep.

The object of the range channel is to sense the radar reflectivity as a function of range. The signal returned to the radar at any particular time consists of a superposition of incremental returns resulting from reflecting matter distributed in space. When only the range channel is considered, we can deal with the reflecting material in terms of incremental spherical shells about the radar. Thus the reflectivity with which we shall deal results from an integration over a shell weighted by the two-way antenna pattern, and only reflection in the direction of the source is considered. Of course, reflection can involve phase shift as well as amplitude change. Let x denote range from the radar.

The first step in deriving the model is to define the radial incremental reflectivity density $\tilde{f}(x)$† of the scene viewed by a given antenna pattern at the carrier frequency ω_0. If $\cos \omega_0 t$ is transmitted, $\tilde{f}(x)$ is that complex number such that the signal returned to the radar, when only the reflecting material in the shell of radii x, $x + dx$ is present, is

$$|\tilde{f}(x)|\, dx \cos\left[\omega_0\left(t - \frac{2x}{c}\right) - \tilde{\alpha}(x)\right]$$

(c is the velocity of light), where $\tilde{f}(x) = |\tilde{f}(x)|e^{j\tilde{\alpha}(x)}$. For convenience, propagation loss (which is directly proportional to x^{-2} for radars viewing the sky, but may be made nearly independent of x for ground-mapping radars) has been incorporated into the function $\tilde{f}$; however, $\tilde{f}$ will be called simply the reflectivity density of the scene since reflectivity is the only quantity influencing $\tilde{f}$ which is considered not fixed.

In an actual radar the signal transmitted is not a monochromatic wave; rather, it occupies some band (or even bands) of frequencies. However, $\tilde{f}$ will not change significantly over the per cent bandwidths used in normal radars. Thus, $\tilde{f}$ will be assumed constant over the spectrum of the transmitted signal.‡

Now, suppose we transmit the pulse $\tilde{A}(t) \cos [\omega_0 t - \tilde{\phi}(t)]$ and all the reflecting material is present (the presence of other reflecting shells has almost no effect on the signal reflected from a given spherical shell). The signal received by the radar, $\tilde{q}(t)$, at time t is the following superposition of incremental returns:

$$\tilde{q}(t) = \int_{-\infty}^{\infty} |\tilde{f}(u)|\tilde{A}\left(t - \frac{2u}{c}\right)\cos\left[\omega_0\left(t - \frac{2u}{c}\right) - \tilde{\phi}\left(t - \frac{2u}{c}\right) - \tilde{\alpha}(u)\right] du$$

For a pulsed radar, $\tilde{A}$ will be nearly zero outside some interval of time which is small compared with $2/c$ times the range interval of interest; hence the integration can be taken from $-\infty$ to ∞. This received signal is now mixed with a local-oscillator signal the frequency of which may or may not be offset from the carrier frequency ω_0. We shall consider in detail the case for which there is no frequency offset, and we shall be led to a low-pass (or video) theory. However, there is an analogous theory for an offset local-

---

† In Sec. 9-1 the tilde does not depict the conjugate of the reflection; it is used simply to provide additional functions.

‡ Some work has been done on the effects of f changing over the bandwidth of the transmitted pulse (see Ref. 12).

oscillator frequency which leads to a bandpass theory. By applying results similar to those developed in Chap. 6, it is easy to show that the bandpass and low-pass cases are mathematically equivalent (more precisely, they are isomorphic under the correspondence between real bandpass functions and low-pass complex functions described in Chap. 6).

Let the received signal $\tilde{q}$ be mixed with $\cos (\omega_0 t + \theta)$, and retain only the difference frequency; then the output of this mixer is

$$\tilde{q}_r(t) = \int_{-\infty}^{\infty} |\tilde{f}(u)| \tilde{A}\left(t - \frac{2u}{c}\right) \cos\left[\frac{2\omega_0}{c} u + \phi\left(t - \frac{2u}{c}\right) + \tilde{\alpha}(u) + \theta\right] du$$

(plus the *input* receiver noise). One could just as well mix the returned signal with $\sin (\omega_0 t + \theta)$. The output of a mixer operating with this quadrature local oscillator would be the same as above except that sine would appear in place of cosine, and this will be denoted by $\tilde{q}_i$. It develops that the radar can more accurately estimate $\tilde{f}$ if both mixers are used.

With both mixers present, an *ordered pair of receiver inputs* is available; hence the receiver input is a single complex-valued function $\tilde{q}_r + j\tilde{q}_i$, which has the following very simple form:

$$\int_{-\infty}^{\infty} \tilde{f}(u) \exp\left[j\left(\theta + \frac{2\omega_0}{c} u\right)\right] \tilde{A}\left(t - \frac{2u}{c}\right) \exp\left[j\phi\left(t - \frac{2u}{c}\right)\right] du$$

It is important to note that receivers using coherent video lead to full-blown complex-valued signals.

The above receiver input is readily recognized to be the convolution of two complex-valued functions. There is a one-to-one correspondence between time and range ($t = 2x/c$), and hence we can eliminate either all the time variables or all the distance variables. Since the overall objective of the system is to sense (measure or estimate) a function of position, the time variables will now be changed to distance variables.

With the following substitutions the equation for the input to the receiver is indeed a simple familiar expression:

1. $f(x) = \tilde{f}(x) \exp [j(\theta + \omega_s x)]$, where $\omega_s = 2\omega_0/c$ is a spatial frequency of $4\pi/\lambda$, that is, 4π radians per wavelength.

2. $k(x) = \tilde{A}(2x/c) \exp [j\phi(2x/c)]$, where k is the impulse response of a filter (normally low-pass).

3. $n(x) = n_r(2x/c) + jn_i(2x/c)$, where the n's refer to noise out of the corresponding mixers.

4. $q(x) = \tilde{q}_r(2x/c) + j\tilde{q}_i(2x/c)$.

Now, we have $q = f * k$, and $q + n$ as the receiver input. To complete†
the model, $q + n$ is filtered; that is, $q + n$ is sent through a system which

† There is a lack of perfect *coherence* in practical systems which should be included in the model for completeness. However, in the interest of simplicity it has been omitted. See Ref. 11 for the analysis which includes imperfect coherence under the heading of phase errors.

will be called the postfilter. The output of the postfilter is the radar
output which is an estimate of f (the output is complex-valued also). A
general complex operator can be synthesized with four real parameter
filters, which need not be describable as a single complex parameter system;
however, for the moment assume that the radar output g is produced by
convolving $q + n$ with a complex-valued function $h(x)$. Of course $h(ct/2)$ is
the impulse response in time of the receiver. The final general model for
the radar system is shown in Figure 9-1, and the receiver is shown in Figure

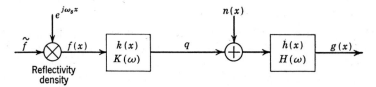

FIGURE 9-1.   Model for radar system.

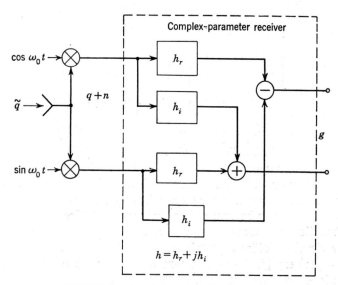

FIGURE 9-2.   Coherent video receiver.

9-2.   Some simple applications of the above formulation will now be
discussed briefly.

EFFECT OF CARRIER FREQUENCY ON THE RANGE CHANNEL OF RADAR

The output of the radar is in response not to the reflectivity $\tilde{f}$, but to
$\tilde{f}(u)e^{j\omega_s u}$. The filters involved are low-pass; hence the output of the radar is
not indicative of energy in the reflectivity distributed at low spatial frequencies, but is indicative of energy centered at the spatial frequency $-\omega_s$.

Such energy in f is produced by fine geometrical structure of the scene, namely, changes which occur over distances of the order of half a wavelength. Thus, a major difference between radars operating at widely different carrier frequencies is that correspondingly different parts of the spectrum of $\tilde{f}$ are sensed by the radars. In fact, this is the reason a radar at, say, S band $(2 \times 10^9 \text{ cps})$ produces a different picture of the world than a radar at X band $(10 \times 10^9 \text{ cps})$. Note that this observation, along with the fact that radars produce outputs, gives us the incidental conclusion that the reflectivity function corresponding to common scenes contains significant energy at very high spatial frequencies.

Approximately 60 cycles/ft corresponds to K_a band.

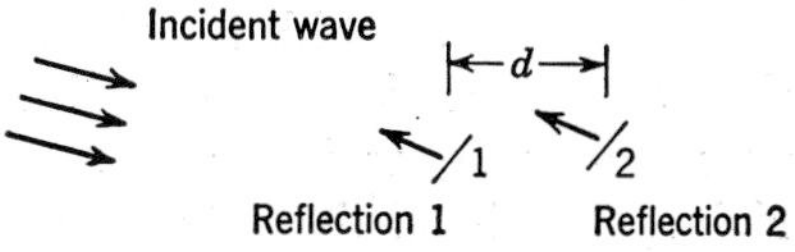

It is easy to see physically that the radar responds to geometrical structure which varies over a distance of half a wavelength. For consider a row of reflecting plates as shown in

FIGURE 9-3.   Role of fine geometrical structure.

Figure 9-3. If the spacing is $d = \lambda/2$, reflection 2 will have the same phase when it reaches plate 1 as the reflection from plate 1. Hence for this spacing we get reinforcement of the various reflections.

RESOLUTION OR RESPONSE TIME

The general philosophy involved in obtaining high resolution will now be described and applied to pulse-compression radar.

For a linear system, resolution can be measured in terms of the width of the output pulse produced by a point target. The idea is that if the responses produced by two point targets do not overlap in time it is clear at the output of the radar that two targets are present, but if the responses overlap we tend not to be able to resolve the total return into two parts. The separation required for resolving the responses is of the order of the duration of an individual response. For a point target, the input $\tilde{f}$ (and hence f) is taken as a delta function and the received signal is then k. Therefore, resolution refers to the width (duration in time or in distance $x = ct/2$) of the overall system impulse response, namely, $k * h$. Let K and H be the transfer functions corresponding to k and h, respectively (that is, K is the Fourier transform of k, etc.). Also, let $Y = KH$ so that Y is the overall transfer function seen by the input.

As is illustrated by specific transform pairs such as

$$H(\omega) = \begin{cases} 0 & \text{for } |\omega| > \Omega \\ 1 & \text{for } |\omega| \leq \Omega \end{cases} \qquad h(t) = F^{-1}(H) = \frac{\sin \Omega t}{\pi t}$$

and as discussed at great length in Chap. 5, we see that broad system bandwidth goes hand in hand with high resolution. However, if we consider a linear FM pulse of fixed duration T, it is seen that an arbitrarily broad bandwidth can be built into a pulse of fixed duration. Thus, as was pointed out in Chap. 5, there is a lower bound on the time-bandwidth product; but there is no upper bound. Broad system bandwidth is only a necessary condition for high resolution.

Insight is obtained if we consider optimizing resolution first by selecting the phase response and then the amplitude response. The elementary radar systems problem should be so decomposed that the phase of $Y = KH$ can be varied by varying only the phase of H, and this has no effect on the noise spectrum produced at the output in response to receiver noise. For any frequency where $K \neq 0$, H could be taken as K^{-1} to produce a very large system bandwidth without transmitting a high-energy density over the broad band; in practice this is not done because the postfilter will then pass too much receiver noise. Actually, in place of equalizing to obtain high system bandwidth, the overall system bandwidth of even high-resolution systems is usually reduced slightly by the receiver in the interest of obtaining good detectability (i.e., low noise in the output).

For the moment, then, assume that $|Y|$ is fixed by such factors as receiver noise. What phase response provides the best possible resolution? Of course, Chap. 5, Theorem 5, states that a constant (or linear) phase is optimum.

Thus, independent of the overall amplitude response, a constant-phase response is optimum and can be obtained without changing the power-density spectrum of the noise out of the system. Recall that when both amplitude and phase were nearly optimum (under various bandwidth constraints), the system resolution was of the order of 1 over the system bandwidth. Of course, if the bandwidth is B, measured in cycles per second, the resolution is approximately $1/B$ sec; and if B is in cycles per foot, the resolution is $1/B$ ft.

It is interesting that if the system is bandwidth-limited in the sense that $Y(\omega) = 0$ for $|\omega| > r$, and the resolution is measured in terms of equivalent rectangle, then (with zero receiver noise) the $Y(\omega)$ which minimizes (optimizes) the resolution also provides the best (least squares) estimate of the reflectivity of the scene. To see this, observe that the output of the system is $f * h * k$ and the error is $\epsilon = f - f * k * h$. In turn, the mean-square error† is

$$A(|\epsilon|^2) = \frac{1}{2\pi} \int_{-\infty}^{\infty} |1 - K(\omega)H(\omega)|^2 S_f(\omega) \, d\omega$$

With the bandwidth restriction,

$$A(|\epsilon|^2) = \frac{1}{2\pi} \int_{-r}^{r} |1 - Y|^2 S_f \, d\omega + \frac{1}{2\pi} \int_{|\omega|>r} S_f \, d\omega$$

† We can view $\epsilon(t)$ as the output of a filter having frequency response $1 - KH$ with f the input. Then the formula for $A|\epsilon|^2$ follows from Chap. 8, Theorem 8.

The best we can do is to make the contribution of the first term zero, that is, make $Y(\omega) = 1$ for $|\omega| < r$. But constant Y minimizes the resolution when resolution is measured in terms of equivalent rectangle (Chap. 5, Theorem 8). This observation enhances equivalent rectangle as a measure of resolution. Also, it raises doubts about the use of tapered illuminations on antennas of limited apertures, but tapering such as cosine weighting is commonly used.

PULSE-COMPRESSION RADAR

Pulse compression as used in chirp radars will now be discussed. Suppose we wish to obtain high resolution. The obvious way is to transmit a narrow pulse; that is, if $k(x) = A(x)e^{j\phi(x)}$, where A is the amplitude modulation and ϕ is the phase modulation, then we simply make the time duration of A small. However, if the transmitter is peak-power-limited, it may be that a narrow pulse-amplitude modulation does not provide enough energy in the returned signal.

Recall (Sec. 8-3) that if the receiver noise $n(x)$ is white noise, then the greatest possible |peak signal|² to mean-square noise at the output of the radar (when the input is a point target) is given by

$$\frac{\text{Energy of received signal}}{\text{Power density of } n}$$

Of course the numerator (within a constant) is

$$\int_{-\infty}^{\infty} |k|^2 \, dt = \int_{-\infty}^{\infty} |A(t)|^2 \, dt$$

Hence, to obtain good detectability and resolution we must transmit a signal having a long duration but offering the potential for high resolution. This may be done in a variety of ways. For example, phase modulation, amplitude modulation, or a combination of phase modulation and amplitude modulation may be used to obtain broad bandwidth. In any case it is only necessary to obtain a broad bandwidth in the transmitted pulse. Phase modulation is generally used; in particular, a linear frequency modulation is often used which results in a broad-bandwidth signal. With such a transmitted signal $K(\omega)$ is nonzero over a broad bandwidth; however, K is far from optimum in phase response. This is eliminated by designing $H(\omega)$ to have the opposite phase response, and then $Y(\omega)$ has constant-phase response over about the same frequency band which was covered by the FM sweep. In this way the resolution corresponding to $Y(\omega)$ can be made arbitrarily better than the resolution corresponding to the transmitted signal. Thus we can select the amplitude modulation to obtain the desired signal energy and then select the phase modulation to obtain a bandwidth which can provide the desired overall system resolution. The received pulse is long, but it produces a short pulse at the output of the radar; the phase response of the receiver compensates (or equalizes) the phase of the Fourier transform of $Ae^{j\phi}$. In turn, the resolution obtained is about 1 over the system bandwidth.

Before considering least-squares optimization of the radar system, it will be shown that the mathematical model derived above, $g = (f * k + n) * h$, also applies to communication systems.

9-2   COMMUNICATION SYSTEM

Let us start in the middle and assume that we are receiving a signal which is centered at the carrier frequency ω_0 and which has amplitude and phase (or frequency) modulation. The received signal will be denoted by

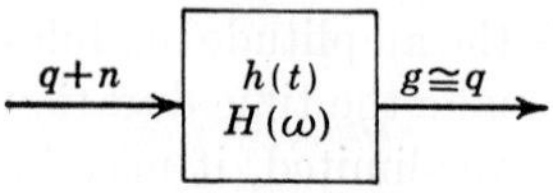

$$|q(t)| \cos [\omega_0 t + \gamma(t)]$$

FIGURE 9-4. Communications receiver.

where $q = |q|e^{j\gamma}$ and of course γ is real-valued. Typically, $|q|$ and/or γ (or $d\gamma/dt$) are the signals being communicated over the channel. As before, we mix the received signal with $\cos \omega_0 t$; that is, we multiply by $\cos \omega_0 t$ and reject the term centered at the frequency $2\omega_0$. Then $|q| \cos \gamma(t)$ is obtained. If we mix with $\sin \omega_0 t$ and retain only the low-frequency term, we get $|q| \sin \gamma(t)$. These real signals are accompanied by noises n_r and n_i as before. Of course, antenna noise and mixer (or receiver) noise contribute to $n = n_r + jn_i$. Just as before, we obtain a complex-valued input,

$$|q| \cos \gamma + n_r + j|q| \sin \gamma + jn_i = q + n$$

for the receiver. The signal $q + n$ can be filtered to obtain (hopefully) a good approximation to q.

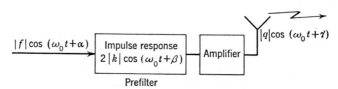

FIGURE 9-5.   Communications transmitter.

A prefilter may not be present in some communication systems; however, it has its place. Suppose the signal we wish to communicate is $|f(t)|$ $\cos [\omega_0 t + \alpha(t)]$, but we filter this to obtain $|q| \cos (\omega_0 t + \gamma)$, which is sent through the power amplifier and out the transmitting antenna. We now have the prefilter shown in Figure 9-5.

As shown in Sec. 6-1, if the filter impulse response is

$$2|k(t)| \cos (\omega_0 t + \beta)$$

then
$$q = |q|e^{j\gamma} = f * k = (|f|e^{j\alpha}) * (|k|e^{j\beta})$$

The object of the prefilter is not to complicate the problem; rather, in the presence of certain constraints on the transmitter it may be possible to obtain better system performance than would be possible without the use of a prefilter. In the terminology of information theory, the prefilter encodes the signal f so as to tend to match the transmitted signal to the rest of the system in some sense. Thus, in the communication system, the prefilter could be referred to as the coding filter (only linear time-invariant coding is considered here). Shortly the receiver (postfilter) frequency response and the coding (prefilter) will both be optimized in a least-squares sense under the constraint that the average power of the transmitter is limited.

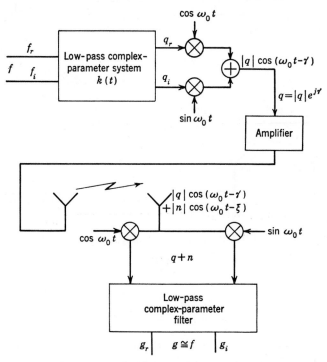

FIGURE 9-6. Low-pass complex-parameter system.

Returning to the various signals under consideration, we see that the coding filter was discussed in terms of a real parameter bandpass filter. On the other hand, the receiver was described in terms of a low-pass complex parameter filter. In view of the isomorphism discussed in Chap. 6 between real bandpass signals and complex low-pass signals, we are led to two (with other more or less obvious variations possible) physical configurations for the communication system. The all-low-pass system is given in Figure 9-6.

Figure 9-7 gives the real bandpass version.

In the bandpass case, the signal $|g| \cos (\omega_0 t - \arg g)$ is usually demodulated to obtain $|g|$ and/or $\arg g$. These two real functions are equivalent to the complex output g.   That is, the final outputs delivered are the same in the two systems, and mathematically the simple model of Figure 9-8 can be used to analyze both versions.   Of course the same model was found for radar.

In both radar and communication systems, real bandpass filters (that is, i-f amplifiers) are usually used.   There simply is not much advantage in using four low-pass real parameter filters to synthesize a complex parameter

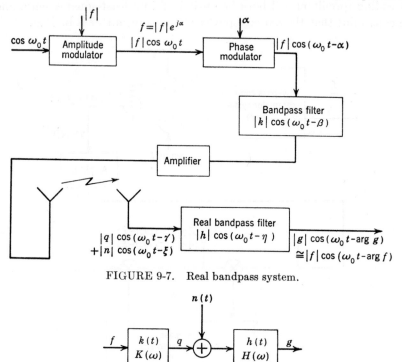

FIGURE 9-7.   Real bandpass system.

FIGURE 9-8.   Model for communications system.

filter when one real bandpass filter can do the job.   Mathematically it is a bit simpler to pretend that low-pass complex parameter systems are used; this eliminates the need to discuss the isomorphism between real bandpass signals and complex low-pass signals.

BANDPASS SYNTHESIS OF GENERAL COMPLEX FILTERS

For the sake of simplicity, general complex filtering has not yet been discussed; however, in some cases such filtering improves system perform- ance (by a limited amount; for example, see Sec. 9-4).   In general complex filtering, four real parameter low-pass filters remain adequate (see Chap. 4). However, two real bandpass filters are generally required rather than only one, which is adequate for an ordinary complex parameter filter.

If the bandpass signal is $|q| \cos (\omega_0 t + \gamma)$, the corresponding low-pass complex signal is $|q|e^{j\gamma}$ and we must filter what corresponds to the conjugate of this. The bandpass function which corresponds to $|q|e^{-j\gamma}$ is obviously $|q| \cos (\omega_0 t - \gamma)$. Thus we (somehow) obtain $|q| \cos (\omega_0 t - \gamma)$ and $|q| \cos (\omega_0 t + \gamma)$ from the received signal and filter these independently. Assuming that we have no passion for having the bandpass filters centered at the same frequency as the received signal, the use of local oscillators above and below the received carrier frequency provides a method for obtaining the two signals required for bandpass synthesis of general complex filters. This is depicted in Figure 9-9.

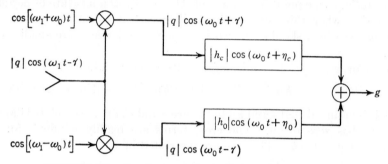

FIGURE 9-9.   Bandpass synthesis of general complex filter.

If general complex filters are to be used, the advantage offered by bandpass operation is no longer very great. However, in practice, general complex filtering is seldom used.

REAL AND IMAGINARY PART MODULATION

As a final little by-product of our general approach to systems analysis, note that mathematically real and/or imaginary part modulation suggests itself. That is, rather than use $|f|$ and/or α for the signals to be communicated (where $f = |f|e^{j\alpha}$), why not use f_r and/or f_i, where $f = f_r + jf_i$? To avoid cross talk between the real and imaginary channels in such a system the local oscillator must be phase-locked as well as frequency-locked to the received carrier. Such synchronization can often be achieved in a practical way. Of course in a system using amplitude and/or frequency modulation, there is no need for such a phase lock.

9-3 LEAST-SQUARES OPTIMIZATION

For the simple model derived, it is a very simple matter to carry out a least-squares optimization. The problem grows if general complex filtering is considered; in fact, with general complex filtering a sizable effort is required for a thorough analysis. This thorough analysis is left for a book covering statistical systems analysis. In Sec. 9-4, general complex filtering is considered in connection with matched filtering; this provides some idea as to the improvement possible with general complex filtering in comparison with ordinary complex filtering, and it introduces some of the additional mathematics needed when general complex filters are present.

Recall the model of Figure 9-8. The error will be taken as $\epsilon = g - f$, and $A(|\epsilon|^2)$ will be considered a measure of the performance of the system, and of course we wish to minimize $A(|\epsilon|^2)$. In many cases it is not obvious that $A(|\epsilon|^2)$ is entirely satisfactory as a measure of system performance. For example, in an amplitude-modulation communication system, $A[(|f| - |g|)^2]$ is a more appropriate measure of performance; it is also a difficult quantity to compute. At this stage in the game such difficulties will be left for future study. One point in support of $A(|f - g|^2)$ as a measure of performance is that when this quantity is small (goes to zero), other measures of performance which should be used in various applications are small (go to zero).

The error is $\epsilon = (n + q) * h - f$, and its autocorrelation function is

$$R_\epsilon = (R_n + R_q) * h * \tilde{h} + R_f - A[(q * h)_{t+\tau}\tilde{f}(t)] - A[(\bar{q} * \tilde{h})_t f(t + \tau)]$$

where it is assumed that f and n (and hence q and n) are uncorrelated† and at least one has zero mean. The cross terms are readily handled; for the moment let $y = k * h$. Then we are interested in

$$A_t \left[\tilde{f}(t) \int_{-\infty}^{\infty} y(u)f(t + \tau - u) \, du \right]$$

since $q * h = f * k * h = f * y$. If the time average and the u integration are interchanged we get

$$\int_{-\infty}^{\infty} y(u)A_t[f(t + \tau - u)\tilde{f}(t)] \, du = \int_{-\infty}^{\infty} y(u)R_f(\tau - u) \, du = y * R_f$$
$$= k * h * R_f$$

The other cross term gives $R_f * \tilde{k} * \tilde{h}$. In turn, the power-density spectrum of the error is

$$S_\epsilon = (S_n + S_q)|H|^2 + S_f - S_f(HK + \bar{H}\bar{K})$$

As in Sec. 8-4, completing the square facilitates finding the optimum receiver frequency response H:

$$S_\epsilon = \left| (S_n + S_q)^{\frac{1}{2}}H - \frac{S_f}{(S_n + S_q)^{\frac{1}{2}}} \bar{K} \right|^2 + S_f - \frac{S_f^2|K|^2}{S_n + S_q}$$

† To see that the cross terms involving n drop out, we have (for one of these cross terms)

$$A_t \int_{-\infty}^{\infty} h(u)n(t + \tau - u)\tilde{f}(t) \, du$$

and if A_t and integration on u are interchanged we get

$$\int_{-\infty}^{\infty} h(u)R_{nf}(\tau - u) \, du = 0$$

if n and f are uncorrelated.

Only the nonrealizable case will be considered in detail; in radar and most communication systems the delay required to obtain a good approximation to the optimum nonrealizable filter is not objectionable. In a radar having a 1-megacycle (per second) bandwidth the required delay is a number of microseconds, and in voice communications the required delay is a number of milliseconds. The optimum receiver is obvious (recall that $S_q = |K|^2 S_f$):

$$H(\omega) = \frac{S_f \bar{K}}{S_n + S_f |K|^2} \tag{9-1}$$

The corresponding mean-square error is

$$A(|\epsilon|^2) = \frac{1}{2\pi} \int_{-\infty}^{\infty} \frac{S_f S_n}{S_n + |K|^2 S_f} \, d\omega \tag{9-2}$$

Note that the overall phase response is always a constant (the phase of H = minus the phase of K) which is optimum for resolution as well. As S_n goes to zero, H goes to $1/K$ so that the overall response is such as to pass all of f without amplitude or phase distortion. As $S_n \to \infty$, H goes to $(S_f/S_n)\bar{K}$, which resembles the matched filter $\bar{K}/S_n$ which is appropriate for a point target (K is the Fourier transform of the received pulse if f is a δ function).

To obtain small error with fixed S_f and S_n, we want $|K|^2$ to be large. In the radar case suppose the energy of the transmitted pulse is limited, that is,

$$\int_{-\infty}^{\infty} |k(t)|^2 \, dt \le C$$

Then, by Parseval's theorem,

$$\frac{1}{2\pi} \int_{-\infty}^{\infty} |K(\omega)|^2 \, d\omega \le C$$

and $|K|^2$ cannot be made arbitrarily large over all frequencies. The problem of finding the best transmitted pulse is seen to be a simple one in the calculus of variations with an integral constraint. That is, we want the $|K(\omega)|$ which minimizes the mean-square error

$$\frac{1}{2\pi} \int_{-\infty}^{\infty} \frac{S_n S_f}{S_n + S_f |K|^2} \, d\omega$$

subject to an integral constraint on $|K|$. In the communications case the average transmitted power might be limited; that is,

$$A(|q|^2) \le C \quad \text{but} \quad A(|q|^2) = \frac{1}{2\pi} \int_{-\infty}^{\infty} S_f |K|^2 \, d\omega$$

so again there is an integral constraint on $|K|^2$. Thus it is clear that we can now go on and find the optimum energy spectrum for the transmitted pulse in the radar case and the optimum coding filter in the communications case. The solution to this will be sketched.

In the radar case the differential equation (provided by the calculus of variations) is†

$$\frac{\partial}{\partial K}\left(\frac{S_n S_f}{S_n + S_f K^2}\right) + \lambda \frac{\partial K^2}{\partial K} = 0$$

or

$$-\frac{S_n S_f{}^2}{(S_n + S_f K^2)^2}K + \lambda K = 0$$

The solutions are

$$|K(\omega)| = 0 \qquad \text{and} \qquad |K(\omega)|^2 = \sqrt{\frac{S_n}{\lambda}} - \frac{S_n}{S_f}$$

Since $|K|^2 \geq 0$, it is not surprising that a careful look at the manipulations leads to

$$|K|^2 = \max\left(0, \sqrt{\frac{S_n}{\lambda}} - \frac{S_n}{S_f}\right)$$

As usual in the calculus of variations, λ is selected to meet the constraint

$$\frac{1}{2\pi}\int_{-\infty}^{\infty} |K|^2\, d\omega = C$$

That is, λ is taken as small as possible compatible with the constraint. For the communications case we obviously get

$$|K(\omega)|^2 = \max\left[0, \sqrt{\frac{S_n(\omega)}{\lambda S_f(\omega)}} - \frac{S_n(\omega)}{S_f(\omega)}\right]$$

where λ is the smallest number for which

$$\frac{1}{2\pi}\int_{-\infty}^{\infty} S_f|K|^2\, d\omega \leq C$$

The intuitive idea is particularly easy to see in the communications case. Consider, say, $\lambda = 1$. Then at frequencies where

$$\sqrt{\frac{S_n}{S_f}} > \frac{S_n}{S_f}$$

that is, where $S_n/S_f < 1$ or $S_f/S_n > 1$, the coding filter passes these frequencies as a result of the favorable signal-to-noise ratio. At frequencies where $S_f/S_n < 1$, $K(\omega) = 0$, we give up. If $\lambda = 1$ now leads to a value of

$$\frac{1}{2\pi}\int_{-\infty}^{\infty} S_f|K|^2\, d\omega$$

less than C, λ is made smaller and new frequencies are passed by the coding filter, etc.

---

† K is now written in place of $|K|$; obviously any phase is acceptable as far as mean-square error is concerned since H compensates for the phase of K.

In summary, the analysis and optimization of two sizable (important) systems have yielded to analytical tools now available. Actually a position of mastery over such systems has nearly been established.

9-4 MATCHED FILTERING

As far as matched filtering in connection with the above model is concerned, there is not much to be done. The primary object of this section is to provide an introduction to analysis and optimization when general

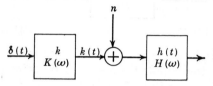

FIGURE 9-10. Point target or very narrow input pulse.

complex filtering is permitted. The use of only ordinary complex filters is a constraint just as the restriction to realizable filters is a constraint. By the way, there are many situations in which the optimum general complex filter turns out to be an ordinary complex filter, so that a good part of the motivation for considering general complex filtering is purely academic.

In the point-target case (or in the case of communicating a very narrow pulse) the input to the system is taken as a δ function as, shown in Figure 9-10. From Chap. 8 it is obvious that the maximum possible value of

$$\frac{S}{N} = \frac{|\text{peak signal out}|^2}{\text{mean-square noise out}}$$

is

$$\frac{S}{N} = \frac{1}{2\pi} \int_{-\infty}^{\infty} \frac{|K(\omega)|^2}{S_n(\omega)} \, d\omega$$

and for white noise of density N_0,

$$\left(\frac{S}{N}\right)_{\text{max}} = \frac{1}{2\pi N_0} \int_{-\infty}^{\infty} |K|^2 \, d\omega = \frac{1}{N_0} \int_{-\infty}^{\infty} |k(t)|^2 \, dt$$

Recall that the receiver frequency response which maximizes said signal-to-noise ratio is $H = (1/S_n)\bar{K}$. As in the other optimizations considered (namely, optimization for resolution and for least-squares estimation of f), phase compensation is present.

We now turn to the use of general complex filtering. The major question is how much improvement can be obtained if general complex filtering is permitted. For $f(t)$ a δ function, a general complex prefilter leads to some received function which will again be called $k(t)$. In the problem at hand, it is not important whether the prefilter is a general complex filter or an ordinary complex filter. To be specific, coherent quadrature mixing is assumed so that the complex function of time $k(t) + n(t)$ is literally available for the receiver.   The received signal is sent through two ordinary complex filters to synthesize a general complex filter, as shown in Figure 9-11 (see Chap. 4).

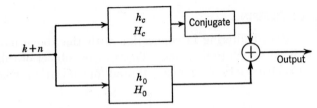

FIGURE 9-11.   General complex receiver.

The signal out is $k * h_0 + \bar{k} * \bar{h}_c$.   The noise out is $z = n * h_0 + \bar{n} * \bar{h}_c$. The first problem is to compute the mean-square noise out.   The correlation function of the noise out will be found; the value at $\tau = 0$ gives the mean-square noise out.   Observe that

$$z(t + \tau)\bar{z}(t) = (n * h_0)_{t+\tau}(\bar{n} * \bar{h}_0)_t + (\bar{n} * \bar{h}_c)_{t+\tau}(n * h_c)_t$$
$$+ (n * h_0)_{t+\tau}(n * h_c)_t + (\bar{n} * \bar{h}_c)_{t+\tau}(\bar{n} * \bar{h}_0)_t$$

We now take the time average of both sides.   The first term is very familiar; it gives $R_n * h_0 * \bar{h}_0$, where $\bar{h}_0(t) = \bar{h}_0(-t)$.   The other three terms give somewhat similar expressions; however, we now need some new time averages for the noise.   The following definitions will be helpful:

1. $R_{n\bar{n}}(\tau) \equiv R_n(\tau) = A[n(t + \tau)\bar{n}(t)]$
2. $R_{\bar{n}n}(\tau) \equiv A[\bar{n}(t + \tau)n(t)] = \overline{R_{n\bar{n}}(\tau)}$
3. $R_{nn}(\tau) \equiv A[n(t + \tau)n(t)]$
4. $R_{\bar{n}\bar{n}}(\tau) \equiv A[\bar{n}(t + \tau)\bar{n}(t)] = \overline{R_{nn}(\tau)}$

To illustrate the derivations involved in the other three terms, consider

$$(n * h_0)_{t+\tau}(n * h_c)_t$$

This can be written as

$$\iint n(t + \tau - u)n(t - v)h_0(u)h_c(v) \, du \, dv$$

If we now take the time average and interchange the time average and the (u, v) integrations, we get

$$\iint R_{nn}(\tau - u + v)h_0(u)h_c(v) \, du \, dv = \iint R_{nn}(\tau - u - v)h_0(u)h_c(-v) \, du \, dv$$

Let $h_{c-}(t) \equiv h_c(-t)$.   Then the result can be written as $R_{nn} * h_0 * h_{c-}$. The other two terms give $R_{\bar{n}n} * h_{c-} * \bar{h}_c$ and $\bar{R}_{nn} * \bar{h}_c * \bar{h}_0$.   Thus

$$R_{z\bar{z}}(\tau) = R_z(\tau) = R_{n\bar{n}} * \bar{h}_0 * h_0 + R_{nn} * h_0 * h_{c-} + \bar{R}_{n\bar{n}} * \bar{h}_c * h_{c-}$$
$$+ \bar{R}_{nn} * \bar{h}_c * \bar{h}_0$$

The following transform pairs will be used:

$$R_{nn} \leftrightarrow S_{nn} \qquad R_{n\bar{n}} \leftrightarrow S_{n\bar{n}} \qquad h_0 \leftrightarrow H_0 \qquad h_c \leftrightarrow H_c$$

Recall that the transform of $\tilde{h}_0$ is $\bar{H}_0$. Note that

$$\int_{-\infty}^{\infty} h(-t)e^{-j\omega t}\, dt = \int_{-\infty}^{\infty} h(t)e^{j\omega t}\, dt$$

Hence the transform of h_{c-} is $H_c(-\omega) = H_{c-}$. Finally, note that

$$\int_{-\infty}^{\infty} \bar{h}(t)e^{-j\omega t}\, dt = \overline{\int_{-\infty}^{\infty} h(t)e^{j\omega t}\, dt} = \bar{H}(-\omega)$$

Thus the transform of $\bar{h}$ is $\tilde{H}$, where $\tilde{H}(\omega) = \bar{H}(-\omega)$. All of this gives the following power-density spectrum for the noise out:

$$S_z(\omega) = S_{n\tilde{n}}|H_0|^2 + \tilde{S}_{n\tilde{n}}\tilde{H}_c H_{c-} + S_{nn}H_0 H_{c-} + \tilde{S}_{nn}\tilde{H}_c \bar{H}_0$$

We now consider an important special case which provides an interesting comparison with ordinary complex filtering. For actual antenna (and/or receiver) noise, it can be shown that $R_{nn} = 0$ and hence $S_{nn} = 0$; this condition will be discussed in some detail later. At any rate, in this special case $S_z(\omega) = S_n|H_0|^2 + \tilde{S}_n(-\omega)\tilde{H}_c H_{c-}$, the integral of which gives the mean-square noise. Note that (since S_n is real)

$$\int_{-\infty}^{\infty} \tilde{S}_n(-\omega)\bar{H}_c(-\omega)H_c(-\omega)\, d\omega = \int_{-\infty}^{\infty} S_n(\omega)|H_c(\omega)|^2\, d\omega$$

Hence the mean-square noise out can be written as

$$\frac{1}{2\pi} \int_{-\infty}^{\infty} S_n(|H_0|^2 + |H_c|^2)\, d\omega$$

The Fourier transform of the signal out is $KH_0 + \tilde{K}\tilde{H}_c$. The signal out at time $t = 0$ is

$$\frac{1}{2\pi} \int_{-\infty}^{\infty} [K(\omega)H_0(\omega) + \bar{K}(-\omega)\bar{H}_c(-\omega)]\, d\omega$$

$$= \frac{1}{2\pi} \int_{-\infty}^{\infty} [K(\omega)H_0(\omega) + \bar{K}(\omega)\bar{H}_c(\omega)]\, d\omega$$

Thus the problem is to find H_0 and H_c so as to maximize

$$\frac{1}{2\pi} \frac{\left| \int_{-\infty}^{\infty} [(K/S_n)H_0 + (\bar{K}/S_n)\bar{H}_c]S_n\, d\omega \right|^2}{\int_{-\infty}^{\infty} (|H_0|^2 + |H_c|^2)S_n\, d\omega}$$

By the more or less obvious generalization of the Schwarz inequality (discussed below) the above ratio is less than or equal to

$$\frac{1}{2\pi} \frac{\left[\int_{-\infty}^{\infty} \left(\frac{|K|^2}{S_n^2} + \frac{|\bar{K}|^2}{S_n^2} \right) S_n\, d\omega \right]\left[\int_{-\infty}^{\infty} (|H_0|^2 + |H_c|)^2 S_n\, d\omega \right]}{\int_{-\infty}^{\infty} (|H_0|^2 + |H_c|^2)S_n\, d\omega}$$

with equality only if $H_0 = C\bar{K}/S_n$ and $H_c = \bar{C}\bar{K}/S_n$.   Thus the best possible signal-to-noise ratio is now

$$\frac{1}{\pi} \int_{-\infty}^{\infty} \frac{|K|^2}{S_n} \, d\omega$$

an improvement by a factor of 2 over an ordinary complex filter.

The above calculation leaves quite a bit of cleanup work to be done. As for the generalization of the Schwarz inequality used, consider the integral to be approximated by a sum thus:

$$\left| \sum_i (k_i h_{0i} + \bar{k}_i \bar{h}_{ci}) S_i \right|^2 \qquad k_i = \frac{K(\omega_i)}{S_n(\omega_i)}$$

Recall that the discrete version of the Schwarz inequality (with nonnegative weights λ_j) is

$$\left| \sum_j \alpha_j \beta_j \lambda_j \right|^2 \leq \left(\sum_j |\alpha_j|^2 \lambda_j \right) \left(\sum_j |\beta_j|^2 \lambda_j \right)$$

For the sum of interest a substitution of the form

$$
\begin{array}{lll}
\alpha_1 = k_1 & \beta_1 = h_{01} & \lambda_1 = S_1 \\
\alpha_2 = \bar{k}_1 & \beta_2 = \bar{h}_{c1} & \lambda_2 = S_1 \\
\alpha_3 = k_2 & \beta_3 = h_{02} & \lambda_3 = S_2 \\
\alpha_4 = \bar{k}_2 & \beta_4 = \bar{h}_{c2} & \lambda_4 = S_2 \\
\cdots\cdots\cdots\cdots\cdots\cdots\cdots
\end{array}
$$

leads to the following result:

$$\left| \sum_i (k_i h_{0i} + \bar{k}_i \bar{h}_{ci}) S_i \right|^2 \leq \left[\sum_i (|k_i|^2 + |\bar{k}_i|^2) S_i \right] \left[\sum_i (|h_{0i}|^2 + |\bar{h}_{ci}|^2) S_i \right]$$

As the sum passes to an integral, we have the desired result.

THE NEED FOR PHASE LOCK

If we return to the derivation of the model and assume that, say, $|k(t)| \cos [\omega_0 t - \alpha(t) - \theta]$ is mixed with $\cos \omega_0 t$ and $\sin \omega_0 t$, the complex signal available is $k(t)e^{j\theta}$ if $k = |k|e^{j\alpha}$.   Thus to receive exactly k, θ must be zero.   In ordinary complex filtering the constant $e^{j\theta}$ appears with the output signal and has no effect on the value of $|\text{signal out}|^2$.   In turn, the lack of a phase lock on the receiver has no effect on the ratio of

$$\frac{|\text{Peak signal out}|^2}{\text{Mean-square noise out}}$$

if ordinary complex filtering is used.   On the other hand, if general complex filtering is used to gain the factor of 2 which was derived above, the factor $e^{j\theta}$ is important.   The signal out becomes $e^{j\theta}(k * h_0) + e^{-j\theta}(\bar{k} * \bar{h}_c)$.   To be specific, let the receiver noise be white.   Then $h_0 = \bar{k}$ and $h_c = \bar{k}$, and note that at $t = 0$, $(k * \tilde{k}) = (\tilde{k} * \bar{\tilde{k}})$ since

$$(k * \tilde{k})_t = \int_{-\infty}^{\infty} k(\tau)\tilde{k}[-(t - \tau)] \, d\tau$$

and

$$(\tilde{k} * \bar{\tilde{k}})_t = \int_{-\infty}^{\infty} \tilde{k}(\tau)k[-(t - \tau)] \, d\tau$$

Let

$$\Gamma \equiv (k * \tilde{k})_{t=0'}$$

Then the signal out at $t = 0$ is

$$\Gamma(e^{j\theta} + e^{-j\theta}) = 2\Gamma \qquad \text{if } \theta = 0$$

But without phase lock we get $2\Gamma \cos \theta$; and it is clear that if θ is not known (no phase lock), the hoped-for performance is not obtained.

Thus to obtain the improved performance possible with general complex filtering, the phase of the received signal must be known; it is sometimes practical to lock the phase of the local oscillator to the phase of the received signal, and the above analysis indicates that improved performance can be obtained when such synchronization can be accomplished. The last loose end to be dealt with is the assumption that $R_{nn} = 0$.

We shall call $A[n(t + \tau)n(t)]$ the complex correlation function of n (n is assumed to be complex-valued) and denote it by R_{nn}. The complex spectrum is S_{nn}, the Fourier transform of R_{nn}.

COMPLEX CORRELATION OF COHERENT VIDEO NOISE

Since the signal received at the antenna is known to occupy a bandwidth which is a small fraction of the carrier frequency we can assume that there is r-f filtering to the extent that the antenna noise is a real bandpass function when it goes into the quadrature mixers. Drawing on Chap. 6, let the real noise prior to mixing be†

$$f_b(t) = |n(t)| \cos [\omega_0 t + \alpha(t)]$$

Recall that the low-pass complex function $n = |n|e^{j\alpha}$ is related to the real bandpass function f_b thus (proved in Chap. 6 only for Fourier-transformable signals, but true for signals of finite average power as well):

Let $S_b(\omega)$ be the power-density spectrum of f_b (double subscripts will now be used only for complex correlations and spectra).

† Some freedom is taken on the sign of the phase modulation $\alpha(t)$.

Note that

$$S_f(\omega) = |V|^2 S_b(\omega) = \begin{cases} 4S_b(\omega) & \text{for } \omega > 0 \\ 0 & \text{for } \omega < 0 \end{cases}$$

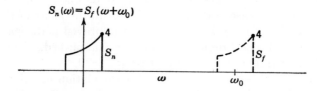

One useful calculation is that of the power-density spectrum of n. Since $n = e^{-j\omega_0 t}f$,

$$n(t + \tau)\bar{n}(t) = e^{-j\omega_0(t+\tau)}e^{j\omega_0 t}f(t + \tau)\bar{f}(t)$$

In turn, averaging over t gives $R_n(\tau) = e^{-j\omega_0\tau}R_f(\tau)$, and then the shift theorem of Fourier transforms gives

$$S_n(\omega) = S_f(\omega + \omega_0)$$

$$S_n \qquad S_f$$

$$\omega \qquad \omega_0$$

Similar considerations are involved in finding S_{nn}. As a preliminary it is easy to show (Prob. 5) that if $g = h * f$ then the complex correlation of g is related to the complex correlation of f thus: $R_{gg} = R_{ff} * h * h-$. In turn, the complex spectra are related thus:

$$S_{gg}(\omega) = S_{ff}(\omega)H(\omega)H(-\omega)$$

In the problem at hand this gives

$$S_{ff}(\omega) = S_b(\omega)V(\omega)V(-\omega)$$

but for any ω either $V(\omega) = 0$ or $V(-\omega) = 0$. That is, $S_{ff}(\omega) = 0$ and hence $R_{ff}(\tau) = 0$. It is easy to believe, and with adequate background not difficult to prove, that $R_{ff} = 0$ implies that $R_{nn} = 0$ if f is antenna noise. The problem consists in finding the following time average:

$$R_{nn}(\tau) = A[n(t + \tau)n(t)] = A[e^{-j2\omega_0 t}e^{-j\omega_0\tau}f(t + \tau)f(t)]$$

If the two functions of t, $e^{-j\omega_0(t+\tau)}e^{-j\omega_0 t}$ and $f(t + \tau)f(t)$, are somewhat uncorrelated, we are tempted to write

$$R_{nn}(\tau) = A[f(t + \tau)f(t)]A(e^{-j2\omega_0 t}e^{-j\omega_0\tau}) = R_{ff}0 = 0$$

In order to avoid discussing the theory of random processes, we simply yield to the temptation and now have the desired result. There is obviously a difficulty present in taking this last step; the step happens to be valid if f is a stationary uniform random process (see Ref. 13), which is the case for antenna and receiver noise. The received (r-f) signal in the absence of noise often cannot be treated as a stationary random process even though the modulations may be stationary processes; hence, we do not have a general conclusion that the complex low-pass receiver input has zero complex correlation, but the part due to receiver and antenna noise does.

Problems

1. Consider a pulse-compression radar in which the transmitted pulse is

$$A \exp\left(-\tfrac{1}{2}at^2\right)\left[\cos\left(\omega_0 t - \tfrac{1}{2}mt^2\right)\right]$$

Assume that an ordinary matched receiver is used. Find the resolution of the system in terms of a and m. Find the resolution in terms of radius of gyration and in terms of equivalent rectangle. Find the compression ratio; e.g., find $1/\sqrt{2a}$ (the radius of gyration of the transmitted pulse) divided by the radius of gyration of the output pulse. Note that the compression can be made arbitrarily large by making m large.

2. Consider a communication system which is intended to communicate $f(t) = f_r + jf_i$, where f_r and f_i are messages of interest. Let $g = g_r + jg_i$ be the output and $\epsilon = f - g$ be the error.

(a) Show that the total mean-square error $A(|\epsilon|^2)$ is merely the sum of the error in the real message $A(f_r - g_r)^2$ and the error in the imaginary message.

(b) Assume that ordinary complex filters are used. Show that if the complex correlations are zero (that is, $R_{ff} = 0$ and $R_{nn} = 0$), then the errors in the real and imaginary channels are equal; that is,

$$A[(f_r - g_r)^2] = A[(f_i - g_i)^2]$$

3. Consider an average-power-limited communication system

$$\frac{1}{2\pi}\int_{-\infty}^{\infty} S_f |K|^2 \le C$$

Suppose that $S_f(\omega) = S e^{-a|\omega|}$ and $S_n(\omega) = N$, where S and N are constants. Find the minimum mean-square error in terms of S, N, and C.

4. Show that the general complex matched filter derived in Sec. 9-4 is quite simple in that it can be reduced to two real filters, as in the diagram.

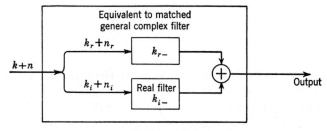

FIGURE P 4

5. Show that if $g = h * f$ (where h is the impulse response of a filter), then $R_{gg} = R_{ff} * h * h-$. Also, show that $S_{gg}(\omega) = S_{ff}(\omega)H(\omega)H(-\omega)$.

6. Find the equivalent-rectangle resolution for the radar discussed in Prob. 1 if the receiver is slightly mismatched in that its impulse response is $A \exp\left(-\tfrac{1}{2}a't^2\right)\cos\left(\omega_0 t + \tfrac{1}{2}m't^2\right)$. With a, m, and m' fixed, find the a' which minimizes the equivalent-rectangle resolution.

10

COMPLEMENTS: MATHEMATICS OF FOURIER TRANSFORMS†

The main objective of this chapter is to prove the inversion theorems listed in Table I at the end of the book (the last one in the table is not proved here). As we strive for generality by dealing with a wild class of functions, improper integrals arise; that is, Cauchy principal parts, Cesàro integrals, and limits in the mean are needed.   As is shown later, if

$$\int_{-\infty}^{\infty} |f(t)| \, dt < \infty$$

† A thorough coverage of this chapter is hardly necessary in applied work.   This chapter is intended as reference material in courses primarily concerned with applications. It also serves well as a short course in the mathematics of Fourier transforms.

if f is continuous, and if

$$F(\omega) = \int_{-\infty}^{\infty} e^{-j\omega t} f(t) \, dt$$

is an absolutely integrable function of ω, then

$$f(t) = \frac{1}{2\pi} \int_{-\infty}^{\infty} e^{j\omega t} F(\omega) \, d\omega$$

In this case the transform and the inverse transform are proper integrals. In Secs. 10-2 through 10-5, we relax the assumptions on f and obtain similar but more sophisticated relations. By the way, recall that if $e^{-\sigma t}q(t)$ satisfies the conditions for f in a Fourier relation, we can obtain a corresponding Laplace relation for q. For example, the formulas above give the following ($p = \sigma + j\omega$):

$$Q(p) = \int_{-\infty}^{\infty} e^{-pt} q(t) \, dt$$

and

$$e^{-\sigma t} q(t) = \frac{1}{2\pi j} \int_{-j\infty}^{j\infty} e^{j\omega t} Q(\sigma + j\omega) \, d(j\omega)$$

or

$$q(t) = \frac{1}{2\pi j} \int_{\sigma-j\infty}^{\sigma+j\infty} e^{pt} Q(p) \, dp$$

From time to time, the roles of the various integrals have been mentioned (Riemann, Lebesgue, and Stieltjes); a brief additional discussion of these integrals is in order and is provided in Sec. 10-1. After Sec. 10-1 we shift gears and become somewhat more concise in an effort to prevent this chapter from diverging into a book in itself.

In Sec. 10-2, the proof of the inversion formula (Theorem 11, Chap. 2) is given along with the inversion theorem for area transforms. The remaining sections give mathematical results not mentioned elsewhere in the book. Specifically, the theories for absolutely integrable and square-integrable functions are given in Secs. 10-3 and 10-4. Finally, Stieltjes transforms and Wiener's generalized transforms are discussed in Sec. 10-5.

10-1 THE ROLES OF THE VARIOUS INTEGRALS

The Riemann integral was adequate for nearly all the previous chapters in this book; however, for the deeper mathematical theory of Secs. 10-3 through 10-5, the Riemann integral is too frail. Recall that

$$\int_a^b f(t) \, dt$$

was defined as the limit of approximating sums,

$$\sum_{k=1}^{n} f(\xi_k)(t_k - t_{k-1})$$

The major shortcoming of the Riemann integral can be viewed in many ways; however, the following gets to the heart of the matter: Each function

f_n of the sequence of functions $\{f_n(t)\}$ can be smooth enough for Riemann integration and

$$\lim_{n \to \infty} f_n(t)$$

can exist for all t, but the limit function

$$f = \lim_{n \to \infty} f_n$$

can end up not smooth enough for Riemann integration.   As an example of this behavior, let $\{r_k\}$ be the rational numbers between $[0, 1]$ in sequence; i.e., let $0 \leq r_k \leq 1$ with r_k rational and with r_1, r_2, r_3, . . . covering each such rational number once (see Ref. 14, page 21, for such a sequence of rationals).   Now let

$$f_n(t) = \begin{cases} 1 & \text{for } t = r_1, r_2, \ldots, r_n \\ 0 & \text{for other } t \end{cases}$$

Then
$$\int_0^1 f_n = 0$$

and
$$f(t) = \lim_{n \to \infty} f_n(t) = \begin{cases} 1 & \text{for } t \text{ rational} \\ 0 & \text{for } t \text{ irrational} \end{cases}$$

As was mentioned in Sec. 2-1, this f is not Riemann-integrable.

Such a shortcoming is not of much importance when we are concerned mostly with simple manipulations or the actual evaluation of integrals. On the other hand, when we wish to develop a rigorous theory in which numerous limiting operations are present, this shortcoming tends to block progress.   It is not obvious at the outset that a remedy for the above ill exists, but of course it does in the form of Lebesgue integration.

LEBESGUE INTEGRATION

There are about half a dozen popular ways to develop the theory of Lebesgue integration.   Reference 15 gives what is probably the slickest, and Ref. 14 gives the approach most suitable for an abstract space.   The definition given below is due to Riesz, but it differs somewhat from his approach in Ref. 15.

Consider a finite interval I (taking I finite only slightly simplifies matters). Then $\alpha(t)$ is a step function if there are a finite number of disjoint subintervals I_1, . . . , I_n such that $\alpha(t) = a_k$ (a constant) for $t \in I_k$ and†

$$\bigcup_{k=1}^{n} I_k = I$$

† If E_k is a set of real numbers for each k,

$$\bigcup_{k=1}^{\infty} E_k = E$$

iff E is the set of real t's such that $t \in E_k$ for at least one k.

The subintervals can be single points, closed intervals, open intervals, or half-open intervals. In other words, α is a step function iff it takes on only a finite number of values, and the inverse image $\alpha^{-1}(a)$ is always an interval or a finite set of intervals [of course, several intervals may be in $\alpha^{-1}(a)$ since some of the values $\{a_k\}$ in the definition of a step function may be equal; also, $\alpha^{-1}(a)$ is the empty set if α does not take on the value a].

We also need the definition of Lebesgue measure zero. The set† $Z \subset I$ is of Lebesgue measure zero iff for any $\epsilon > 0$ there exists a sequence of (not necessarily disjoint) intervals $I_1, I_2, \ldots$ such that

$$Z \subset \bigcup_{k=1}^{\infty} I_k \quad \text{and} \quad \sum_{k=1}^{\infty} m(I_k) < \epsilon$$

where $m(I_k)$ is the length of the interval I_k. As an example, let Z be the rational numbers on the interval $I = [0, 1]$. Let the rationals be ordered $r_1, r_2, \ldots$. Let I_k be the interval about r_k thus:

$$I_k = \left[r_k - \frac{\delta}{2^k}, r_k + \frac{\delta}{2^k} \right]$$

Then $$\sum_{k=1}^{\infty} m(I_k) = \sum_{k=1}^{\infty} \frac{2\delta}{2^k} = 2\delta(\tfrac{1}{2} + \tfrac{1}{4} + \tfrac{1}{8} + \cdots) = 2\delta$$

Thus, for any $\epsilon > 0$ we take $\delta < \epsilon/2$ and we get

$$\sum_{k=1}^{\infty} m(I_k) < \epsilon$$

which proves that the rationals in $[0, 1]$ have Lebesgue measure zero.

In order to integrate a function, it must be adequately well behaved in two respects: it must be smooth enough and it must have values which are not too large in some sense. The concept of being adequately smooth is made precise by defining measurability. The function $f(t)$ is (Lebesgue) measurable iff there exists a sequence of step functions $\{\alpha_n\}$ which converges to f save possibly on a set of measure zero. That is, f is measurable iff there exists a sequence of step functions $\{\alpha_n\}$ such that

$$\lim_{n \to \infty} \alpha_n(t) = f(t) \quad \text{for } t \in (I - Z)$$

and Z is of measure zero.‡

Let α be a step function with $\alpha(t) = a_k$ for $t \in I_k$,

$$\bigcup_{k=1}^{n} I_k = I$$

---

† $B \supset A$ if $t \in A$ implies $t \in B$. Note $A = B$ iff $A \supset B$ and $B \supset A$.
‡ The set $C = A - B$ is all $t \in A$ which are not elements of B.

and the I_k's are disjoint intervals. Then we define

$$\int_I \alpha(t) \; dt = \sum_{k=1}^{n} a_k m(I_k) = \int_I \alpha$$

If E is a set of real numbers, let

$$\phi_E(t) = \begin{cases} 1 & \text{if } t \in E \\ 0 & \text{if } t \text{ is not an element of } E \end{cases}$$

The function ϕ_E is called the characteristic function of the set E. If A is a finite set of intervals, the product $\phi_A \alpha$ is a step function. We define

$$\int_A \alpha \; dt \qquad \text{as} \qquad \int_I (\phi_A \alpha) \; dt$$

If f is measurable, we plan to define

$$\int_I f$$

as a limit on integrals of step functions which converge to f. Something must be done about restricting the size of f—since f will be assumed measurable, only size remains as an issue. Note that if α is a step function, and A is a finite set of intervals, then

$$\lim_{m(A) \to 0} \int_A \alpha = 0$$

where $m(A)$ is the sum of the lengths of the intervals which make up the set A. Let $\{\alpha_n\}$ be a sequence of step functions on I. Then the sequence

$$\left\{ \int_A \alpha_n \right\}$$

is viewed as a sequence of real-valued functions of A; this sequence is *equiabsolutely continuous* iff

$$\lim_{m(A) \to 0} \int_A \alpha_n = 0$$

uniformly in n. That is, the sequence

$$\left\{ \int_A \alpha_n \right\}$$

is equiabsolutely continuous iff, for any $\epsilon > 0$, there exists $\delta > 0$ such that

$$\left| \int_A \alpha_n \right| < \epsilon$$

for all n whenever $m(A) < \delta$.

Let f be measurable; then f is integrable iff there exists a sequence of step functions $\{\alpha_n\}$ which converges to f almost everywhere and for which

$$\left\{ \int_A \alpha_n \right\}$$

is equiabsolutely continuous.

Theorem 1.   Let f be integrable and let $\{\alpha_n\}$ be a sequence of the type defining integrability; then

$$\lim_{n \to \infty} \int_I \alpha_n$$

exists and depends only on f—not on the particular (equiabsolutely continuous) sequence which converges to f.   In turn, we define

$$\int_I f \equiv \lim_{n \to \infty} \int_I \alpha_n$$

The proof is left for a course on integration theory.   Two more theorems will be mentioned.

Theorem 2.   Let $\{f_n\}$ be a sequence of measurable functions which converge almost everywhere, and let

$$f(t) = \lim_{n \to \infty} f_n(t)$$

for t in the set where $\{f_n\}$ converges (and f has arbitrary values elsewhere). Then f is measurable.   That is, the property of being smooth enough for integration is not lost when limits are taken.

Theorems on interchanging limits and integrals follow without great difficulty.   Specifically, the following theorem is basic to the approach outlined here.

Theorem 3.   Let $\{f_n\}$ be a sequence of measurable functions which converge almost everywhere to f, and let

$$\left\{ \int_A f_n \right\}$$

be equiabsolutely continuous; then

$$\lim_{n \to \infty} \int_I f_n = \int_I f$$

This theorem implies the dominated convergence theorem (Chap. 2, Theorem 7) since if $|f_n| \leq g$ with g integrable, we have

$$\left| \int_A f_n \right| \leq \int_A g = \lim_{k \to \infty} \int \alpha_k$$

where $\{\alpha_k\}$ is a sequence which defines the integral of g.   In turn, since

$$\left\{ \int_A \alpha_n \right\}$$

is equiabsolutely continuous, for any $\epsilon > 0$ there exists a $\delta > 0$ such that

$$\left| \int_A \alpha_n \right| < \frac{\epsilon}{2} \qquad \text{if } m(A) < \delta$$

from which it follows that

$$\left| \lim_{n \to \infty} \int_A \alpha_n \right| < \epsilon$$

and hence

$$\left| \int_A f_n \right| < \epsilon$$

That is, the existence of the dominating function g implies equiabsolute continuity for

$$\left\{ \int_A f_n \right\}$$

Of course, if f is complex-valued, f is integrable iff its real and imaginary parts are integrable; and in this case, the integral of f is the integral of its real part plus j times the integral of its imaginary part.

On the interval $(-\infty, \infty)$ we require that

$$\int_{|t| < T} |f(t)| \, dt$$

exist and be bounded (as T varies). Then

$$\int_{-\infty}^{\infty} f(t) \, dt \equiv \lim_{T \to \infty} \int_{-T}^{T} f(t) \, dt$$

If E is a set of real numbers, E is measurable iff ϕ_E is a measurable function. The measure of E is

$$m(E) \equiv \int_{-\infty}^{\infty} \phi_E(t) \, dt$$

When this integral diverges, E is said to have infinite measure.

STIELTJES INTEGRAL

The Riemann integral is sometimes introduced as a generalization of the notion of sum. However, although approximating sums are involved in the definition of Riemann integrals, a sum of the form

$$\sum_{k=1}^{n} f(t_k)$$

cannot be written as an integral of the form

$$\int_a^b f(t) p(t) \, dt$$

unless p is taken as a combination of δ functions. In many respects, δ functions suffice as a means for writing sums in terms of integrals; however, it is worthwhile to also use Stieltjes integrals in this and other roles.

To introduce the Stieltjes integral, consider a mass distributed along the x axis. Let $p(x)$ depict the mass density so that $p(x) \, dx$ is the mass residing between x and $x + dx$. The moment of inertia of this mass about the appropriate axis might be of interest. It is obviously given by

$$\int_{-\infty}^{\infty} x^2 p(x)\, dx$$

Now, if we add some point masses of sizes $p_1, p_2, \ldots, p_n$ at positions $x_1, \ldots, x_n$, the total inertia becomes

$$\int_{-\infty}^{\infty} x^2 p(x)\, dx + \sum_{k=1}^{n} (x_k)^2 p_k$$

or, in terms of δ functions,

$$\int_{-\infty}^{\infty} x^2 \left[p(x) + \sum_{k=1}^{n} p_k \delta(x - x_k) \right] dx$$

By introducing a cumulative mass distribution P in place of the density distribution p, continuous and discrete masses can be accommodated simultaneously in another way. Let $P(a)$ be the total mass residing at points to the left of a, more precisely, at all $x \le a$. If there is a point mass of size p_k at x_k, then $P(x)$ will have a jump discontinuity at $x = x_k$ and the size of the jump will be p_k. The mass in the interval $\alpha < x \le \beta$ is $P(\beta) - P(\alpha)$. If $\beta - \alpha$ is small, the mass in the interval (α, β) contributes approximately $\theta^2[P(\beta) - P(\alpha)]$ to the inertia about $x = 0$ if $\alpha < \theta \le \beta$. To simplify matters, suppose all the mass is located on the finite interval $[a, b]$. Then it is natural to formulate the total inertia thus: partition $[a, b]$ with $a = x_0 < x_1 < \cdots < x_n = b$ and let $x_{i-1} < \theta_i \le x_i$; then the total inertia is approximately

$$\sum_{k=1}^{n} \theta_k^2 [P(x_k) - P(x_{k-1})]$$

and the approximation gets better as

$$\Delta = \max_k (x_k - x_{k-1})$$

gets small. The limit of the above sum as Δ goes to zero is defined as the Riemann-Stieltjes integral of x^2 with respect to $P(x)$. More generally, the Riemann-Stieltjes integral of $f(x)$ with respect to $P(x)$ is

$$\lim_{\Delta \to 0} \sum_{k=1}^{n} f(\theta_k)[P(x_k) - P(x_{k-1})]$$

and it is denoted by

$$\int_a^b f(x)\, dP(x) \qquad \text{or} \qquad \int_a^b f\, dP$$

If f is continuous and P is of bounded variation, it is easy enough to show that

$$\int_a^b f\, dP$$

exists.   In particular, if P is of bounded variation,

$$\int_a^b e^{j\omega t}\, dP(t)$$

exists and is of considerable interest to us in Sec. 10-5. If "the mass" is permitted to run over the entire real line, the integral can be defined by forming the limit of a sum as above with arbitrary $[a, b]$ and then

$$\int_{-\infty}^{\infty} f(x)\, dP(x) = \lim_{a \to -\infty} \lim_{b \to \infty} \int_a^b f(x)\, dP(x)$$

The Riemann-Stieltjes integral is frail as far as limit operations are concerned, just as the Riemann integral was.   However, it is simple enough to proceed to the Lebesgue-Stieltjes integral.   About all one does is to replace the length of intervals with the difference of P at the end points; i.e., one generalizes the notion of the length of the interval.   To develop the theory, one considers a monotone $P(x)$ and if I is the interval $(a, b]$, we take $m(I) \equiv P(b) - P(a)$ in place of $b - a$.   Then the Lebesgue-Stieltjes integral is defined in essentially the same way that the Lebesgue integral was defined.   After the theory is developed for a monotone P, it is trivial to generalize to functions of bounded variation (see Sec. 2-1).

Recall that, with a Stieltjes integral, we can formulate

$$\int_a^b f(x)p(x)\, dx + \sum_k a_k f(x_k)$$

as a single Stieltjes integral.   It is natural to pose the following question: Can all Stieltjes integrals be decomposed into an integral involving a continuous weighting p, plus a sum (generally infinite sum)?   This is a deep, exciting problem in analysis.   The sum obviously comes from the jump discontinuities in P, and p would be the derivative of what remains after the jumps in P are "removed."   If such a decomposition were always possible, Stieltjes integrals would offer nothing over ordinary integrals with δ functions thrown in to cover the discrete sum.   Alas, such is not the case. The problem can be viewed in terms of a decomposition of monotone functions, and the important result is the Lebesgue decomposition theorem. Let P have jumps of size $\{a_k\}$ at the points $\{x_k\}$.   Then

$$P_1(x) = P(x) - \sum_{k=-\infty}^{\infty} a_k U(x - x_k)$$

is continuous if $U(\xi) = 1$ for $\xi \geq 1$ and $U(\xi) = 0$ elsewhere and P is continuous from the right [that is, $P(x + 0) = P(x)$ for all x].   Now the sum involving U takes care of the jumps, and if it is denoted by $J(x)$ we have $P = J + P_1$.   We might now hope that if $p = dP_1/dx$, then

$$P_1(x) = \int_0^x p(\xi)\, d\xi + P_1(0)$$

This simply is not the case. The first fear may be that dP_1/dx will not exist; however, with a great deal of effort, this fear can be put to rest. Specifically (Lebesgue's theorem), the derivative of a monotone function exists everywhere save possibly on a set of measure zero. That is, monotone functions have a derivative almost everywhere. Be that as it may, the integral of this derivative may not recover the function. Let $p = dP_1/dx$, and let

$$P_2(x) = \int_0^x p(\xi)\, d\xi + P_1(0)$$

By the way, p is clearly measurable; it can be written as the limit of a sequence of measurable functions thus:

$$P(x) = \lim_{n \to \infty} n\left[P_1\left(x + \frac{1}{n}\right) - P_1(x) \right]$$

and then Theorem 2 implies that p is measurable. Size is no problem in integrating p if P_1 is bounded on the interval of integration; this is not quite obvious but easy enough to prove.

Now, let $P_3 = P - J - P_2$; then P_3 may not be zero. This part of the decomposition of P is called the singular part (if it is present). The important problem is to show that singular functions exist; a singular function is continuous and has a derivative almost everywhere; but this derivative is zero almost everywhere, and yet the function is not identically zero. As an example, the Cantor function (Ref. 14, page 193) starts with $f(0) = 0$ and has $f(1) = 1$, $f'(x) = 0$ where f' exists (and it exists on all but a set of points of measure zero—by the way, this exceptional set of measure zero has an uncountable infinity of points), and f is continuous. If we think of such an f as, say, the displacement of a moving object, the instantaneous velocity is zero when it exists; the object makes no positive jumps, yet by a generous infinity of "zeroish" jumps, the object gets up and moves.

The existence of singular functions prevents Riemann (or Lebesgue) integrals along with δ functions from supplanting Stieltjes integrals in certain mathematical theories. From here on, the integrals will be Lebesgue or Lebesgue-Stieltjes integrals.

10-2 LOOSE ENDS: INVERSION FOR FUNCTIONS OF BOUNDED VARIATION AND FOR AREA TRANSFORMS

Let

$$\int_{-\infty}^{\infty} |f(t)|\, dt < \infty$$

and let

$$F(\omega) = \int_{-\infty}^{\infty} e^{-j\omega t} f(t)\, dt$$

Consider

$$\frac{1}{2\pi} \int_{-R}^{R} e^{-j\omega t} F(\omega)\, d\omega \quad \text{or} \quad \frac{1}{2\pi} \int_{-R}^{R} e^{j\omega t} \left[\int_{-\infty}^{\infty} e^{-j\omega u} f(u)\, du \right] d\omega$$

Since

$$\int_{-R}^{R} \left[\int_{-\infty}^{\infty} |e^{j\omega t} e^{-j\omega u} f(u)| \, du \right] d\omega < \infty$$

by Fubini's theorem (Chap. 2, Theorem 8) the ω integration can be done first and we get

$$\int_{-\infty}^{\infty} f(u) \frac{\sin R(t - u)}{\pi(t - u)} \, du$$

Our interest is in taking the limit as R goes to infinity. Such a limit occurred in the discussion of the basic Theorem 11, Chap. 2. Several lemmas will be given to deal with this problem.

Lemma 1 (Continuity in the Mean). Let

$$\int_{a}^{b} |f(t)| \, dt < \infty$$

and assign $f(t) = 0$ for $t < a$ and $t > b$. Then

$$\lim_{\theta \to 0} \int_{a}^{b} |f(t + \theta) - f(t)| \, dt = 0$$

PROOF: Let α_n be a sequence of step functions which defines the integral of f. Then

$$\int_{A} |\alpha_n - f| \leq \int_{A} |\alpha_n| + \int_{A} |f|$$

and the right side is less than ϵ if $m(A)$ is small. That is,

$$\left\{ \int_{A} |\alpha_n - f| \right\}$$

is equiabsolutely continuous. It follows from Theorem 3 that

$$\lim_{n \to \infty} \int_{I} |\alpha_n - f| = \int \lim_{n \to \infty} |\alpha_n - f| = 0 \qquad \text{since } \lim_{n \to \infty} |\alpha_n - f| = 0$$

almost everywhere.

Note that

$$\lim_{\theta \to 0} |\alpha_n(t + \theta) - \alpha_n(t)| = 0$$

for almost all $t \in [a, b]$ and since α_n is bounded by some constant, the dominated convergence theorem (a constant is integrable on $[a, b]$) gives

$$\lim_{\theta \to 0} \int_{a}^{b} |\alpha_n(t + \theta) - \alpha_n(t)| \, dt = 0$$

Observe that

$$|f(t + \theta) - f(t)| = |[f(t + \theta) - \alpha_n(t + \theta)] - [f(t) - \alpha_n(t)]$$
$$- [\alpha_n(t) - \alpha_n(t + \theta)]| \leq |f(t + \theta) - \alpha_n(t + \theta)| + |f(t) - \alpha_n(t)|$$
$$+ |\alpha_n(t) - \alpha_n(t + \theta)|$$

In turn

$$\int_a^b |f(t + \theta) - f(t)| \, dt \leq 2 \int_a^b |f(t) - \alpha_n(t)| \, dt + \int_a^b |\alpha_n(t) - \alpha_n(t + \theta)| \, dt$$

Now as θ goes to zero, the second term on the right goes to zero and we get both the $\overline{\lim}_{\theta \to 0}$ and $\underline{\lim}_{\theta \to 0}$ of

$$\int_a^b |f(t + \theta) - f(t)| \, dt$$

less than or equal to

$$2 \int_a^b |f(t) - \alpha_n(t)| \, dt \qquad \text{for all n}$$

Finally, since

$$\lim_{n \to \infty} \int_a^b |f(t) - \alpha_n(t)| \, dt = 0$$

this implies that

$$\lim_{\theta \to 0} \int_a^b |f(t + \theta) - f(t)| \, dt = 0$$

as was to be shown.

Lemma 2 (Riemann-Lebesgue Lemma).   If

$$\int_{-\infty}^{\infty} |f(t)| \, dt < \infty \qquad \text{and} \qquad F(\omega) = \int_{-\infty}^{\infty} e^{-j\omega t} f(t) \, dt$$

then

$$\lim_{\omega \to \pm \infty} F(\omega) = 0$$

PROOF: Note that

$$\int_{-\infty}^{\infty} \exp\left[-j\omega \left(t + \frac{\pi}{\omega} \right) \right] f(t) \, dt = -F(\omega)$$

or

$$-F(\omega) = \int_{-\infty}^{\infty} e^{-j\omega u} f\left(u - \frac{\pi}{\omega} \right) du$$

In turn

$$2F(\omega) = \int_{-\infty}^{\infty} e^{-j\omega t} \left[f(t) - f\left(t - \frac{\pi}{\omega} \right) \right] dt$$

and hence

$$|2F(\omega)| \leq \int_{-\infty}^{\infty} \left| f(t) - f\left(t - \frac{\pi}{\omega} \right) \right| dt$$

Save for the infinite interval, Lemma 1 now gives

$$\lim_{\omega \to \pm \infty} |2F(\omega)| = \lim_{\theta \to 0} \int_{-\infty}^{\infty} |f(t) - f(t - \theta)| \, dt = 0$$

As for the infinite interval, there is the usual argument that for any $\epsilon > 0$ there exists a T sufficiently large that

$$\int_{|t| > T} |f(t) - f(t - \theta)| \, dt \leq 2 \int |f(t)| \, dt < \epsilon$$

if the integral is over $|t| > T - |\theta_0|$. Then, on $|t| < T$,

$$\lim_{\theta \to 0} \int_{|t| < T} |f(t) - f(t - \theta)| \, dt = 0$$

by Lemma 1, and hence both $\overline{\lim}$ and $\underline{\lim}$ of

$$\int_{-\infty}^{\infty} |f(t) - f(t - \theta)| \, dt$$

are less than ϵ for arbitrary ϵ; therefore,

$$\lim_{\theta \to 0} \int_{-\infty}^{\infty} |f(t) - f(t - \theta)| \, dt = 0$$

In the next two lemmas, the functions discussed are real-valued.

Lemma 3 (*First Theorem of the Mean*). Let $p(t)$ be integrable on $[a, b]$ and let $p \geq 0$; also, let $f(t) = (d/dt)F(t)$ for every $t \in [a, b]$ with f bounded; then

$$\int_a^b f(t)p(t) \, dt = f(t_0) \int_a^b p(t) \, dt \qquad \text{for some } t_0 \in [a, b]$$

PROOF: Let U be the least upper bound of f and let L be the greatest lower bound of f. Then since $Lp \leq fp \leq Up$,

$$L \int_a^b p \leq \int_a^b fp \leq U \int_a^b p \qquad \text{and} \qquad \int_a^b fp = M \int_a^b p$$

where $L \leq M \leq U$. If $p = 0$ almost everywhere, any t_0 will do. If $p(t) > 0$ on a set $E \subset [a, b]$ with $m(E) > 0$ and if $M = U$, $f(t)$ must equal U on E save for a subset of E of measure zero, and again there are plenty of suitable values for t_0. Similar reasoning can be applied if $M = L$. Suppose then that $L < M < U$. In this case $f(t)$ takes on values greater than as well as less than M. It is well known that if a function, which is a derivative, takes on, say, values $f(t_1) = a_1$ and $f(t_2) = a_2$ and if $a_1 < M < a_2$, then there exists a t_0 between t_1 and t_2 at which $f(t_0) = M$. Having come this far, we might as well prove this last remark, which completes the proof of the lemma. Let $g(t) = F(t) - Mt$; then, $g'(t) = f(t) - M$ and $g'(t_1) < 0$ and $g'(t_2) > 0$. It follows that the minimum value of $g(t)$ on $[t_1, t_2]$ occurs at a point t_0 with $t_1 < t_0 < t_2$. Since $g'(t_0)$ exists and g has a minimum at t_0, $g'(t_0) = 0$; that is, $f(t_0) = M$, as was to be shown.

Lemma 4 (*Second Theorem of the Mean*). Let p be integrable on $[a, b]$, let f be bounded and nondecreasing on $[a, b]$, let $L \leq f(a + 0)$, and let $U \geq f(b - 0)$; then there exists a point $t_0 \in [a, b]$ such that

$$\int_a^b fp = L \int_a^{t_0} p + U \int_{t_0}^b p$$

PROOF: To simplify matters, note that the theorem is true for (f, U, L) iff it is true for $(f + C, U + C, L + C)$, where C is a constant. That is,

$$\int_a^b (f + C)p = (U + C) \int_a^{t_0} p + (L + C) \int_{t_0}^b p$$

iff
$$\int_a^b fp = U \int_a^{t_0} p + L \int_{t_0}^b p$$

Therefore, we shall take $U = 0$. Let

$$P(t) = \int_a^t p(\xi)\, d\xi$$

First, suppose f is a polygonal line $U = f(b)$, $L = f(a)$. Then we can integrate

$$\int_a^b fp$$

by parts to obtain

$$\int_a^b fp\, dt = fP \Big]_a^b - \int_a^b f'(t) P(t)\, dt$$

However, $P(a) = 0$ and $f(b) = U = 0$; thus, we have

$$- \int_a^b f'(t) P(t)\, dt$$

By Lemma 3, this is equal to

$$-P(t_0) \int_a^b f'(t)\, dt$$

since $f' \geq 0$ and $P(t)$ is everywhere the derivative of

$$\int_0^t P(\xi)\, d\xi$$

This is true since P is continuous† and hence, by the fundamental theorem of elementary calculus,

$$\frac{d}{dt} \int_0^t P(\xi)\, d\xi = P(t)$$

Of course,

$$\int_a^b f'(t)\, dt = f(b) - f(a) = -L$$

Hence

$$\int_a^b fp\, dt = L \int_a^{t_0} p(\xi)\, d\xi$$

as was to be shown for the special case under consideration.

Now we approximate an arbitrary monotone bounded f with a polygonal f_n having vertices (a, L), $[t_1, f(t_1)]$, . . . , $[t_n, f(t_n)]$, $(b, 0)$, where

$$t_k = a + k\, \frac{b - a}{n + 1} \qquad \text{for } 1 \leq k \leq n$$

† One way to see that

$$\int_a^t p(\xi)\, d\xi \qquad \text{or} \qquad \int_a^t P(\xi)\, d\xi$$

is continuous is to write it as

$$\int_a^b \phi_t(\xi) p(\xi)\, d\xi \qquad \phi_t(\xi) = \begin{cases} 1 & \text{if } a < \xi \leq t \\ 0 & \text{if } t < \xi \leq b \end{cases}$$

Then

$$\lim_{t \to t_0} \int_a^b \phi_t p = \int_a^b \phi_{t_0} p$$

by the dominated convergence theorem since $|\phi p| \leq |p|$, which serves as a dominating function.

It is easy to see that

$$\lim_{n \to \infty} f_n(t) = f(t)$$

almost everywhere; the only possible exceptional points are a, b, and jumps in f. Since $|f_n p| \le |Lp|$ (except possibly at $t = a$),

$$\lim_{n \to \infty} \int_a^b f_n p = \int_a^b fp$$

However,

$$\int_a^b f_n p \, dt = L \int_a^{t_{0n}} p \, dt$$

and if we take a subsequence from $\{t_{0n}\}$ which converges (all bounded sequences have subsequences which converge) to $\tilde{t}$, then since all subsequences of

$$\{\textstyle\int\!\int f_n p\}$$

converge to the same limit, we have

$$\lim_{n \to \infty} \int_a^b f_n p = \lim_{k \to \infty} \int_a^b f_{n(k)} p = L \lim_{k \to \infty} \int_a^{t_{0n(k)}} p = L \int_a^{\tilde{t}} p(\xi) \, d\xi$$

since

$$\int_a^t p(\xi) \, d\xi$$

is a continuous function of t (as shown in the last footnote).

The hard work is over for a while.   We return to the original problem:

$$\lim_{R \to \infty} \int_{-\infty}^{\infty} f(u) \frac{\sin R(t - u)}{\pi(t - u)} \, du$$

It is somewhat convenient to let $t - u = v$ in the integral on $[-\infty, t]$; this gives

$$\int_0^{\infty} f(t - v) \frac{\sin Rv}{\pi v} \, dv$$

On $[t, \infty]$, let $t - u = -v$; this gives

$$\int_0^{\infty} f(t + v) \frac{\sin Rv}{\pi v} \, dv$$

Thus, the integral can be written as

$$\int_0^{\infty} [f(t + v) + f(t - v)] \frac{\sin Rv}{\pi v} \, dv$$

Consider the special case

$$\int_0^{\infty} \phi(v) \frac{\sin Rv}{\pi v} \, dv$$

with $\phi(0+) = 0$ and ϕ real nondecreasing on $[0, a]$ with $a > 0$. Let $0 < \delta < a$; then†

$$\overline{\lim_{R \to \infty}} \int_0^\delta \phi(v) \frac{\sin Rv}{\pi v} \, dv + \overline{\lim_{R \to \infty}} \int_\delta^\infty \phi(v) \frac{\sin Rv}{\pi v} \, dv$$

is equal to

$$\overline{\lim_{R \to \infty}} \int_0^\delta \phi(v) \frac{\sin Rv}{\pi v} \, dv$$

by Lemma 2 since ϕ is assumed to be absolutely integrable on $[0, \infty]$ and, in turn, ϕ/v is absolutely integrable on $[\delta, \infty]$.‡ By Lemma 4,

$$\int_0^\delta \phi(v) \frac{\sin Rv}{\pi v} \, dv = \phi(0+) \int_0^{v_0} \frac{\sin Rv}{\pi v} \, dv + \phi(\delta-) \int_{v_0}^\delta \frac{\sin Rv}{\pi v} \, dv$$

$$= \phi(\delta-) \int_{v_0}^\delta \frac{\sin Rv}{\pi v} \, dv = \phi(\delta-) \int_{Rv_0}^{R\delta} \frac{\sin \theta}{\pi \theta} \, d\theta$$

It is easy to see that

$$\int_{Rv_0}^{R\delta} \frac{\sin \theta}{\pi \theta} \, d\theta$$

is bounded in R, say by A. Since δ can be made arbitrarily small and

$$\lim_{\delta \to 0+} \phi(\delta-) = \phi(0+) = 0$$

we have that for any R we can take δ so that

$$\left| \phi(\delta-) \int_{Rv_0}^{R\delta} \frac{\sin \theta}{\pi \theta} \, d\theta \right| \leq \epsilon A$$

which now implies that

$$0 \leq \overline{\lim_{R \to \infty}} \left| \int_0^\infty \phi(v) \frac{\sin Rv}{\pi v} \, dv \right| \leq \epsilon A$$

for arbitrary $\epsilon > 0$. Since it is true for any $\epsilon > 0$, clearly,

$$\lim_{R \to \infty} \int_0^\infty \phi(v) \frac{\sin Rv}{\pi v} \, dv = 0$$

as hoped.

† $\overline{\lim_{R \to \infty}}$ means either the limit inferior or the limit superior and is used prior to showing that the limits in question exist.

‡ Of course we can write the integral as

$$\int_\delta^\infty \frac{\phi(v)}{jv} e^{jRv} \, dv - \int_\delta^\infty \frac{\phi(v)}{jv} e^{-jRv} \, dv$$

to apply the exponential form of the Riemann-Lebesgue lemma.

Next, suppose $\phi(0+) \neq 0$; let $\gamma(v) = \phi(v) - \phi(0+)$. Then $\gamma(0+) = 0$. In turn

$$\lim_{R \to \infty} \int_0^\delta \phi(v) \frac{\sin Rv}{\pi v} = \lim_{R \to \infty} \int_0^\delta \gamma(v) \frac{\sin Rv}{\pi v} + \phi(0+) \lim_{R \to \infty} \int_0^\delta \frac{\sin Rv}{\pi v} \, dv$$

$$= 0 + \phi(0+) \lim_{R \to \infty} \int_0^{R\delta} \frac{\sin \theta}{\pi \theta} \, d\theta = \frac{1}{2} \phi(0+)$$

Of course, by Lemma 2,

$$\lim_{R \to \infty} \int_0^\infty \phi(v) \frac{\sin Rv}{\pi v} \, dv = \lim_{R \to \infty} \int_0^\delta \phi(v) \frac{\sin Rv}{\pi v} \, d$$

which was just shown to equal $\frac{1}{2}\phi(0+)$.

We return now to

$$\int_0^\delta f(t + v) \frac{\sin Rv}{\pi v} \, dv + \int_0^\delta f(t - v) \frac{\sin Rv}{\pi v} \, dv$$

which again, by Lemma 2, is all we need consider. The above shows that for (real) monotone f, the first integral gives $\frac{1}{2}f(t + 0)$ and the second gives $\frac{1}{2}f(t - 0)$. If f is complex and of bounded variation in a neighborhood of t, the real and imaginary parts of f can be written in terms of real nondecreasing functions, and the general result is obtained. The major result obtained is recorded in the following theorem.

Theorem 4.   If

$$\int_{-\infty}^\infty |f(t)| \, dt < \infty$$

f is of bounded variation on finite intervals, and

$$F(\omega) = \int_{-\infty}^\infty f(t) e^{-j\omega t} \, dt$$

Then $$\frac{1}{2}[f(t + 0) + f(t - 0)] = \lim_{R \to \infty} \frac{1}{2\pi} \int_{-R}^R F(\omega) e^{j\omega t} \, d\omega$$

INVERSION FOR AREA TRANSFORMS†

Let F be a real-valued function of two real variables; it will be called *nondecreasing* iff whenever $x_2 \geq x_1$ and $y_2 \geq y_1$ it follows that $F(x_2, y_2) \geq F(x_1, y_1)$. A real-valued function of two real variables is of *bounded variation* on the xy plane iff it is the difference of two bounded nondecreasing functions. A complex-valued function is of bounded variation iff its real and imaginary parts are of bounded variation.

† This subsection can be skipped as far as the main objectives of this chapter are concerned; however, it is complementary to the introduction to area transforms given in Chap. 3.

Recall that $f(t)$ is *area-transformable* iff there exists a complex-valued function $F(\omega, \sigma)$ of bounded variation on the (σ, ω) plane such that

$$f(t) = \frac{1}{4\pi^2} \int_{-\infty}^{\infty} \int_{-\infty}^{\infty} e^{pt} \, dF(\omega, \sigma)$$

where $p = \sigma + j\omega$. The problem is the following: We are given f and we are given that f is area-transformable; find a suitable F. To handle this problem, we need the two-dimensional version of Theorem 19 (the basic theorem on Stieltjes transforms). This result is assumed available for this section and is stated here as a lemma.

Lemma 5. If $H(\omega, \mu)$ is of bounded variation on the (ω, μ) plane and

$$h(x, y) = \frac{1}{4\pi^2} \iint \exp(j\omega x + j\mu y) \, dH(\omega, \mu)$$

then if H is continuous at the four points $(\omega \pm a, \omega \pm b)$

$$\frac{H(\omega + a, \mu + b) - H(\omega + a, \mu - b) - H(\omega - a, \mu + b) + H(\omega - a, \mu - b)}{4ab}$$

$$= \lim_{A \to \infty} \int_{-A}^{A} \int_{-A}^{A} \frac{\sin a\omega}{a\omega} \frac{\sin b\mu}{b\mu} \exp(-j\omega x - j\mu y) h(x, y) \, dx \, dy$$

By the way, if

$$\int_{-\infty}^{\infty} \int_{-\infty}^{\infty} |h(x, y)| \, dx \, dy < \infty$$

h serves as a dominating function and we can take the limit (under the integral sign) as a and b go to zero to obtain

$$\frac{\partial^2 H}{\partial \omega \, \partial \mu} = \int_{-\infty}^{\infty} \int_{-\infty}^{\infty} \exp(-j\omega x - j\mu y) h(x, y) \, dx \, dy$$

and in turn

$$h(x, y) = \frac{1}{4\pi^2} \int_{-\infty}^{\infty} \int_{-\infty}^{\infty} \exp(j\omega x + j\mu y) \frac{\partial^2 H}{\partial \omega \, \partial \mu} \, d\omega \, d\mu$$

which is obviously a two-dimensional variation of Theorem 4.

The point of Lemma 5 is that, given either h or H (with H satisfying appropriate conditions), then the other function of the two-dimensional Fourier-Stieltjes transform pair can be found. One is led to the area transform formula by considering the possibility of finding a function of two variables, $h(x, y)$, which will provide the area transform of f in terms of the Fourier-Stieltjes transform of this function h. Given $f(t)$, suppose we find a function $h(x, y)$ such that h can be analytically continued in the second variable (when so continued, the second variable will be denoted by z) to obtain f in terms of h thus: $f(t) = h(t, -jt)$. We hope for more from h, namely, that $h(x, y)$ can be analytically continued under the integral sign thus:

$$h(x, z) = \frac{1}{4\pi^2} \iint \exp\left(j\omega x + j\mu z\right) dH(\omega, \mu)$$

for all complex z (omitted integration limits are infinite integration limits). Obviously, if such a function $h(x, y)$ can be found, a transform for f has been found since

$$f(t) = h(t, -jt) = \frac{1}{4\pi^2} \iint \exp\left(j\omega t + \mu t\right) dH(\omega, \mu)$$

If we set $\sigma = \mu$ and $p = \sigma + j\omega$,

$$f(t) = \frac{1}{4\pi^2} \iint \exp\left(pt\right) dH(\omega, \sigma)$$

and H has provided an area transform for f.

The above scheme for finding the area transform may seem rather far-fetched; however, it is generally easy to apply. Theorem 5 guarantees that an appropriate h always exists, and Example 3 provides a rather general method for finding h.

To obtain a theory which is easy to handle mathematically, only area transforms which are absolutely convergent will be considered. Such transforms will be termed proper. The results obtained with this assumption often apply even when the assumption of absolute convergence is not met. From the viewpoint of obtaining a simple unified theory, it is unfortunate that the consideration of improper [nonabsolutely convergent integrals of the form

$$\widetilde{\iint} \exp\left(pt\right) dF(\omega, \sigma)$$

where $\sim$ might indicate Cauchy principal part or limit in the mean] transforms is quite fruitful. With the exception of Theorems 5 and 19, all of this chapter involves improper integrals in the various inversion formulas.

Theorem 5. The function $f(t)$ is properly area-transformable if and only if there exists a function $h(x, y)$ of two real variables (the two-dimensional Fourier-Stieltjes transform of h providing an area transform of f) which has the following properties:

1. h can be analytically continued in its second variable; when so continued, the notation $h(x, z)$ will be used.

2. $f(t) = h(t, -jt)$.

3. $h(x, y)$ has an ordinary proper two-dimensional Fourier-Stieltjes transform $H(\omega, \mu)$.

4. If $h(x, z)$ is the continued version of $h(x, y)$, then

$$h(x, z) = \frac{1}{4\pi^2} \iint \exp(j\omega x + j\mu z) \, dH(\omega, \mu)$$

as a proper integral for all real x and all complex z.

PROOF: The *if* part of the theorem is obvious since from properties 2 and 4 we have (with σ written in place of μ)

$$f(t) = h(t, -jt) = \frac{1}{4\pi^2} \iint \exp(j\omega t + \sigma t) \, dH(\omega, \sigma)$$

and clearly f is area-transformable in that H provides a Stieltjes weighting of the p plane for f.

For the *only if* part of the theorem, we are given that f can be written thus:

$$f(t) = \frac{1}{4\pi^2} \iint \exp(pt) \, dF(\omega, \sigma)$$

for some function F. We try the following for an $h(x, y)$:

$$h(x, y) = \frac{1}{4\pi^2} \iint \exp(j\omega x + j\sigma y) \, dF(\omega, \sigma)$$

Recall that this integral involving the complex F can be written as four integrals involving real bounded monotone weight functions. Hence, from here on we consider F as one of these real nondecreasing functions. The absolute integrability is taken to mean that $\iint |e^{pt}| \, dF < \infty$; that is, $\iint e^{\sigma t} \, dF < \infty$ for all real t. It follows that

$$\int_{-\infty}^{0} \int_{-\infty}^{\infty} e^{-\sigma t} \, dF \qquad \text{and} \qquad \int_{0}^{\infty} \int_{-\infty}^{\infty} e^{\sigma t} \, dF$$

each converge (for all real t); hence,

$$\int_{-\infty}^{\infty} \int_{-\infty}^{\infty} e^{|\sigma t|} \, dF < \infty \qquad \text{for arbitrary } t$$

Note that $|\exp(j\omega x + j\sigma z)| = e^{-\sigma v}$ if $z = u + jv$, where u and v are real. For any specific v, we can take $t > |v|$ and then $e^{|\sigma t|} > e^{-v\sigma}$ for all σ; hence

$$h(x, z) = \frac{1}{4\pi^2} \int_{-\infty}^{\infty} \int_{-\infty}^{\infty} \exp(j\omega x + j\omega z) \, dF$$

exists since the integrand is dominated by $e^{|\sigma t|}$, which is a convergent integrand.

We have shown that if f is properly area-transformable, there exists an $h(x, z)$ such that $f(t) = h(t, -jt)$ and $h(x, y)$ has the required Fourier-Stieltjes transform. It remains to be shown that $h(x, z)$ is regular in z for arbitrary real x. This is useful in that given f we tend to first construct

$h(x, jv)$, and it is hoped that we can proceed from this to $h(x, z)$ and then to $h(x, y)$, which finally provides the area transform of f. The regularity in z will now be proved, and in fact we shall prove that the derivative with respect to z can be taken under the integral sign.

The difference quotient is

$$\iint \exp\ (j\omega x + j\sigma z)\ \frac{e^{j\sigma\,\Delta z} - 1}{\Delta z}\ dF$$

To find a dominating function so that we can apply the dominated convergence theorem, observe that

$$e^{j\sigma\,\Delta z} - 1 = \sigma\,\Delta z + \frac{(j\sigma\,\Delta z)^2}{2!} + \cdots$$

$$\left|\frac{e^{j\sigma\,\Delta z} - 1}{\Delta z}\right| \leq |\sigma|\left(1 + |\sigma\,\Delta z| + \frac{|\sigma\,\Delta z|^2}{2!} + \cdots\right)$$

$$\leq |\sigma|\ \exp\ (|\sigma\,\Delta z|)$$

Therefore, the integrand is dominated by $|\sigma|e^{-\sigma v}e^{|\sigma\,\Delta z|}$. This, in turn, is dominated by $Ae^{|\sigma t|}$ for all $|\Delta z| < \delta$ if $t > |v| + 2\delta$ and A is taken sufficiently large. Since $e^{|\sigma t|}$ is integrable (with respect to F), a dominating function has been found and we can pass to the limit under the integral sign. That is, for any fixed real x,

$$\frac{d}{dz}\,h(x, z) = \frac{1}{4\pi^2}\iint j\sigma\,\exp\ (j\omega x + j\sigma z)\ dF$$

and the proof is complete.

Before considering some examples, two major *computational theorems* for area transforms will be mentioned.

Theorem 6. Let f have† the area transform dF and let $\iint p\,\exp\ (pt)\ dF$ converge absolutely; then f' exists and has the area transform $p\,dF$.

The proof consists in trying to differentiate

$$f(t) = \iint \exp\ (pt)\ dF$$

under the integral sign. A dominating function is found in a manner similar to the construction in the proof of Theorem 5.

Theorem 7. Let f have the proper area transform F, let $h_s(t)$ be the step response of a (Stieltjes) convoluting circuit, and let

$$I = \iiint \exp\ p(t - \tau)\ dh_s(\tau)\ dF(\omega, \sigma)$$

converge absolutely; then

1. $H(p) = \displaystyle\int_{-\infty}^{\infty} \exp\ (-p\tau)\ dh_s(\tau)$ exists.‡

2. $g(t) = \displaystyle\int_{-\infty}^{\infty} f(t - \tau)\ dh_s(\tau)$ exists.‡

---

† It is sometimes convenient to refer to the differential dF as the transform.

‡ In the usual sense used with Fubini's theorem, i.e., for almost all p in item 1 and almost all t in item 2.

3. $H(p) \, dF$ is the area transform of g in that

$$g(t) = \frac{1}{4\pi^2} \iint \exp \, (pt) H(p) \, dF(p)$$

That is, g has an area transform G where $dG = H \, dF$.

Of course, the above is a (very general) convolution theorem; unlike some formulations of convolution theorems, the above theorem, with its proof, makes it obvious that the convolution theorem is simply Fubini's theorem applied to specific functions. For if the (ω, σ) integral is done first, we get

$$I = \frac{1}{4\pi^2} \int_{-\infty}^{\infty} \left\{ \iint \exp \, [p(t - \tau)] \, dF(\omega, \sigma) \right\} dh_s(\tau)$$

$$= \int_{-\infty}^{\infty} f(t - \tau) \, dh_s(\tau)$$

and if the τ integration is done first, we get

$$I = \frac{1}{4\pi^2} \iint \exp \, (pt) \left[\int_{-\infty}^{\infty} \exp \, (-p\tau) \, dh_s(\tau) \right] dF(\omega, \sigma)$$

$$= \frac{1}{4\pi^2} \iint \exp \, (pt) H(p) \, dF(\omega, \sigma)$$

which completes the proof.

Now some specific transform pairs will be given, the computational theorems will be illustrated, and a method (usually applicable) for directly constructing the function h of Theorem 5 will be described. In all these examples, only Riemann area transforms will be considered.

Example 1. Suppose

$$f(t) = \frac{\sin t}{t} \frac{\sinh t}{t}$$

Then we can take

$$h(x, y) = \frac{\sin x}{x} \frac{\sin y}{y}$$

and then $f(t) = h(t, -jt)$. The two-dimensional Fourier transform of h is well known:

$$H(\omega, \mu) = \iint \exp \, (-j\omega x - j\mu y) \frac{\sin x}{x} \frac{\sin y}{y} \, dx \, dy$$

$$= \begin{cases} \pi^2 & \text{if } |\omega| < 1 \text{ and } |\mu| < 1 \\ 0 & \text{for other } (\omega, \mu) \end{cases}$$

This H is $\partial^2 H_s / \partial\omega \, \partial\mu$ if H_s is the function used in the Stieltjes case (Theorem 5). In turn,

$$h(x, y) = \tfrac{1}{4} \int_{-1}^{1} \int_{-1}^{1} \exp \, (j\omega x + j\mu y) \, d\omega \, d\mu$$

which can obviously be analytically continued, and then

$$f(t) = \tfrac{1}{4} \int_{-1}^{1} \int_{-1}^{1} \exp(pt) \, d\omega \, d\sigma$$

Thus, $\dfrac{\sin t}{t} \dfrac{\sinh t}{t}$ can be viewed as the superposition of complex frequencies in the p plane which are inside a square centered at $p = 0$ with uniform (continuous) weighting on this square.

Example 2. Suppose $f(t) = \exp(t^2/2)$. This is the usual example given of a function which is not transformable by any of the previously available theories. However, here we simply consider $h(y) = \exp(-y^2/2)$, and then $H(\mu) = \sqrt{2\pi} \exp(-\mu^2/2)$ by the well-known transform pair of Gaussian functions. In turn,

$$h(y) = \frac{1}{\sqrt{2\pi}} \int_{-\infty}^{\infty} \exp(j\mu y) \exp\left(-\frac{\mu^2}{2}\right) d\mu$$

This can readily be analytically continued in y (under the integral sign) because of the presence of $\exp(-\mu^2/2)$. If the integration variable μ is called σ, and y is replaced with $-jt$, we get

$$f(t) = h(-jt) = \frac{1}{\sqrt{2\pi}} \int_{-\infty}^{\infty} \exp(\sigma t) \exp\left(-\frac{\sigma^2}{2}\right) d\sigma$$

Thus, $\exp(t^2/2)$ can be viewed as the superposition of frequencies along the real axis in the complex p plane with a continuous weighting of the form $\exp(-\sigma^2/2)$. Of course, the formula

$$\exp\frac{t^2}{2} = \frac{1}{\sqrt{2\pi}} \int_{-\infty}^{\infty} \exp(\sigma t) \exp\left(-\frac{\sigma^2}{2}\right) d\sigma$$

is easily verified by completing the square in the exponent; however, the theory of area transforms leads us naturally to the above representation of $\exp(t^2/2)$. In this example, there was no need to use frequencies off the real axis; however, a two-dimensional formulation can be used. The following is the Stieltjes version: Let $F(\omega, \sigma) = 4\pi^2 U(\omega)\phi(\sigma)$, where $U(\omega)$ is the unit step function and

$$\phi(\sigma) = \frac{1}{\sqrt{2\pi}} \int_0^{\sigma} \exp\frac{-\lambda^2}{2} \, d\lambda$$

Then $$f(t) = \frac{1}{4\pi^2} \iint \exp(pt) \, dF(\omega, \sigma)$$

Example 3. A General Construction for h. In the first two examples, it was a simple matter to guess an $h(x, y)$; in this example, a very general method for constructing an h will be described. The method follows from Example 2. Let $f(t)$ be given and suppose we can find an α such that

$$g(t) \equiv f(t) \exp \frac{-t^2}{2\alpha^2}$$

is absolutely integrable; hence this product has an ordinary one-dimensional Fourier transform. Such an α can be found for quite a rich class of functions. Let the Fourier transform of g be $G(\omega)$. Take h thus:

$$h(x, y) = g(x) \exp \frac{-y^2}{2\alpha^2}$$

Then
$$H(\omega, \mu) = G(\omega) \sqrt{2\pi}\, \alpha \exp\left(-\tfrac{1}{2}\mu^2\alpha^2\right)$$

In turn,

$$h(x, y) = \frac{\sqrt{2\pi}\, \alpha}{4\pi^2} \iint \exp\left(j\omega x + j\mu y\right)G(\omega) \exp\left(-\tfrac{1}{2}\mu^2\alpha^2\right) d\omega\, d\mu$$

The factor $\exp\left(-\tfrac{1}{2}\mu^2\alpha^2\right)$ ensures that h can be analytically continued in y under the integral sign, and we get

$$f(t) = h(t, -jt) = g(t) \exp \frac{t^2}{2\alpha^2}$$

$$= \frac{\sqrt{2\pi}\, \alpha}{4\pi^2} \iint \exp\left(pt\right)G(\omega) \exp\left(-\tfrac{1}{2}\alpha^2\sigma^2\right) d\omega\, d\sigma$$

and, of course, $\sqrt{2\pi}\alpha G(\omega) \exp\left(-\tfrac{1}{2}\alpha^2\sigma^2\right)$ is a *Riemann area transform* of f.

If f is a function of finite average power, the above method can be used; an alternative for this case is given in Sec. 10-5. As another specific case, observe that an exponential function itself can be written as a continuous weighting of exponentials over the entire plane. Normally, to express an exponential in terms of a transform, discrete (or δ function) weighting is used with a Stieltjes integral. The method outlined above gives

$$\exp\left(at\right) = \exp\left(at\right)\left(\exp \frac{-t^2}{2}\right)\exp \frac{t^2}{2}$$

and
$$G(\omega) = \sqrt{2\pi} \exp\left[-\frac{1}{2}\left(\omega - \frac{a}{j}\right)^2\right]$$

Therefore,

$$\exp\left(at\right) = \frac{\sqrt{2\pi}}{4\pi^2} \iint \exp\left(pt\right) \exp\left(-\frac{1}{2}\sigma^2\right)\exp\left[-\frac{1}{2}\left(\omega - \frac{a}{j}\right)^2\right] d\omega\, d\sigma$$

which is a rather strange way to express a simple exponential function. The formula does illustrate the fact that continuous (Riemann) weighting with area transforms can often be used in place of Stieltjes weighting in ordinary (or even Stieltjes area) transforms.

In view of Examples 2 and 3, one wonders how fast area-transformable functions might grow as t goes to infinity. The importance of Example 3 would be enhanced if area-transformable functions were no higher order than $\exp(t^2/2\alpha^2)$, where α would depend on the function under consideration. However, area-transformable functions can grow even faster than $\exp t^n$ for any n (see Ref. 8).

Example 4. All the above examples were concerned with transform pairs, and they provided insight as to the nature of area-transformable functions. The value of area transforms is largely conceptual; however, it is very simple to illustrate the use of Theorem 6, and Theorem 7 will be illustrated here.

Suppose

$$f(t) = \exp \frac{t^2}{8} \qquad d(t) = \exp\left(-\frac{t^2}{2}\right) \qquad g = d * f$$

One could not find g (legitimately) by previously available transforms since some of the transforms involved would not exist; however, Theorem 7 handles this problem quite easily. Of course,

$$H(p) = \int_{-\infty}^{\infty} e^{-pt} d(t) \, dt = \sqrt{2\pi} \exp \frac{p^2}{2}$$

$$F(\omega, \sigma) = 2 \exp \frac{-4\sigma^2}{2} U(\omega) \frac{4\pi^2}{\sqrt{2\pi}}$$

and

$$g(t) = 2 \iint \exp(pt) \exp \frac{p^2}{2} \exp \frac{-4\sigma^2}{2} \, dU(\omega) \, d\sigma$$

or

$$g(t) = \frac{2\sqrt{2\pi}}{\sqrt{3}} \exp \frac{t^2}{6}$$

as one might possibly guess.

The above calculation is rigorous in view of the fact that

$$\iiint \exp(pt) \exp\left[-\frac{(t-\tau)^2}{2}\right] \exp(-2\sigma^2) \, dU(\omega) \, d\sigma \, l\tau$$

converges absolutely [the ω integral is no problem and

$$\exp(-2\sigma^2) \exp \frac{-\tau^2}{2}$$

takes care of the other two variables].

10-3 GENERAL INVERSION FOR ABSOLUTELY INTEGRABLE FUNCTIONS

Here an inversion formula is proved without assuming bounded variation on finite intervals.

A Cesàro limit is used, and a few words about this are in order.   Let

$$\int_{-T}^{T} f(t)\, dt < \infty$$

Then $\displaystyle\int_{C_{-\infty}}^{\infty} f(t)\, dt = A$ iff $\displaystyle\lim_{T\to\infty}\int_{-T}^{T}\left(1 - \frac{|t|}{T}\right) f(t)\, dt = A$

This can be viewed in the following way: Suppose

$$q(u) = \int_{-u}^{u} f(t)\, dt$$

does not approach a limit as u goes to infinity and hence

$$\int_{-\infty}^{\infty} f(t)\, dt$$

does not exist.   It may be that $q(u)$ varies about some average value; that is, $q(u)$ may have a well-defined "d-c level" in that

$$\lim_{T\to\infty}\frac{1}{T}\int_{0}^{T} q(u)\, du$$

does exist.   This d-c level is

$$\int_{C_{-\infty}}^{\infty} f(t)\, dt$$

as established by the following lemma.

   Lemma 6.   If

$$\int_{-T}^{T} f(t)\, dt < \infty \qquad \text{for all finite } T$$

then $\displaystyle\lim_{T\to\infty}\int_{-T}^{T}\left(1 - \frac{|t|}{T}\right) f(t)\, dt$ and $\displaystyle\lim_{T\to\infty}\frac{1}{T}\int_{0}^{T}\left[\int_{-u}^{u} f(t)\, dt\right] du$

are equivalent.

   PROOF: Let

$$\Gamma(u,\, t) = \begin{cases} 1 & \text{if } |t| \le u \\ 0 & \text{if } |t| > u \end{cases}$$

and only $u \ge 0$ is considered.   Then

$$\frac{1}{T}\int_{0}^{T} q(u)\, du$$

is given by

$$\frac{1}{T}\int_{0}^{T}\left[\int_{-u}^{u} f(t)\, dt\right] du = \frac{1}{T}\int_{0}^{T}\int_{-\infty}^{\infty} \Gamma(u,\, t) f(t)\, dt\, du$$

For finite T, Fubini's theorem gives

$$\frac{1}{T} \int_{-\infty}^{\infty} f(t) \left[\int_{0}^{T} \Gamma(u, t) \, du \right] dt$$

Observe that Γ has the value 1 in the wedge depicted in Figure 10-1. If

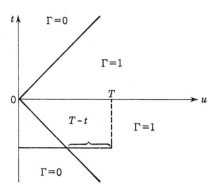

FIGURE 10-1.   Graph of values of Γ.

$T > t$, the u integration gives $T - |t|$; if $T < t$, the u integration gives zero. That is,

$$\int_{0}^{T} \Gamma(u, t) \, du = \begin{cases} T - |t| & \text{if } |t| < T \\ 0 & \text{if } |t| > T \end{cases}$$

In turn,

$$\frac{1}{T} \int_{0}^{T} q(u) \, du = \frac{1}{T} \int_{-T}^{T} f(t)(T - |t|) \, dt$$

which gives the desired simple result.

Lemma 7.   If

$$\lim_{u \to \infty} \int_{-u}^{u} f(t) \, dt = A$$

then

$$\int_{C \, -\infty}^{\infty} f(t) \, dt = A$$

That is, the use of the Cesàro limit is compatible with

$$\lim_{u \to \infty} q(u)$$

in case this limit does in fact exist.

PROOF: Let $\epsilon > 0$. Then there exists a θ such that $|q(u) - A| < \epsilon$ if $u > \theta$. Consider

$$\frac{1}{T} \int_{0}^{T} q(u) \, du = \frac{1}{T} \int_{0}^{\theta} q(u) \, du + \frac{1}{T} \int_{\theta}^{T} q(u) \, du$$

By taking T large, the first term can be made arbitrarily small, say less than ϵ.   For the second term, we have

$$(A - \epsilon)\left(1 - \frac{\theta}{T}\right) \leq \frac{1}{T} \int_{\theta}^{T} q \, du \leq (A + \epsilon)\left(1 - \frac{\theta}{T}\right)$$

From this it is seen that we can take T large enough to get, say,

$$\left| \frac{1}{T} \int_{\theta}^{T} q \, du - A \right| < 2\epsilon$$

Then

$$\left| \frac{1}{T} \int_{0}^{T} q \, du - A \right| \leq \left| \frac{1}{T} \int_{0}^{\theta} q \right| + \left| \frac{1}{T} \int_{\theta}^{T} q - A \right| < 3\epsilon$$

That is, by taking T large, we can make

$$\frac{1}{T} \int_{0}^{T} q \, du$$

arbitrarily close to A, as was to be shown.

An additional lemma is needed.   Actually, most of the lemmas of this chapter are basic results in integration theory.   Since we did not start with a development of the theory of integration, we are more or less building the theory of Fourier transforms on a base of quicksand.   Our lemmas amount to scattered steppingstones not easily seen with the few lights provided by Sec. 10-1 and not easily reached by the analytical abilities developed so far in the book.

As is illustrated in Ref. 16, one can progress very easily if all the major results from integration theory are assumed at the outset.   However, a good portion of these results were motivated by the study of Fourier analysis; hence, it is somewhat superficial to omit their proofs.

Lemma 8.   If $E_1, E_2, \ldots$ is a sequence of sets of measure zero, then

$$E = \bigcup_{k=1}^{\infty} E_k$$

is a set of measure zero.   That is, the countable union of sets of measure zero is a set of measure zero.

PROOF: We could easily prove this directly from the definition of measure zero given in Sec. 10-1; however, it is faster to note that it is implied by the dominated convergence theorem.   Let

$$F_n = \bigcup_{k=1}^{n} E_k$$

Then

$$\phi_E(t) = \lim_{n \to \infty} \phi_{F_n}(t)$$

where ϕ_A denotes the characteristic function of A; that is, $\phi_A(t) = 1$ if $t \in A$ and $\phi_A(t) = 0$ otherwise.   On a finite interval $(-T, T)$ we have

$$\int_{-T}^{T} \phi_E(t)\, dt = \int_{-T}^{T} \lim_{n \to \infty} \phi_{F_n}(t)\, dt = \lim_{n \to \infty} \int_{-T}^{T} \phi_{F_n}(t)\, dt$$

This interchange is valid since $|\phi_{F_n}| \le 1$ and 1 is integrable on $(-T, T)$. Now

$$0 \le \phi_{F_n} \le \sum_{k=1}^{n} \phi_{E_n}$$

and hence

$$0 \le \int_{-T}^{T} \phi_{F_n} \le \sum_{k=1}^{n} \int_{-T}^{T} \phi_{E_k} = 0$$

since each E_k is of measure zero.   Since

$$\int_{-T}^{T} \phi_{F_n} = 0 \qquad \text{for all } n$$

$$\lim_{n \to \infty} \int_{-T}^{T} \phi_{F_n} = 0 = \int_{-T}^{T} \phi_E$$

In turn,

$$\lim_{T \to \infty} \int_{-T}^{T} \phi_E = 0$$

That is, E is of measure zero, as was to be shown.

We have used the *fundamental theorem of calculus* from time to time.   In connection with Riemann integration, the integrand is usually assumed to be continuous.   Then

$$\frac{d}{dx}\left[\int_{a}^{x} f(t)\, dt \right] = f(x)$$

for all x.   In Lebesgue calculus, one need only assume that f is Lebesgue-integrable (possibly discontinuous everywhere) and then (we omit this proof also)

$$\frac{d}{dx}\left[\int_{a}^{x} f(t)\, dt \right] = f(x)$$

for almost all x, that is, for all x save possibly for a set of x of measure zero. Thus,

$$\lim_{\theta \to 0}\left[\frac{1}{\theta} \int_{a}^{x+\theta} f(t)\, dt - \frac{1}{\theta} \int_{a}^{x} f(t)\, dt \right] = \lim_{\theta \to 0} \frac{1}{\theta} \int_{x}^{x+\theta} f(t)\, dt = f(x)$$

What is the same thing,

$$\lim_{\theta \to 0} \frac{1}{\theta} \int_{x}^{x+\theta} [f(t) - f(x)]\, dt = 0$$

for almost all x.   The following lemma is a troublesome corollary to the fundamental theorem of Lebesgue calculus; all we want is to be able to put absolute-value signs on the last integrand above.

Lemma 9. If f is integrable, then

$$\lim_{\theta \to 0} \frac{1}{\theta} \int_x^{x+\theta} |f(x) - f(t)| \, dt = 0$$

for almost all x. Note that, in particular, the limit is zero if f is continuous at x. This last remark is obvious since for any $\epsilon > 0$ we can take θ small enough that

$$|f(x) - f(t)| < \epsilon$$

and, in turn,

$$\frac{1}{\theta} \int_x^{x+\theta} |f(x) - f(t)| \, dt \le \frac{1}{\theta} (\epsilon\theta) = \epsilon$$

which, by definition, means that the limit is zero.

PROOF: If

$$f_r = \operatorname{Re} f \qquad \text{and} \qquad f_i = \operatorname{Im} f$$

then

$$|f(x) - f(t)| \le |f_r(x) - f_r(t)| + |f_i(x) - f_i(t)|$$

from which it is seen that it is sufficient to consider real f in the lemma. We could now prove more than required, namely, that the set of x's for each of which there exists a real γ such that

$$\lim_{\theta \to 0} \frac{1}{\theta} \int_x^{x+\theta} |\gamma - f(t)| \, dt \ne |\gamma - f(x)|$$

is a measure of zero. Except for this set (call it E) we are free to take any value for γ and get equality; in particular, with $\gamma = f(x)$ we get

$$\lim_{\theta \to 0} \frac{1}{\theta} \int_x^{x+\theta} |f(t) - f(x)| \, dt = 0$$

The set of points not in E is called the Lebesgue set of f.

Since there is a clever way to prove just what we need, the strong form (arbitrary γ) will not be proved here. The following proof of Lemma 9 was suggested by Dr. Harold M. Horwitz.

Note that not only can we restrict consideration to real functions, but it is sufficient to consider real nonnegative functions. That is, let

$$f_1(t) = f(t) \qquad \text{when } f(t) \ge 0$$

and

$$f_1(t) = 0 \qquad \text{when } f(t) < 0$$

and let

$$f_2(t) = f_1(t) - f(t)$$

Then
$$|f(t) - f(x)| \le |f_1(t) - f_1(x)| + |f_2(t) - f_2(x)|$$
Hence, assume that f is real and nonnegative, and then let
$$g = f^{\frac{1}{2}}$$
We can then write
$$Q = \frac{1}{\theta} \int_x^{x+\theta} |f(t) - f(x)|\, dt = \frac{1}{\theta} \int_x^{x+\theta} |g(t) + g(x)|\, |g(t) - g(x)|\, dt$$

By the Schwarz inequality (Chap. 5, Theorem 6)
$$0 \le Q^2 \le \frac{1}{\theta} \int_x^{x+\theta} [g(t) + g(x)]^2\, dt\, \frac{1}{\theta} \int_x^{x+\theta} [g(t) - g(x)]^2\, dt$$

We are now rid of the absolute-value signs and can proceed with ease. Expansion of the second integral gives
$$\frac{1}{\theta} \int_x^{x+\theta} f(t)\, dt - 2g(x) \frac{1}{\theta} \int_x^{x+\theta} g(t)\, dt + f(x)$$

Of course, the first integral gives
$$\frac{1}{\theta} \int_x^{x+\theta} f(t)\, dt + 2g(x) \frac{1}{\theta} \int_x^{x+\theta} g(t)\, dt + f(x)$$

Finally, by the fundamental theorem of calculus, the (almost everywhere) limit as $\theta \to 0$ is
$$[f(x) + 2f(x) + f(x)][f(x) - 2f(x) + f(x)] = 0$$

as was to be shown.

Finally, we get to the big scene for this section.

Theorem 8. Let
$$\int_{-\infty}^{\infty} |f(t)|\, dt < \infty$$
and let
$$F(\omega) = \int_{-\infty}^{\infty} e^{-j\omega t} f(t)\, dt$$
Then
$$f(t) = \frac{1}{2\pi} \int_{-\infty}^{\infty} e^{j\omega t} F(\omega)\, d\omega$$

almost everywhere. That is,
$$f(t) = \lim_{R \to \infty} \frac{1}{2\pi} \int_{-R}^{R} \left(1 - \frac{|\omega|}{R}\right) e^{j\omega t} F(\omega)\, d\omega$$

for all t save for a set of t's of measure zero. This exceptional set of measure zero is (contained in) the set E of Lemma 9; hence, the inversion formula holds specifically at continuity points of f. Before the proof is given, two obvious corollaries will be mentioned.

Corollary 1. If f is continuous and absolutely integrable and if, in addition, the Fourier transform of f is absolutely integrable, then

$$f(t) = \frac{1}{2\pi} \int_{-\infty}^{\infty} e^{j\omega t} F(\omega) \, d\omega$$

everywhere. This is obvious from Lemma 7.

Corollary 2 (*Uniqueness*). Let f and g be absolutely integrable. Then $f(t) = g(t)$ almost everywhere iff $F(\omega) = G(\omega)$ almost everywhere. This follows readily from Theorem 8 since changing the values of an integrand on a set of measure zero does not change the value of the integral.

PROOF OF THEOREM 8: Let

$$P_R(t) = \frac{1}{2\pi} \int_{-R}^{R} \left(1 - \frac{|\omega|}{R}\right) e^{j\omega t} F(\omega) \, d\omega$$

$$= \frac{1}{2\pi} \int_{-R}^{R} \left(1 - \frac{|\omega|}{R}\right) e^{j\omega t} \left[\int_{-\infty}^{\infty} e^{-j\omega u} f(u) \, du\right] d\omega$$

Since

$$\int_{-R}^{R} \left[\int_{-\infty}^{\infty} \left|\left(1 - \frac{|\omega|}{R}\right) e^{j\omega t} e^{-j\omega u} f(u)\right| du\right] d\omega$$

is finite, we can interchange orders of integration.

The ω integration is

$$\int_{-R}^{R} \left(1 - \frac{|\omega|}{R}\right) e^{j(t-u)\omega} \, d\omega$$

which is easily evaluated and is found to equal

$$2\frac{1 - \cos R(t - u)}{R(t - u)^2}$$

Recall that $1 - \cos \gamma = 2\sin^2(\gamma/2)$. Therefore,

$$P_R(t) = \frac{2}{\pi} \int_{-\infty}^{\infty} f(u) \frac{\sin^2\left[\frac{1}{2}R(t - u)\right]}{R(t - u)^2} \, du$$

The limit problem we now face is similar to that in Theorem 5; however,

$$\frac{\sin^2\left(\frac{1}{2}R\theta\right)}{R\theta^2}$$

is an absolutely integrable kernel, while the Dirichlet kernel is not absolutely integrable. Because of this difference, it is nearly trivial to proceed if f is assumed to be continuous, and Lemma 9 is about all we need for an arbitrary integrable f.

It is somewhat more convenient to write

$$P_R(t) = \int_0^\infty [f(t-u) + f(t+u)] \left[\frac{2}{\pi} \frac{\sin^2 \left(\frac{1}{2}Ru\right)}{Ru^2} \right] du$$

The integral of the kernel is of interest (let $Ru = \theta$); then integration by parts gives

$$\int_0^\infty \frac{\sin^2 \left(\frac{1}{2}\theta\right)}{\theta^2} d\theta = -\frac{\sin^2 \left(\frac{1}{2}\theta\right)}{\theta} \Big]_0^\infty + \int_0^\infty \frac{\sin \left(\frac{1}{2}\theta\right) \cos \left(\frac{1}{2}\theta\right)}{\theta} d\theta$$

$$= \frac{1}{2} \int_0^\infty \frac{\sin \theta}{\theta} d\theta = \frac{\pi}{4}$$

Thus, we can write

$$f(t) = \int_0^\infty 2f(t) \left[\frac{2}{\pi} \frac{\sin^2 \left(\frac{1}{2}Ru\right)}{Ru^2} \right] du$$

We now deal with

$$P_R(t) - f(t) = \int_0^\infty [f(t-u) + f(t+u) - 2f(t)] \left[\frac{2}{\pi} \frac{\sin^2 \left(\frac{1}{2}Ru\right)}{Ru^2} \right] du$$

and of course we now must show that the limit is zero for almost all t. Write the integral for $P_R(t) - f(t)$ as

$$\int_0^\delta + \int_\delta^\infty = I_1 + I_2$$

Then

$$|I_1| \leq \int_0^\delta \phi(u) \left[\frac{2}{\pi} \frac{\sin^2 \left(\frac{1}{2}Ru\right)}{Ru^2} \right] du$$

where $\phi(u) = |f(t-u) + f(t+u) - 2f(t)|$. Let

$$\Phi(u) = \int_0^u \phi(\xi) \, d\xi$$

and restrict t to the Lebesgue set of f.

Of course,

$$\frac{1}{\theta} \int_0^\theta |f(t+u) - f(t)| \, du = \frac{1}{\theta} \int_t^{t+\theta} |f(\xi) - f(t)| \, d\xi$$

and

$$\frac{1}{\theta} \int_0^\theta |f(t-u) - f(t)| \, du = -\frac{1}{\theta} \int_t^{t-\theta} |f(\xi) - f(t)| \, d\xi$$

Also, $\phi(t) \leq |f(t+u) - f(t)| + |f(t-u) - f(t)|$; hence, if t is in the Lebesgue set for f,

$$\lim_{\theta \to 0} \frac{\Phi(\theta)}{\theta} = 0$$

In turn, given $\epsilon > 0$, we can take δ such that for $\theta < \delta$, $\Phi(\theta) < \epsilon\theta$ for $0 \leq \theta \leq \delta$. Break I_1 down thus:

$$I_1 = \int_0^\delta \phi(u) \left[\frac{2}{\pi} \frac{\sin^2 \left(\frac{1}{2}Ru\right)}{Ru^2} \right] du = \int_0^{1/R} + \int_{1/R}^\delta = I_a + I_b$$

Then since $\sin^2 (z/2) = \frac{1}{2} - \frac{1}{2} \cos z \le \frac{1}{2}(z^2/2)$,

$$|I_a| \le \frac{1}{2\pi} \int_0^{1/R} \frac{(Ru)^2}{Ru^2} \phi(u) \, du$$

or

$$|I_a| \le \frac{R}{2\pi} \int_0^{1/R} \phi(u) \, du = \frac{R}{2\pi} \Phi\left(\frac{1}{R}\right)$$

That is, $|I_a| \le \epsilon/2\pi$.   As for I_b,

$$I_b \le \frac{2}{\pi} \int_{1/R}^{\delta} \frac{\phi(u)}{Ru^2} \, du$$

which we integrate by parts to obtain

$$I_b \le \frac{2}{\pi}\left[\frac{\Phi(\delta)}{R\delta^2} - R\Phi\left(\frac{1}{R}\right) + 2 \int_{1/R}^{\delta} \frac{\Phi(u)}{Ru^3} \right] du$$

We can drop the term $R\Phi(1/R)$, and note that

$$\int_{1/R}^{\delta} \frac{\Phi(u)}{Ru^3} \, du \le \epsilon \int_{1/R}^{\delta} \frac{du}{Ru^2} \le \epsilon \int_1^{\infty} \frac{d\theta}{\theta^2} = \epsilon$$

Therefore, $I_b \le \dfrac{2}{\pi}\left(\dfrac{\epsilon\delta}{R\delta^2} + 2\epsilon\right)$ or $I_b \le \dfrac{2}{\pi}(3\epsilon)$

since $\delta > 1/R$.   In turn,

$$|I_1| \le \frac{2}{\pi}\left(3\epsilon + \frac{\epsilon}{4}\right) \le \frac{2}{\pi}(4\epsilon)$$

Returning to I_2,

$$|I_2| \le \frac{2}{\pi R} \int_{\delta}^{\infty} \frac{\phi(u)}{u^2} \, du$$

but

$$\int_{\delta}^{\infty} \frac{\phi(u)}{u^2} \, du < \infty$$

and hence

$$\lim_{R\to\infty} |I_2| = 0$$

Thus, we get

$$\varlimsup_{R\to\infty} |P_R(t) - f(t)| \le \varlimsup_{R\to\infty} |I_1| + \varlimsup_{R\to\infty} |I_2| \le \frac{8}{\pi}\epsilon$$

for any $\epsilon > 0$.   That is,

$$0 \le \varlimsup_{R\to\infty} |P_R(t) - f(t)| \le \frac{8}{\pi}\epsilon$$

for any ϵ; hence

$$\lim_{R\to\infty} P_R(t) = f(t)$$

if t is in the Lebesgue set of f, as was to be shown.

In view of the intimacy gained so far, we are overdue in calling the class of absolutely integrable functions by its popular name.   This fine aggregate is called L_1.

The class of functions for which

$$\int_{-\infty}^{\infty} |f(t)|^p \, dt < \infty$$

is L_p; we are ready to strike up an acquaintance with L_2. Before proceeding, recall the following theorem (Theorem 19, Sec. 2-3) which is implied by Fubini's theorem and a change of variable.

Theorem 9 (Convolution Theorem). If f and h are in L_1, then

$$g(t) = \int_{-\infty}^{\infty} f(t - \tau)h(\tau) \, d\tau$$

exists for almost all t and is in L_1 and $G = FH$, where the capital letters denote Fourier transforms.

10-4 SQUARE-INTEGRABLE FUNCTIONS

The following theorem (along with the completeness of L_2 mentioned later) brings about the avalanche of results of interest in this section.

Theorem 10. Let f be in L_1 and in L_2; that is, let

$$\int_{-\infty}^{\infty} |f|^p \, dt < \infty \qquad \text{for } p = 1 \text{ and } 2$$

Then
$$F(\omega) = \int_{-\infty}^{\infty} e^{j\omega t} f(t) \, dt$$

is in L_2 as a function of ω, that is,

$$\int_{-\infty}^{\infty} |F(\omega)|^2 \, d\omega < \infty$$

and
$$\frac{1}{2\pi} \int_{-\infty}^{\infty} |F(\omega)|^2 \, d\omega = \int_{-\infty}^{\infty} |f(t)|^2 \, dt$$

PROOF: Recall that

$$\int_{-\infty}^{\infty} e^{j\omega t} \exp\left(-\frac{\omega^2}{2n}\right) d\omega = \sqrt{2\pi n} \exp\left(-\frac{nt^2}{2}\right)$$

and note that

$$|F(\omega)|^2 = \int_{-\infty}^{\infty} e^{-j\omega t} f(t) \, dt \int_{-\infty}^{\infty} e^{j\omega u} \bar{f}(u) \, du$$

Now multiply both sides by $\exp(-\omega^2/2n)$ and integrate over ω; this gives

$$\int_{-\infty}^{\infty} \exp\left(-\frac{\omega^2}{2n}\right) |F(\omega)|^2 \, d\omega$$
$$= \int_{-\infty}^{\infty} \int_{-\infty}^{\infty} f(t)\bar{f}(u) \left[\int_{-\infty}^{\infty} e^{j\omega(u-t)} \exp\left(-\frac{\omega^2}{2n}\right) d\omega\right] du \, dt$$

Since $f \in L_1$ and $\exp(-\omega^2/2n) \in L_1$, it is clear that we have absolute convergence for the integral and hence we can interchange orders of integration. This gives

$$\int_{-\infty}^{\infty} \exp\left(-\frac{\omega^2}{2n}\right) |F(\omega)|^2 \, d\omega$$

$$= \int_{-\infty}^{\infty} \int_{-\infty}^{\infty} f(t)\bar{f}(u) \sqrt{2\pi n} \exp\left[-n\frac{(u-t)^2}{2}\right] du \, dt$$

$$\int_{-\infty}^{\infty} \exp\left(-\frac{\omega^2}{2n}\right) |F(\omega)|^2 \, d\omega$$

$$= \sqrt{2\pi n} \int_{-\infty}^{\infty} \exp\left[-\frac{nt^2}{2} \int_{-\infty}^{\infty} f(t+u)\bar{f}(u) \, du\right] dt$$

Let

$$R(t) = \int_{-\infty}^{\infty} f(t+u)\bar{f}(u) \, du$$

Then a change of variable on the right gives

$$\int_{-\infty}^{\infty} \exp\left(-\frac{\omega^2}{2n}\right) |F(\omega)|^2 \, d\omega = \sqrt{2\pi} \int_{-\infty}^{\infty} \exp\left(-\frac{\theta^2}{2}\right) R\left(\frac{\theta}{\sqrt{n}}\right) d\theta$$

Two problems now present themselves which we state here as lemmas to be proved later.

Lemma 10. $R(t)$ is continuous (everywhere, but we want only its continuity at $t = 0$) and $|R(t)| \le R(0)$.

Lemma 11 (Monotone Convergence Theorem). For $n = 1, 2, \ldots$, let $g_{n+1}(\omega) \ge g_n(\omega)$ for (almost) all ω, and let $g_n \in L_1$ for all n; then

$$g(\omega) = \lim_{n \to \infty} g_n$$

is in L_1 iff

$$\lim_{n \to \infty} \int_{-\infty}^{\infty} g_n(\omega) \, d\omega$$

is finite. If said limit is finite,

$$\int_{-\infty}^{\infty} g(\omega) \, d\omega = \lim_{n \to \infty} \int_{-\infty}^{\infty} g_n(\omega) \, d\omega$$

If we accept these lemmas for the moment, then

$$\left| \exp\left(-\frac{\theta^2}{2}\right) R\left(\frac{\theta}{\sqrt{n}}\right) \right| \le R(0) \exp\left(-\frac{\theta^2}{2}\right)$$

so that we have a dominating function. Also,

$$\lim_{n \to \infty} \exp\left(-\frac{\theta^2}{2}\right) R\left(\frac{\theta}{\sqrt{n}}\right) = R(0) \exp\left(-\frac{\theta^2}{2}\right)$$

(by Lemma 10).   Then, by the dominated convergence theorem,

$$\lim_{n \to \infty} \sqrt{2\pi} \int_{-\infty}^{\infty} \exp\left(-\frac{\theta^2}{2}\right) R\left(\frac{\theta}{\sqrt{n}}\right) d\theta = \sqrt{2\pi} \, R(0) \int_{-\infty}^{\infty} e^{-\theta^2/2} \, d\theta = 2\pi R(0)$$

$$= 2\pi \int_{-\infty}^{\infty} |f(t)|^2 \, dt$$

That is,
$$\lim_{n \to \infty} \int_{-\infty}^{\infty} \exp\left(-\frac{\omega^2}{2n}\right) |F(\omega)|^2 \, d\omega < \infty$$

and then, by the monotone convergence theorem (Lemma 11), $|F(\omega)|^2$ is integrable, that is, $F(\omega) \in L_2$, as was to be shown.   Of course, we have also proved that

$$\frac{1}{2\pi} \int_{-\infty}^{\infty} |F(\omega)|^2 \, d\omega = \int_{-\infty}^{\infty} f(t)^2 \, dt$$

if $f \in L_1$ and $f \in L_2$.   This key result will soon be shown to hold merely if $f \in L_2$, but we must first define the Fourier transform for arbitrary $f \in L_2$.

PROOF OF LEMMA 10: Since only continuity at $t = 0$ is needed, consider

$$R(t) - R(0) = \int_{-\infty}^{\infty} [f(t + u) - f(u)]\bar{f}(u) \, du$$

and hence

$$|R(t) - R(0)| \leq \int_{-\infty}^{\infty} |f(t + u) - f(u)| \, |f(u)| \, du$$

For the method of proof to be used here, it is helpful to restrict f to being real and nonnegative.   This is no limitation since if $f_r = \text{Re } f$ and $f_i = \text{Im } f$, we have

$$|f(t + u) - f(u)| \leq |f_r(t + u) - f_r(u)| + |f_i(t + u) - f_i(u)|$$

Then, if $f_1 = f_r \vee 0$, which means

$$f_1(t) = \begin{cases} f_r(t) & \text{if } f_r(t) \geq 0 \\ 0 & \text{if } f_r(t) < 0 \end{cases}$$

and
$$f_2(t) = -f_r \vee 0 = -(f_r - f_1)$$

then
$$|f_r(t + u) - f_r(u)| \leq |f_1(t + u) - f_1(u)| + |f_2(t + u) - f_2(u)|$$

Therefore, let f_k denote one of the four real nonnegative functions we deal with in breaking f down.   Then

$$|R(t) - R(0)| \leq \int_{-\infty}^{\infty} \sum_k |f_k(t + u) - f_k(u)| \, |f(u)| \, du = \sum_k Q_k$$

By the Schwarz inequality (Chap. 5, Theorem 6),

$$Q_k^2 \leq \int_{-\infty}^{\infty} |f_k(t + u) - f_k(u)|^2 \, du \int_{-\infty}^{\infty} |f(u)|^2 \, du$$

What we need now is a generalization of Lemma 1; that is, we want

$$\lim_{t \to 0} \int_{-\infty}^{\infty} |f_k(t + u) - f_k(u)|^2 \, du = 0$$

However, with f real and nonnegative, this is an obvious corollary to Lemma 1. For recall that $|a - b|^2 \leq |a^2 - b^2|$ since

$$|a^2 - b^2| = |a - b| \, |a + b|$$

and $|a + b| \geq |a - b|$ if both a and b are real and nonnegative. Thus

$$\int_{-\infty}^{\infty} |f_k(t + u) - f_k(u)|^2 \, du \leq \int_{-\infty}^{\infty} |f_k^2(t + u) - f_k^2(u)| \, du$$

and $f_k^2 \in L_1$. Thus, by Lemma 1,

$$\lim_{t \to 0} Q_k = 0$$

which completes the proof.

PROOF OF LEMMA 11: For the *only if* part, we are given that

$$\lim_{n \to \infty} g_n = g$$

is in L_1 and we wish to show first that

$$\lim_{n \to \infty} \int g_n < \infty$$

This is obvious since $g_n \leq g$; hence, for all n, $\int g_n \leq \int g$. In turn, $\{\int g_n\}$ is a monotone bounded sequence; such a sequence has a finite limit. The interchange is also valid since $g_1 < g_n \leq g$ (almost everywhere); hence, $|g_n| \leq (-g_1) \vee g$. Finally, $(-g_1) \vee g$ is integrable since

$$(-g_1) \vee g = \frac{-g_1 + g}{2} + \frac{|-g_1 - g|}{2}$$

which is integrable since $|-g_1 - g| \leq |g_1| + |g|$ and taking absolute value does not affect (Lebesgue) integrability; i.e., the dominated convergence theorem can be used to justify the interchange.

We now want the *if* part of the lemma: Given that

$$\lim_{n \to \infty} \int g_n < \infty$$

we want to show that

$$\lim_{n \to \infty} g_n = g$$

is in L_1. To prove this, it is helpful to introduce $h_n = g_{n+1} - g_n$ for $n = 1, 2, \ldots$. Then

$$\sum_{n=1}^{N} h_n = g_{N+1} - g_1$$

and

$$\sum_{n=1}^{\infty} \int h_n = \lim_{N \to \infty} \int g_{N+1} - \int g_1 < \infty$$

Therefore, for any $\epsilon > 0$, there exists an N_ϵ such that

$$\sum_{n=N_\epsilon}^{\infty} \int_{-\infty}^{\infty} h_n < \frac{\epsilon}{2}$$

Of course, since $h_n \geq 0$,

$$\sum_{n=N_\epsilon}^{\infty} \int_A h_n < \frac{\epsilon}{2}$$

for any set of intervals A.   Also, there exists a $\delta > 0$ such that

$$\left| \int_A g_n \right| < \frac{\epsilon}{2}$$

for $n = 1, 2, \ldots, N_\epsilon$ if $m(A) < \delta$ (this was shown after Theorem 3). Finally, for $n > N_\epsilon$,

$$g_n = g_{N_\epsilon} + \sum_{k=N_\epsilon}^{n-1} h_k$$

and hence

$$\left| \int_A g_n \right| \leq \left| \int_A g_{N_\epsilon} \right| + \sum_{k=N_\epsilon}^{\infty} \int_A h_k$$

which $< \epsilon$ if $m(A) < \delta$.   That is,

$$\left\{ \int_A g_n \right\}$$

is equiabsolutely continuous; and hence, by Theorem 3,

$$\lim_{n \to \infty} g_n = g \in L_1 \qquad \text{and} \qquad \lim_{n \to \infty} \int g_n = \int g$$

as was to be shown.

At a fairly good pace, we can now derive the major results for Fourier transforms on L_2.   Recall that, in the theory for functions of bounded variation, a Cauchy principal part was used.   Then, for L_1 more generally, a *Cesàro integral* was used.   The use of such "improper integrals" is more or less a part of life in the mathematics of Fourier transforms, and L_2 is no exception.   On L_2 we go to a limit in the mean.   Let $f \in L_2$ and let $f_n \in L_2$ for $n = 1, 2, \ldots$; then

$$\text{l.i.m.}_{n \to \infty} f_n(t) = f(t)$$

iff the following ordinary limit on the integral is satisfied:

$$\lim_{n \to \infty} \int_{-\infty}^{\infty} |f_n(t) - f(t)|^2 \, dt$$

A rather meaty digression into some general properties of L_2 is in order; however, only a few facts will be mentioned so that we can push on in the subject of Fourier transforms.

Recall that $\{a_n\}$ is a Cauchy sequence of numbers iff for any $\epsilon > 0$, there is an N (depending on ϵ) such that $|a_n - a_m| < \epsilon$ if n and m are greater than N. In other words,

$$\lim_{\substack{n \to \infty \\ m \to \infty}} |a_n - a_m| = 0$$

The rational numbers are "incomplete" in that there exist Cauchy sequences of rational numbers which do not approach a rational number as a limit. On the other hand, the real number system is complete; in fact, it is usually grown by completing the rational number system. In a similar fashion, $\{f_n\}$ is a Cauchy sequence of elements of L_2 iff for any $\epsilon > 0$ there exists an N (depending on ϵ) such that

$$\int_{-\infty}^{\infty} |f_n(t) - f_m(t)|^2 \, dt < \epsilon$$

whenever n and m exceed N. If we considered L_2 with Riemann integration, L_2 would not be complete. On the other hand, L_2 (Lebesgue) is complete as stated by the following theorem.

Theorem 11. If $\{f_n\}$ is a Cauchy sequence of elements of L_2, then there exists a function $f \in L_2$ such that

$$\mathrm{l.i.m.}_{n \to \infty} f_n(t) = f(t)$$

and if g is another function for which

$$\mathrm{l.i.m.}_{n \to \infty} f_n = g$$

then $f(t) = g(t)$ for almost all t.

It would be rather strenuous for us to prove this theorem; only a few remarks will be made. The usual method of proof involves finding a subsequence $f_{n(k)}$ such that for almost all t, $f_{n(k)}(t)$ is a Cauchy sequence of numbers; hence

$$\lim_{k \to \infty} f_{n(k)}(t)$$

exists and serves to display an $f(t)$ which turns out to be the limit in the mean of $\{f_n\}$. Thus, we have the following as a corollary to the proof of Theorem 11.

Corollary 3. If $\{f_n\}$ converges almost everywhere to g in the ordinary sense and

$$\mathrm{l.i.m.}_{n \to \infty} f_n = f$$

then $f(t) = g(t)$ almost everywhere. This is obvious since, if $n(k)$ gives the subsequence referred to above, then

$$\lim_{k \to \infty} f_{n(k)}(t) = f(t)$$

almost everywhere. On the other hand,

$$\lim_{n \to \infty} f_n(t) = g(t)$$

almost everywhere; but then

$$\lim_{j \to \infty} f_{n(j)}(t) = g(t)$$

for any subsequence $n(j)$ and, in turn, $g(t) = f(t)$ almost everywhere since $n(k)$ denotes some specific subsequence.

The rather difficult part of Theorem 11 is the existence of an f, not its uniqueness; the uniqueness is easy to show, as is indicated after the following lemma.

Lemma 12. Let f and g be square-integrable functions; then $f + g$ is square-integrable, and

$$(\textstyle\int |f + g|^2)^{\frac{1}{2}} \leq (\textstyle\int |f|^2)^{\frac{1}{2}} + (\textstyle\int |g|^2)^{\frac{1}{2}}$$

PROOF: This follows from the Schwarz inequality since

$$\textstyle\int |f + g|^2 = \int |f|^2 + \int |g|^2 + \int f \bar{g} + \int \bar{f} g \leq \int |f|^2 + \int |g|^2 + 2(\int |f|^2)^{\frac{1}{2}}(\int |g|^2)^{\frac{1}{2}}$$

That is,

$$\textstyle\int |f + g|^2 \leq [(\int |f|^2)^{\frac{1}{2}} + (\int |g|^2)^{\frac{1}{2}}]^2$$

as was to be shown. As for uniqueness for limit in the mean, let

$$\operatorname*{l.i.m.}_{n \to \infty} f_n = f \qquad \text{and} \qquad \operatorname*{l.i.m.}_{n \to \infty} f_n = g$$

Consider

$$0 \leq (\textstyle\int |f - g|^2 \, dt)^{\frac{1}{2}} = [\int |(f - f_n) - (g - f_n)|^2]^{\frac{1}{2}} \leq (\int |f - f_n|^2)^{\frac{1}{2}} + (\int |g - f_n|^2)^{\frac{1}{2}}$$

Now as n goes to ∞, $\int |f - g|^2 \, dt$ is sandwiched to zero. Thus,

$$\textstyle\int |f - g|^2 \, dt = 0$$

from which it is easy to see that $f = g$ almost everywhere.

The Fourier transform on L_2 can now be defined. Let

$$f_n(t) \equiv \begin{cases} f(t) & \text{for } |t| \leq n \\ 0 & \text{for } |t| > n \end{cases}$$

Let $f \in L_2$. Then F, the Fourier transform of f, is defined as a limit in the mean thus:

$$F(\omega) = \operatorname*{l.i.m.}_{n \to \infty} F_n(\omega)$$

where F_n is the L_1 Fourier transform of f_n.

Theorem 12.   Let $f \in L_2$ and let f_n and F_n be defined as above; then $\{F_n\}$ is a Cauchy sequence and hence there exists an $F(\omega) \in L_2$ such that

$$\underset{n \to \infty}{\text{l.i.m.}} \ F_n = F$$

That is, the Fourier transform on L_2 is well defined.

PROOF: Since

$$\int_{-\infty}^{\infty} |f_n(t)| \ dt = \int_{-n}^{n} |f(t)| \ dt \leq \left(\int_{-n}^{n} |f|^2 \ dt \right)^{\frac{1}{2}} \left(\int_{-n}^{n} 1 \ dt \right)^{\frac{1}{2}}$$

by Schwarz inequality, we have

$$\int_{-\infty}^{\infty} |f_n| \leq \sqrt{2n} \left(\int_{-\infty}^{\infty} |f|^2 \right)$$

and hence f_n is in L_1 as well as in L_2.   Now by Theorem 10, $F_n \in L_2$ and

$$\int_{-\infty}^{\infty} |f_n|^2 \ dt = \frac{1}{2\pi} \int_{-\infty}^{\infty} |F_n(\omega)|^2 \ d\omega$$

What is more (and actually of interest to us), $F_n - F_m$ is the L_1 Fourier transform of $f_n - f_m$ and, of course $f_n - f_m$ is in L_1 and in L_2 (both L_1 and L_2 are linear spaces).   Hence

$$\frac{1}{2\pi} \int_{-\infty}^{\infty} |F_n - F_m|^2 \ d\omega = \int_{-\infty}^{\infty} |f_n - f_m|^2 \ dt = \int_{-m}^{-n} |f|^2 \ dt + \int_{n}^{m} |f|^2 \ dt$$

Therefore (if $m > n$),

$$\frac{1}{2\pi} \int_{-\infty}^{\infty} |F_n - F_m|^2 \ d\omega \leq \int_{-\infty}^{-n} |f|^2 + \int_{n}^{\infty} |f|^2$$

which can be made small (for all m) by taking n large since

$$\int_{-\infty}^{\infty} |f|^2 \ dt < \infty$$

Note that if $f \in L_2$, then

$$F(\omega) = \underset{n \to \infty}{\text{l.i.m.}} \int_{-n}^{n} e^{j\omega t} f(t) \ dt$$

and if f is also in L_1, its L_1 transform is

$$F_1(\omega) = \int_{-\infty}^{\infty} e^{-j\omega t} f(t) \ dt = \lim_{n \to \infty} \int_{-n}^{n} e^{j\omega t} f(t) \ dt$$

By Corollary 3, $F_1(\omega) = F(\omega)$ almost everywhere.   That is, when both the L_1 and L_2 transforms are applicable, they agree.   Now that the Fourier transform on L_2 has been defined, we work toward an inversion formula (analogous to Theorems 4 and 8).

Theorem 13 (*Parseval's Theorem—Generalization of Theorem* 10).   Let $f \in L_2$.   Then the Fourier transform of f is in L_2 and

$$\int_{-\infty}^{\infty} |f|^2 \, dt = \frac{1}{2\pi} \int_{-\infty}^{\infty} |F(\omega)|^2 \, d\omega$$

PROOF: Note that

$$|(\int |f|^2)^{\frac{1}{2}} - (\int |g|^2)^{\frac{1}{2}}| \leq (\int |f - g|^2)^{\frac{1}{2}}$$

To see this we have

$$\int |f - g|^2 \geq \int ((|f| - |g|))^2 = \int |f|^2 + \int |g|^2 - 2\int |f| \, |g|$$

and then, by the Schwarz inequality,

$$\int |f - g|^2 \geq \int |f|^2 + \int |g|^2 - 2(\int |f|^2)^{\frac{1}{2}}(\int |g|^2)^{\frac{1}{2}}$$

or

$$\int |f - g|^2 \geq [(\int |f|^2)^{\frac{1}{2}} - (\int |g|^2)^{\frac{1}{2}}]^2$$

as was to be shown.   Now, since

$$0 \leq |(\int |F_n|^2)^{\frac{1}{2}} - (\int |F|^2)^{\frac{1}{2}}| \leq (\int |F - F_n|^2)^{\frac{1}{2}}$$

and

$$\operatorname*{l.i.m.}_{n \to \infty} F_n = F$$

that is,

$$\lim_{n \to \infty} \int |F - F_n|^2 = 0$$

$$\lim_{n \to \infty} \int |F_n|^2 = \int |F|^2$$

By the definition of f_n,

$$\lim_{n \to \infty} \int |f_n|^2 = \int |f|^2$$

Since $f_n \in L_1$ and $f_n \in L_2$, Theorem 10 gives

$$\int |f_n|^2 = \frac{1}{2\pi} \int |F_n|^2$$

Finally, $$\int |F|^2 = \lim_{n \to \infty} \int |F_n|^2 = 2\pi \lim_{n \to \infty} \int |f_n|^2 = 2\pi \int |f|^2$$

as was to be shown.

Theorem 14 (*Generalization and Yet a Corollary to Theorem* 13).   Let $f \in L_2$ and $g \in L_2$.   Then

$$\int_{-\infty}^{\infty} f\bar{g} \, dt = \frac{1}{2\pi} \int_{-\infty}^{\infty} F(\omega)\bar{G}(\omega) \, d\omega$$

PROOF: By Theorem 13,

$$\int |f + g|^2 \, dt = \frac{1}{2\pi} \int |F + G|^2 \, d\omega$$

since $F + G$ is the Fourier transform of $f + g$.   Expanding, we get

$$\int f\bar{g} + \int \bar{f}g = \frac{1}{2\pi} \int F\bar{G} + \frac{1}{2\pi} \int \bar{F}G$$

Since F and G were arbitrary, we can substitute jg (and jG) in the above equation to obtain

$$-j \int f\bar{g} + j \int \bar{j}g = \frac{-j}{2\pi} \int F\bar{G} + \frac{j}{2\pi} \int \bar{F}G$$

or

$$\int f\bar{g} - \int \bar{j}g = \frac{1}{2\pi} \int F\bar{G} - \frac{1}{2\pi} \int \bar{F}G$$

Adding this to the formula derived for f and g, we get

$$\int f\bar{g} = \frac{1}{2\pi} \int F\bar{G}$$

as was to be shown.

Lemma 13.   Let

$$\operatorname*{l.i.m.}_{n \to \infty} f_n = f$$

Then for any $g \in L_2$,

$$\lim_{n \to \infty} \int f_n g \, dt = \int fg \, dt$$

PROOF: Consider

$$0 \leq |\int (f_n - f)g \, dt|^2 \leq \int |f_n - f|^2 \, dt \int |g|^2 \, dt$$

by the Schwarz inequality.   However,

$$\lim_{n \to \infty} \int_{-\infty}^{\infty} |f - f_n|^2 \, dt = 0$$

which completes the proof.

Recall that if $f \in L_2$, then $F \in L_2$; there is no need to use different variables (t and ω), and in the next theorem we deal with functions and the Fourier transform of functions in one integrand.

Theorem 15.   Let $f \in L_2$ and $g \in L_2$.   Then

$$\int_{-\infty}^{\infty} f(t)G(t) \, dt = \int_{-\infty}^{\infty} F(t)g(t) \, dt$$

where capital letters denote Fourier transforms.

PROOF: Let f_n and g_n denote truncated functions as usual, and let

$$F_m(\omega) = \int_{-\infty}^{\infty} e^{-j\omega t} f_m(t) \, dt$$

$$G_n(\omega) = \int_{-\infty}^{\infty} e^{-j\omega t} g_n(t) \, dt$$

Now

$$\int_{-\infty}^{\infty} F_m(t)g_n(t) \, dt = \int_{-\infty}^{\infty} g_n(t) \left[\int_{-\infty}^{\infty} e^{-jtu} f_m(u) \, du \right] dt$$

By Fubini's theorem, we can interchange orders of integration (f_m and g_n

are in L_1), and hence

$$\int_{-\infty}^{\infty} F_m(t)g_n(t)\ dt = \int_{-\infty}^{\infty} f_m(u)G_n(u)\ du$$

Since $\operatorname{l.i.m.}_{n\to\infty} g_n = g$ and $\operatorname{l.i.m.}_{n\to\infty} G_n = G$

and since F_m and f_m are in L_2, we can let $n \to \infty$, and Lemma 13 gives

$$\int_{-\infty}^{\infty} F_m g\ dt = \int f_m G\ dt$$

Now g and G are in L_2, and another application of Lemma 13 (with $m \to \infty$) gives

$$\int_{-\infty}^{\infty} F(t)g(t)\ dt = \int_{-\infty}^{\infty} f(t)G(t)\ dt$$

Theorem 16.   Let $f \in L_2$ and let $g(t) = \bar{F}(t)$, where F is the Fourier transform of f; then, if G is the Fourier transform of g,

$$f(t) = \frac{1}{2\pi}\bar{G}(t)$$

(almost everywhere).
   PROOF: Consider

$$\int \left| f(t) - \frac{1}{2\pi}\bar{G}(t) \right|^2 dt = \int |f|^2 + \frac{1}{4\pi^2}\int |G|^2 - \frac{1}{2\pi}\int fG - \frac{1}{2\pi}\int \bar{f}\bar{G}$$

Now, by Theorem 15,

$$\int f(t)G(t)\ dt = \int F(t)g(t)\ dt = \int |F(\omega)|^2\ d\omega = 2\pi\int |f|^2$$

by Parseval's theorem.   Also, $\int \bar{f}\bar{G}\ dt = 2\pi\int |f|^2$.   Therefore,

$$\int \left| f(t) - \frac{1}{2\pi}\bar{G}(t) \right|^2 dt = \frac{1}{4\pi^2}\int |G|^2 - \int |f|^2$$

but $\int |G|^2 = 2\pi\int |g|^2 = 2\pi\int |F|^2 = 4\pi^2\int |f|^2$

That is,

$$\int_{-\infty}^{\infty} \left| f(t) - \frac{1}{2\pi}\bar{G}(t) \right|^2 dt = 0   \text{or}   f(t) = \frac{1}{2\pi}\bar{G}(t)$$

almost everywhere, as was to be shown.   We have arrived.
   Corollary 4 (*Inversion of L_2 Fourier Transforms*).   If $f \in L_2$ and F is the Fourier transform of f, then

$$f(t) = \operatorname{l.i.m.}_{n\to\infty} \frac{1}{2\pi}\int_{-n}^{n} e^{j\omega t}F(\omega)\ d\omega$$

   PROOF: Let $g(t) = \bar{F}(t)$; then, by Theorem 16, $\bar{f}(t) = (1/2\pi)G(t)$.   That is,

$$\bar{f}(t) = \operatorname{l.i.m.}_{n\to\infty} \frac{1}{2\pi}\int_{-n}^{n} e^{-jut}g(u)\ du = \operatorname{l.i.m.}_{n\to\infty} \frac{1}{2\pi}\int_{-n}^{n} e^{-jut}\bar{F}(u)\ du$$

If we conjugate the equation (and replace u with ω),

$$f(t) = \underset{n \to \infty}{\text{l.i.m.}} \frac{1}{2\pi} \int_{-n}^{n} e^{j\omega t} F(\omega) \, d\omega$$

as was to be shown.

The following summarizes the major results of this section.

Theorem **17** (*Plancherel's Theorem*). If $f \in L_2$, then there exists an $F \in L_2$ such that:

1. $F(\omega) = \underset{n \to \infty}{\text{l.i.m.}} \int_{-n}^{n} e^{-j\omega t} f(t) \, dt$.

2. F is essentially unique [that is, $F(\omega)$ is determined by f save for values on a set of measure zero].

3. $f(t) = \underset{n \to \infty}{\text{l.i.m.}} \dfrac{1}{2\pi} \int_{-n}^{n} e^{j\omega t} F(\omega) \, d\omega$.

4. $\displaystyle\int_{-\infty}^{\infty} |f(t)|^2 \, dt = \frac{1}{2\pi} \int_{-\infty}^{\infty} |F(\omega)|^2 \, d\omega$.

PROOF: Theorem 17 simply combines Theorems 12 and 13 and Corollary 4.

We conclude with a few remarks about operators on L_2. Let $H(\omega)$ denote the frequency response of a linear time-invariant system. If f is the input and g is the corresponding output, we expect $G = HF$. In the context of this section, we can simply start with a nearly arbitrary function $H(\omega)$ and induce an operator on L_2. If Φ denotes the operator corresponding to H, then $g = \Phi(f)$ is defined as the inverse (L_2 — limit in the mean) Fourier transform of HF, where F is the transform of f. This all goes very well if HF is in L_2. We are led to the following question: How do we characterize the allowed transfer functions $H(\omega)$ such that the above scheme yields operators on L_2? Here an operator on L_2 means that for arbitrary $f \in L_2$, $\Phi(f)$ is an element of L_2.

Theorem **18.** For arbitrary $f \in L_2$, let $\Phi(f) = g$ be taken as

$$g(t) = \underset{n \to \infty}{\text{l.i.m.}} \frac{1}{2\pi} \int_{-n}^{n} e^{j\omega t} H(\omega) F(\omega) \, d\omega$$

where $$F(\omega) = \underset{n \to \infty}{\text{l.i.m.}} \int_{-n}^{n} e^{-j\omega t} f(t) \, dt$$

Then the operator Φ is well defined with its range in L_2 iff H is measurable and essentially bounded,† that is, iff H is measurable and there exists an M such that $|H(\omega)| \leq M$ for almost all ω.

† Recall that h is the impulse response of a stable convoluting system iff

$$\int_{-\infty}^{\infty} |h| < \infty$$

Note that for such h, $H(\omega)$ is bounded and hence all absolutely integrable impulse responses provide operators for L_2. That is, with finite energy inputs, stable systems deliver finite energy outputs.

PROOF: If H is essentially bounded, then

$$\int_{-\infty}^{\infty} |HF|^2 \, d\omega \leq M^2 \int_{-\infty}^{\infty} |F|^2 \, d\omega < \infty$$

Hence $G \in L_2$ and, in turn, g exists and is an element of L_2. Suppose that $|H(\omega)|^2$ is not essentially bounded; then, let A_n be the set of ω's for which $n < |H(\omega)|^2 \leq n + 1$, where $n = 1, 2, \ldots$. Infinitely many A_n have positive measure, for otherwise H would be essentially bounded. Let $\{A_{n(k)}\}$ be a subsequence of $\{A_n\}$ with measures $m(A_{n(k)}) > 0$, and let $B_k = A_{n(k)}$. On B_k, $H(\omega) \geq k$. The problem is to find an $f \in L_2$ $(F \in L_2)$ such that HF is not in L_2, for then g will not be in L_2 (g will not exist, as far as we know). Try the following candidate for F:

$$|F(\omega)|^2 = \begin{cases} \dfrac{1}{k^2 m(B_k)} & \text{for } \omega \in B_k \\ 0 & \text{for other } \omega \end{cases}$$

Then
$$\int_{-\infty}^{\infty} |F|^2 \, d\omega = \sum_{k=1}^{\infty} \frac{1}{k^2} < \infty$$

That is, $F \in L_2$ and hence $f \in L_2$. However,

$$\int_{-\infty}^{\infty} |FH|^2 \, d\omega \geq \sum_{k=1}^{\infty} \frac{1}{k^2} k = \sum_{k=1}^{\infty} \frac{1}{k} = \infty$$

That is, G is not in L_2, which completes the proof.

Of course by restricting attention to a subspace of L_2, frequency-response functions which are not essentially bounded can be accommodated. For example, $H(\omega) = j\omega$ and $\Phi(f) = f'$ is well behaved on that part of L_2 for which

$$\int_{-\infty}^{\infty} \omega^2 |F(\omega)|^2 \, d\omega < \infty$$

10-5 STIELTJES TRANSFORMS AND WIENER'S GENERALIZED HARMONIC ANALYSIS

We first consider functions of t which can be written as a superposition of frequencies along the $j\omega$ axis with a Stieltjes weighting thus:

$$f(t) = \frac{1}{2\pi} \int_{-\infty}^{\infty} e^{j\omega t} \, dF(\omega)$$

where the real and imaginary parts of F are of bounded variation on $-\infty < \omega < \infty$.

Theorem 19 (Inversion Formula for Stieltjes Transform). If

$$f(t) = \frac{1}{2\pi} \int_{-\infty}^{\infty} e^{j\omega t} \, dF(\omega)$$

where the real and imaginary parts of F are of bounded variation, and if F is continuous at $\omega + \theta$ and at $\omega - \theta$, then

$$\frac{F(\omega + \theta) - F(\omega - \theta)}{2\theta} = \lim_{T \to \infty} \int_{-T}^{T} e^{-j\omega t} \frac{\sin \theta t}{\theta t} f(t) \, dt$$

Before giving the proof, a corollary will be mentioned.

Corollary 5. If, in addition,

$$\int_{-\infty}^{\infty} |f(t)| \, dt < \infty$$

then $dF/d\omega$ exists and is equal to

$$\int_{-\infty}^{\infty} e^{-j\omega t} f(t) \, dt$$

and, of course,

$$f(t) = \frac{1}{2\pi} \int_{-\infty}^{\infty} e^{j\omega t} \frac{dF}{d\omega} \, d\omega$$

Thus, under restricting conditions, Theorem 19 leads to the same transform formula as found under other conditions. Specifically, this corollary is the same as Corollary 1.

PROOF: As an aside, note that

$$f(t) = \frac{1}{2\pi} \int_{-\infty}^{\infty} e^{j\omega t} \, dF(\omega)$$

is continuous since

$$\lim_{\to t_0} \int_{-\infty}^{\infty} e^{j\omega t} \, dF(\omega) = \int_{-\infty}^{\infty} e^{j\omega t_0} \, dF(\omega)$$

by the dominated convergence theorem; that is, $|e^{j\omega t}| \leq 1$ and since F is of bounded variation, 1 is integrable with respect to F. Consider

$$Q = \int_{-T}^{T} e^{-j\omega t} \frac{\sin \theta t}{t} f(t) \, dt = \int_{-T}^{T} e^{-j\omega t} \frac{\sin \theta t}{t} \left[\frac{1}{2\pi} \int_{-\infty}^{\infty} e^{jut} \, dF(u) \right] dt$$

and observe that

$$\left| e^{jt(u-\omega)} \frac{\sin \theta t}{t} \right| \leq \theta$$

Then, since F is of bounded variation, we can interchange orders of integration to obtain

$$Q = \frac{1}{2\pi} \int_{-\infty}^{\infty} \left[\int_{-T}^{T} \frac{\sin \theta t}{t} e^{jt(u-\omega)} \, dt \right] dF(u)$$

The bracket gives

$$2 \int_0^T \frac{\sin \theta t \cos t(u - \omega)}{t} \, dt$$

or

$$\int_0^T \frac{\sin (u - \omega + \theta)t}{t} \, dt - \int_0^T \frac{\sin (u - \omega - \theta)t}{t} \, dt$$

Let

$$s(v, T) = \int_0^T \frac{\sin vt}{t} \, dt = \int_0^{vT} \frac{\sin \beta}{\beta} \, d\beta$$

It is easy to see that s is bounded for all (v, T) and that

$$\lim_{T \to \infty} s(v, T) = \begin{cases} \dfrac{\pi}{2} & \text{if } v > 0 \\ 0 & \text{if } v = 0 \\ \dfrac{-\pi}{2} & \text{if } v < 0 \end{cases}$$

Now

$$Q = \frac{1}{2\pi} \int_{-\infty}^{\infty} [s(u - \omega + \theta, T) - s(u - \omega - \theta, T)] \, dF(u)$$

Since s is bounded, the integrand is dominated by a constant which is integrable with respect to F. Therefore, we can apply the dominated convergence theorem. The integrand (after we take the limit as $T \to \infty$ with $\theta > 0$) becomes

$$\frac{1}{\pi} [s(u - \omega + \theta, \infty) - s(u - \omega - \theta, \infty)] = \begin{cases} 0 & \text{if } u < \omega - \theta \\ \frac{1}{2} & \text{if } u = \omega - \theta \\ 1 & \text{if } \omega - \theta < u < \omega + \theta \\ \frac{1}{2} & \text{if } u = \omega + \theta \\ 0 & \text{if } u > \omega + \theta \end{cases}$$

That is,

$$\lim_{T \to \infty} \int_{-T}^T e^{-j\omega t} \frac{\sin \theta t}{t} f(t) \, dt = \frac{1}{2} \int_{\omega - \theta}^{\omega + \theta} dF(u)$$

and if F is continuous at $\omega + \theta$ and at $\omega - \theta$, we have

$$\int_{\omega - \theta}^{\omega + \theta} dF(u) = F(\omega + \theta) - F(\omega - \theta)$$

which completes the proof.

For the corollary, if

$$\int_{-\infty}^{\infty} |f(t)| \, dt < \infty$$

then

$$\left| e^{-j\omega t} \frac{\sin \theta t}{\theta t} f(t) \right| \le |f(t)|$$

and we have a dominating function; therefore,

$$\lim_{\theta \to \infty} \int_{-\infty}^{\infty} e^{-j\omega t} f(t) \frac{\sin \theta t}{\theta t} \, dt = \int_{-\infty}^{\infty} e^{-j\omega t} f(t) \, dt$$

Hence, for all ω

$$\lim_{\theta \to 0} \frac{F(\omega + \theta) - F(\omega - \theta)}{2\theta} = \frac{dF}{d\omega}$$

exists and equals

$$\int_{-\infty}^{\infty} e^{-j\omega t} f(t) \, dt$$

Since $f \in L_1$, $dF/d\omega$ is continuous; so we return to the entirely proper equations mentioned at the beginning of this chapter and first obtained as Corollary 1. At this point, it would be fitting to prove Bochner's theorem (i.e., the Wiener-Kinchin theorem given as Theorem 3 in Chap. 5); however, the proof is a bit weighty, and we shall close with a few remarks on Wiener's generalized harmonic analysis.

Chapter 8 gave those parts of Wiener's generalized harmonic analysis which are used in applied problems. The material in Chap. 8 can be viewed as a theory which provides a spectral distribution of the average power in a function which has finite total average power. That is, if

$$\lim_{T \to \infty} \frac{1}{2T} \int_{-T}^{T} |f|^2 \, dt < \infty$$

we were able to define a $\mathcal{S}_f(\omega)$ such that $\mathcal{S}_f(\beta) - \mathcal{S}_f(\alpha)$ was the power in f residing in the frequencies $\alpha < \omega \leq \beta$. The thing missing in Chap. 8 was an expression for f itself as a superposition of frequencies along the $j\omega$ axis. Wiener obtained such an expression for functions of finite average power—a gigantic result of great conceptual value. Nearly all the tricks of this chapter are needed in this transform and its inverse.

Theorem 20. Let

$$\lim_{T \to \infty} \frac{1}{2T} \int_{-T}^{T} |f(t)|^2 \, dt < \infty$$

Then

$$\frac{F(\omega + \theta) - F(\omega - \theta)}{2\theta} = \text{l.i.m.} \int_{-T}^{T} e^{-j\omega t} \frac{\sin \theta t}{\theta t} f(t) \, dt$$

exists and

$$f(t) = \frac{1}{2\pi} \int_{-\infty}^{\infty} e^{j\omega t} \, dF(\omega)$$

That is,

$$2\pi f(t) = \lim_{R \to \infty} \frac{1}{R} \int_{0}^{R} \left[\int_{-\alpha}^{\alpha} e^{j\omega t} \, dF(\omega) \right] d\alpha$$

for almost all t. The proof will be omitted (see Ref. 17). Since F is not always of bounded variation, the proof requires some preliminary work so that

$$\int_{-\alpha}^{\alpha} e^{j\omega t} \, dF(\omega)$$

will be meaningful.   Since

$$f(t)\, \frac{\sin \theta t}{t}$$

is in L_2, Plancherel's theorem ensures the existence of $F(\omega)$, and the conclusion of this theorem is in line with the result of Theorem 19.

Most of the inversion formulas developed in this chapter are listed in Table I.   For the record, the following basic theorems were not proved during the development (but are covered in any study of integration theory): one interchange theorem (equiabsolute continuity), Fubini's theorem, fundamental theorem of calculus. and completeness of L_2 (Lebesgue).

TRANSFORM RELATIONS AND PAIRS

The various Fourier inversion formulas are collected in Table I. Recall that in any of the Fourier inversion formulas, if $q(t)e^{-\sigma t}$ satisfies the conditions imposed on f, then a Laplace inversion formula is obtained for q from the formula given for f.

A few Laplace transform pairs are given in Table II.

TABLE I. INVERSION FORMULAS

Conditions on $f(t)$ and $F(\omega)$	Transform Formula	Inversion Formula
1. Continuous f, f and F in L_1 (and hence F continuous)	$F(\omega) = \displaystyle\int_{-\infty}^{\infty} e^{-j\omega t}f(t)\,dt$	$f(t) = \dfrac{1}{2\pi}\displaystyle\int_{-\infty}^{\infty} e^{j\omega t}F(\omega)\,d\omega$
2. f in L_1 with f of bounded variation on finite intervals	$F(\omega) = \displaystyle\int_{-\infty}^{\infty} e^{-j\omega t}f(t)\,dt$	$\tfrac{1}{2}[f(t+0)+f(t-0)] = \displaystyle\lim_{R\to\infty}\dfrac{1}{2\pi}\int_{-R}^{R} e^{j\omega t}F(\omega)\,d\omega$
3. f in L_1	$F(\omega) = \displaystyle\int_{-\infty}^{\infty} e^{-j\omega t}f(t)\,dt$	$f(t) = \dfrac{1}{2\pi}\displaystyle\int_{\substack{-\infty\\ C}}^{\infty} e^{j\omega t}F(\omega)\,d\omega \quad \text{a.e.}\dagger$ where $\displaystyle\int_{\substack{-\infty\\ C}}^{\infty} Q(\omega)\,d\omega = \lim_{R\to\infty}\dfrac{1}{R}\int_0^{R}\left[\int_{-\alpha}^{\alpha} Q(\omega)\,d\omega\right]d\alpha$
4. f in L_2	$F(\omega) = \operatorname{l.i.m.}\limits_{n\to\infty}\displaystyle\int_{-n}^{n} e^{-j\omega t}f(t)\,dt$	$f(t) = \operatorname{l.i.m.}\limits_{n\to\infty}\dfrac{1}{2\pi}\displaystyle\int_{-n}^{n} e^{j\omega t}F(\omega)\,d\omega$
5. f has the quadratic-form property (see Chap. 5, Theorem 3) or is a complex linear combination of function with said property	$\dfrac{F(\omega+\theta)-F(\omega-\theta)}{2\theta} = \displaystyle\lim_{T\to\infty}\int_{-T}^{T} e^{-j\omega t}\dfrac{\sin\theta t}{\theta t}f(t)\,dt$	$f(t) = \dfrac{1}{2\pi}\displaystyle\int_{-\infty}^{\infty} e^{j\omega t}\,dF(\omega)$
6. f has finite average power	$\dfrac{F(\omega+\theta)-F(\omega-\theta)}{2\theta} = \operatorname{l.i.m.}\limits_{T\to\infty}\displaystyle\int_{-T}^{T} e^{j\omega t}\dfrac{\sin\theta t}{\theta t}f(t)\,dt$	$f(t) = \dfrac{1}{2\pi}\displaystyle\int_{\substack{-\infty\\ C}}^{\infty} e^{j\omega t}\,dF(\omega) \quad \text{a.e.}\dagger$

† Almost everywhere.

TABLE II. SOME TRANSFORM PAIRS†

$$L(f)_p \equiv F(p) = \int_{-\infty}^{\infty} e^{-pt} f(t)\, dt \qquad \sigma_1 < \mathrm{Re}\ p < \sigma_2$$

$$L^{-1}[F(p)]_t = \frac{1}{2\pi j} \int_{\sigma-j\infty}^{\sigma+j\infty} e^{pt} F(p)\, dp \qquad \sigma_1 < \sigma < \sigma_2$$

$$U(t) = \begin{cases} 1 & \text{for } t \geq 0 \\ 0 & \text{for } t < 0 \end{cases} \qquad a_r = \mathrm{Re}\ a$$

J and K denote Bessel functions

No.	$f(t)$	$F(p)$	(σ_1, σ_2)
1	$e^{at} f(t)$	$F(p - a)$	$(\sigma_1 + a_r, \sigma_2 + a_r)$
2	$U(t)$	$\dfrac{1}{p}$	$(0, \infty)$
3	$-U(-t)$	$\dfrac{1}{p}$	$(-\infty, 0)$
4	$\begin{cases} 1 \text{ for } |t| < T \\ 0 \text{ for } |t| > T \end{cases}$	$\dfrac{1}{p}\,(e^{pT} - e^{-pT})$	$(-\infty, \infty)$
5	$\dfrac{\sin Wt}{\pi t}$	$F(j\omega) = \begin{cases} 1 & \text{for } |\omega| < W \\ 0 & \text{for } |\omega| > W \end{cases}$	$\mathrm{Re}\ p = 0$
6	$\dfrac{1}{\sqrt{2\pi a}} \exp\left(-\dfrac{t^2}{2a^2}\right)$ $\mathrm{Re}\ a^{-2} > 0$	$\exp \dfrac{a^2 p^2}{2}$	$(-\infty, \infty)$
7	$\dfrac{t^{n-1}}{(n-1)!}\, e^{at} U(t) \qquad n > 0$	$\dfrac{1}{(p-a)^n}$	(a_r, ∞)
8	$\dfrac{-t^{n-1}}{(n-1)!}\, e^{at} U(-t) \qquad n > 0$	$\dfrac{1}{(p-a)^n}$	$(-\infty, a_r)$
9	$U(t) \sin \alpha t \qquad \alpha \text{ real}$	$\dfrac{\alpha}{p^2 + \alpha^2}$	$(0, \infty)$
10	$U(t) \cos \alpha t \qquad \alpha \text{ real}$	$\dfrac{p}{p^2 + \alpha^2}$	$(0, \infty)$
11	$U(t) \log t$	$\dfrac{-\log p - E}{p}$ where $E = 0.577215665 \cdots$ is Euler's constant	$(0, \infty)$
12	$\sqrt{t(t+a)}\, U(t) \qquad a > 0$	$\exp \dfrac{ap}{2}\, K_0\left(\dfrac{ap}{2}\right)$	$(0, \infty)$
13	$\dfrac{U(t)}{\sqrt{t^3}} \exp\left(-\dfrac{a^2}{4t}\right) \qquad a > 0$	$\dfrac{2\sqrt{\pi}}{\alpha} \exp\left(-a\sqrt{p}\right)$	$(0, \infty)$
14	$U(t) J_n(\alpha x)$ $\alpha > 0 \text{ and } n > -1$	$\dfrac{(\sqrt{\alpha^2 + p^2} - p)^n}{\alpha^n \sqrt{\alpha^2 + p^2}}$	$(0, \infty)$
15	$\dfrac{1}{t^2 + a^2} \qquad a > 0$	$F(j\omega) = \dfrac{\pi}{a} \exp\left(-a|\omega|\right)$	$\mathrm{Re}\ p = 0$
16	$\dfrac{1}{\sqrt{t^2 + a^2}} \qquad a > 0$	$F(j\omega) = 2K_0(a|\omega|)$	$\mathrm{Re}\ p = 0$

† The last six entries are from W. Gröbner and N. Hofreiter, "Integraltafel," vol. 2, Springer-Verlag OHG, Berlin, 1958.

REFERENCES

1. Kelley, J. L.: "General Topology," D. Van Nostrand Company, Inc., Princeton, N.J., 1955.
2. Riemann, B. G.: Ueber die Darstellbarkeit einer Function durch eine trigonometrische Reihe (first delivered in 1854), in Heinrich Weber and Richard Dedekind (eds.), "The Collected Works of Bernhard Riemann," Dover Publications, Inc., New York, 1953.
3. Lebesgue, H.: "Leçons sur les Séries Trigonométriques," Paris, 1906.
4. Doetsch, G.: "Theorie und Anwendung der Laplace-Transformation," Springer-Verlag OHG, Berlin, 1937; Dover Publications, Inc., New York, 1943.
5. Hille, E.: "Analytic Function Theory," vol. I, Ginn and Company, Boston, 1960.
6. Schwartz, L.: "Théorie des Distributions," Publications de l'Institut de Mathématique de l'Université, Hermann and Cie, Paris, 1950.
7. Lighthill, M. T.: "Generalized Functions," Cambridge University Press, New York, 1960.
8. Brown, W. M.: Area Transforms, *IRE Trans. Circuit Theory*, vol. CT-9, no. 2, pp. 163–168, June, 1962.
9. Elmore, W. C.: The Transient Response of Damped Linear Networks with Particular Regard to Wideband Amplifiers, *J. Appl. Phys.*, vol. 19, pp. 55–63, January, 1948.
10. Davenport, W. B., and W. L. Root: "Introduction to Random Signals and Noise," McGraw-Hill Book Company, Inc., New York, 1958.
11. Brown, W. M., and C. J. Palermo: Theory of Coherent Systems, *IRE Trans. Military Electron.*, 2d Special Issue on Advanced Radar Techniques, vol. MIL-6, no. 2, pp. 187–196, April, 1962.
12. Brown, W. M., and C. J. Palermo: Effects of Phase Errors on the Ambiguity Function, *IEEE Intern. Conv. Record*, 1963.
13. Brown, W. M.: Time Statistics of Noise, *IRE Trans. Inform. Theory*, vol. IT-4, no. 4, pp. 137–145, December, 1958.

14. Munroe, M. E.: "Introduction to Measure and Integration," Addison-Wesley Publishing Company, Inc., Reading, Mass., 1953.
15. Riesz, F., and B. Sz.-Nagy: "Functional Analysis," trans. from 2d French ed. by Leo F. Boron, Frederick Ungar Publishing Co., New York, 1955.
16. Goldberg, R. R.: "Fourier Transforms," Cambridge Tracts in Mathematics and Mathematical Physics, Cambridge University Press, New York, 1961.
17. Wiener, N.: Generalized Harmonic Analysis, *Acta Mathematica*, vol. 55, pp. 117–258, 1930.

INDEX